Computational Modelling of Free and Moving Boundary Problems II

SECOND INTERNATIONAL CONFERENCE ON COMPUTATIONAL MODELLING OF FREE AND MOVING BOUNDARY PROBLEMS 93

INTERNATIONAL SCIENTIFIC ADVISORY COMMITTEE

Acknowledgement is made to N. Tosaka *et al.* for the use of figure 9(b) on page 205 which appears on the front cover of this book.

Computational Modelling of Free and Moving Boundary Problems II

Editors:

L.C. Wrobel

Wessex Institute of Technology

&

C.A. Brebbia

Wessex Institute of Technology

Computational Mechanics Publications

Southampton Boston

L.C. Wrobel
Wessex Institute of Technology
University of Portsmouth
Ashurst Lodge
Ashurst
Southampton
SO4 2AA UK

C.A. Brebbia
Wessex Institute of Technology
University of Portsmouth
Ashurst Lodge
Ashurst
Southampton
SO4 2AA UK

Published by

Computational Mechanics Publications
Ashurst Lodge, Ashurst, Southampton, SO4 2AA, UK
Tel:44 (0) 703 293223 Fax:44 (0) 703 292853
Email:CMI@uk.ac.rl.ib

For USA, Canada and Mexico

Computational Mechanics Inc
25 Bridge Street, Billerica, MA 01821, USA
Tel:508 667 5841 Fax:508 667 7582

British Library Cataloguing-in-Publication Data

A Catalogue record for this book is available
from the British Library

ISBN:1-85312-242-4 Computational Mechanics Publications, Southampton
ISBN:1-56252-165-9 Computational Mechanics Publications, Boston

Library of Congress Catalog Card Number 93-71021

*The texts of the various papers in this volume were set
individually by the authors or under their supervision*

PREFACE

Free and moving boundary problems are of importance in a large variety of physical situations. The common feature is the presence, in the mathematical modelling, of an initially unknown surface, or a surface which moves throughout the analysis, the determination of which is an essential part of the solution procedure. These nonlinear problems are difficult to solve analytically but for the simplest cases; because of this, one usually has to resort to a numerical method of solution. Whichever method is chosen, an efficient computational implementation will require advanced features such as grid adaptivity, moving meshes, particle tracking, or other algorithms.

Although the physical problems under consideration can be completely different in nature, there are several common features in their mathematical modelling and computer methods of solution. Thus, scientists working in a wide variety of fields can benefit from each others' experience on the development of numerical models for free and moving boundary problems. With this in mind, the First International Conference on Computational Modelling of Free and Moving Boundary Problems was organized in Southampton, UK, in July 1991. The success of this meeting prompted the organizers to reconvene the conference in Milan, Italy, in June 1993. This book contains the edited version of the papers presented at Moving Boundaries '93. Once again, the main purpose of the conference was to promote the interaction between engineers, applied mathematicians and numerical analysts involved in the creation, development and application of computational methods to free and moving boundary problems.

The conference was organized and sponsored by the Wessex Institute of Technology, Southampton, UK. The editors are particularly grateful to the members of the Scientific Advisory Committee and invited speakers for thier support, to the assistance from the conference secretary, Mrs. A. Lampard, and to the staff of Computational Mechanics Publications for the preparation of this volume.

Milan, June 1993
The Editors

CONTENTS

SECTION 1: FLOW THROUGH POROUS MEDIA

SECTION 2: WAVE PROPAGATION

SECTION 3: STOKES FLOW

SECTION 4: CAVITATIONAL FLOW

SECTION 5: FREE SURFACE FLOW

SECTION 6: SEDIMENT TRANSPORT

SECTION 7: COMPUTATIONAL HYDRAULICS

SECTION 8: SOLIDIFICATION AND MELTING

SECTION 1: FLOW THROUGH POROUS MEDIA

Transient simulation of water table aquifers using a pressure dependent storage law

A. Dassargues

Laboratoires de Géologie de l'Ingénieur, d'Hydrogéologie, et de Prospection Géophysique (L.G.I.H.), University of Liège Bat. B19, 4000 Liège, Belgium

ABSTRACT

In groundwater problems involving unconfined aquifers, the shape and the location of the water table surface have to be determined as a part of the solution of the flow problem. The transient changes affecting the position of this free surface alter the geometry of the flow system so that the relationship between changes at boundaries and changes in piezometric heads and flows must be non linear. Methods have been developed recently using fixed mesh grids and non linear codes. They are based generally on non linear variation laws of the hydraulic conductivity of the porous medium in function of the pore pressure.

Other methods based on the variation of the storage are exposed. When coupled with the hydraulic conductivity variation law, they lead to solving the generalised well-known Richards equation described and used by many authors to simulate the unsaturated flow. Considering here only the saturated flow, different relations based on arctangent and polynomial functions, linking the storage of the porous medium to the water pressure are proposed in order to reach a very good accuracy in the determination of the water table surface which is the moving boundary of the saturated domain.

DEFINITION AND CONDITIONS CHARACTERIZING A WATER TABLE SURFACE

The water table surface of an unconfined (or water table) aquifer is defined as the locus where the macroscopic pore pressure is equal to the atmospheric pressure. However, above this surface, moisture does occupy a part of the pore space. The shape and the location of the water table surface have to be determined as a part of the solution of the flow problem. Two conditions express the definition of a free surface [1] : (1) the pore pressure p is equal to zero (or atmospheric pressure):

$$p = 0 \quad \text{and} \quad h = z \qquad \text{with } h = \text{piezometric head} \qquad (1)$$

(2) except recharge or evaporation, no flux across the free surface is considered, corresponding to a prescribed flux boundary :

$$\partial h / \partial n = f \qquad \text{where } f \text{ is the flux (negative if evaporation)} \qquad (2)$$

FLOW EQUATION IN CONFINED AND UNCONFINED AQUIFERS

Adding the Darcy law to the continuity equation expressing the mass conservation, the well-known equation describing the transient flow in a saturated porous medium is written (in term of pore presure p):

$$div\left[\underline{\underline{K}}.(grad\,p+\rho.g.\underline{grad}z)\right]=S_s.(\partial p/\partial t) \tag{3}$$

where $\underline{\underline{K}}$ is the tensor of the permeability coefficients, ρ is the mass per unit volume of water, z is the elevation above a reference level, and S_s is the specific storage coefficient of a saturated porous medium. It characterizes the aquifer capacity to store or release a volume of water in function of the pore pressure in the formation. Considering the classical assumptions of non-compressible flows [2], it can be written:

$$S_s=\rho.g.(\alpha+n.\beta) \tag{4}$$

where α is the volumetric compressibility coefficient of the porous medium and β is the water compressibility coefficient. The coupling between the transient flow and the consolidation process is shown as the specific storage coefficient is expressed in function of the compressibility coefficients of the porous medium and water.

   Usually, a storage coefficient is defined as the vertical integration of the specific storage coefficient on the thickness of the confined aquifer. It corresponds to the water volume stored or expelled per surface unit of the aquifer and per unit variation in piezometric head. For a water table aquifer, the variation of the piezometric heads induces the motion of the free surface, increasing or decreasing the amount of stored water by saturation or drainage of the porous medium. Consequently, in these conditions , the water storage per unit variation of piezometric head is mainly depending of the effective porosity. The storage coefficient of a water table is then defined by :

$$S_{coeff}=n_e+\int_{z_1}^{h}S_s.dz \tag{5}$$

where S_s is the specific storage coefficient in saturated (confined) conditions. In practice, the second term of this equation (5) is often neglected as 0.03 to 0.35 is a current range for n_e values in aquifers, whereas S_s reaches rarely values upper than 10^{-4} (m^{-1}). Although a same definition, the storage coefficients of confined and unconfined aquifers correspond mainly to largely different physical processes: drainage in water table aquifer and expulsion of water in confined aquifer for any decrease in piezometric head . The equation of the flow in a water table aquifer, is very often written considering the integration on the saturated thickness of the aquifer. By this way, the $\partial h/\partial z$ terms vanish, and all the vertical components of the flow are neglected :

$$div\left[\left(\int_{z_1}^{h}\underline{\underline{K}}.dz\right)\underline{grad}h\right]=n_e.\frac{\partial h}{\partial t} \tag{6}$$

In some cases of intensive water withdrawal, a confined aquifer may become a free or water table aquifer by lowering the piezometric head under the top of the upperlying aquitard. In such particular conditions, the storage coefficient passes from its confined value to the value of the effective porosity (n_e) ; there is a discontinuity.

METHODS USUALLY APPLIED WITH F.E.M. PROGRAMS

In transient conditions, the position of the water table can change significantly from its initial position, the geometry of the flow domain is altered so that the relationship between changes at boundaries and changes in piezometric heads and flows must be non linear [1]. The classical way to linearize this problem starts with a first estimation of the free surface position giving the initial boundary of the saturated domain. The piezometric heads are prescribed ($h = z$) on it. In each time step, after a first integration of the equation, the value of the computed flux $K(\partial h/\partial n)$ across the free surface is compared to the f value of equation (2). If the flow conditions are not satisfied (to a specified tolerance), the position of the free surface is adjusted in the desired direction and the problem is solved again and again, until the free surface flow conditions are met. For one time step, this "internal" process may need many adjustments (cycles) of the new position of the free surface, especially in geometrically complex cases or if the initial position has been roughly estimated. Most often, assuming the Dupuit approximation, the mesh is not changed at each cycle, but the value of the transmissivity (which is defined as the permeability coefficient integrated vertically on the saturated thickness), is actualized using the new piezometric head corresponding to the adjusted water table surface. For the computations, this change modifies the rigidity matrix, so that at each cycle a new problem is solved numerically.

Another current technique using the Finite Element Method consists in discretizing only the water saturated domain according to an initial free surface. The flow problem is solved and similarly to the first method described above, the computed value of the flux across the free surface is compared to the admitted value and its position is eventually adjusted. Here, the Finite Element mesh has to follow this moving. A new mesh is established at each "internal" iteration. As the discretization is changed, the solution of a new equation system must be found. To keep the effort to a minimum, only the geometric locations of the nodal points near the free surface are adjusted. If the mesh adjustments are made by an automatic meshing procedure, some distorted finite elements could appear in this zone, increasing the risk of instability or non-convergence in the numerical computations.

Methods, based mainly on the works of Bathe and Khoshgoftaar [3], have been developed using non linear laws. One of these methods is based on a variation law of the permeability coefficient (non linearity of K). The water table surface is not really considered as a boundary but as a particular zone where the porous medium is passing continuously from the saturated state to the unsaturated state or vice-versa. Looking in details at this zone, and considering in a first step the particular case of hydrostatic conditions, the medium is partly saturated above the water table surface. Water occupies a part of the voids (the rest being filled with air) and constitutes the wetting fluid [4]. The pressure of the water phase is smaller than the atmospheric pressure. This negative pressure reaches the capillary pressure (p_c) for the suction head value ($h = \psi$). In transient conditions, a tremendous simplification of the flow problem is achieved assuming that the partly saturated zone is translated together with the free surface [4]. This assumption can be accepted if the changes of the free surface are considered sufficiently slow that the partly saturated zone can adapt itself instantaneously to the new position of the water table. According to Vachaud [5], this requirement is as more verified as the ratio ψ/z_{sat} is lower than 1.0 (i.e. $\psi << z_{sat}$)

where z_{sat} is the saturated thickness in the aquifer. As mentioned by Dysli and Rybisar [6], from an hydrogeological point of view, the unsaturated zone can be characterized by a relationship linking the permeability coefficient to the suction pressure. To simulate the flow conditions in this zone, a permeability coefficient varying with the saturation conditions must be used [5,...].

As the curves of water content in function of the suction pressure can show quite different behaviours for the different geological media, different relationships between K and the pore pressure (p) can be chosen depending on the nature of the studied porous medium. Numerically, the permeability coefficient can be introduced as a function of the pore pressure. Empirical relations are used and experimentally adjusted in each case. Moreover the relation $K(h)$ or $K(p)$ is affected by hysteresis phenomena according to whether the porous medium is in drainage conditions or in wetting conditions, and according to whether the drainage or wetting processes are fully or partly completed before an inversion of the process. This capillary hysteresis, is usually not taken into account in the flow analysis [7].

Considering the 3D simulations of highly heterogeneous regional aquifers, the techniques described above are certainly not efficient. They are rejected because we really need a 3D approach (without Dupuit assumption), and because of the complexity of the meshing network. Consequently, a non linear method based on the introduction of non linear variations of the storage is presented hereafter.

METHOD USING THE NON-LINEARITY OF THE STORAGE

A variation of the water storage can also be introduced in the non linear code, as a function of the pore pressure. The method has been imagined [8] from the modelling by "enthalpic technique" of the phase changes in heat conduction problems : the phase changes occur at constant temperature, with heat storage [9]. In our case, the geological porous medium passes from unsaturated to saturated state at a constant zero pressure with storage of water. This storage corresponds mainly to the effective porosity of the medium. The obtained storage law is largely discontinuous (Fig. 1), the magnitude of the discontinuity being equal to the effective porosity of the medium.

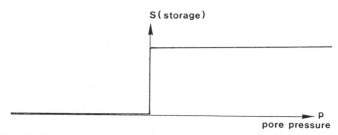

Fig. 1 Discontinuous storage law obtained by analogy to the heat storage law in thermic phase changes.

In reality, looking at the unsaturated flow with more accuracy, Musy and Soutter [7] mentioned that the well known Richards equation can be written :

$$div\left(\underline{\underline{K}}(h).\underline{grad}h\right) = -c(h).(\partial h/\partial t) \tag{7}$$

where the coefficient $c(h)$ is called the capillary capacity in m^{-1} , with h taking negative values in the unsaturated zone and the permeability coefficient depending of h (cfr above). The capillary capacity of the porous medium is defined as the variation of the water content per unit variation of the negative piezometric head in the unsaturated zone. In fact, $c(h)$ is completely equivalent in definition and units to the specific storage coefficient in the saturated part (Fig. 2). So that we could "generalize" the term of specific storage coefficient in both unsaturated and saturated zones. In the saturated zone S_s is constant (if the effects of the consolidation are disregarded at this stage), and in the unsaturated zone $S_s(h)$ is highly variable (Fig. 2):

$$c(h) = S_s(h) = (\partial\theta/\partial h) \text{ with } \theta \text{ the water content in the unsaturated zone} \quad (8)$$

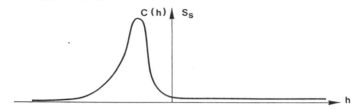

Fig. 2 Evolution of the "generalized" specific storage coefficient in both unsaturated and saturated zones, in function of h.

The variation of the water content per unit variation of the piezometric head in the unsaturated zone is equal to the variation of the storage (S) for the same variation of negative piezometric head (Fig. 3):

$$\partial\theta/\partial h = \partial S/\partial h \quad (9)$$

The relation $S(h)$ can also be drawn in function of the pore pressure p (Fig. 4). For sandy and clayey materials the relations obtained experimentally are very contrasted, and a very abrupt decrease of the storage is observed in sandy layers when the pore pressure passes from 0 to -10 kPa (Fig. 4). In this last case, the curves can be drawn in ($log\ p$, S) or ($ln\ p$, S) diagrams. From equation (9), we obtain the relation:

$$\theta = S + \text{ constant} \quad (10)$$

where the constant is equal to the water content corresponding to the residual saturation degree. This constant is less important for sandy aquifers than for clayey layers. However, this relation between S and p (or h) is affected by hysteresis phenomena, as exposed by Musy and Soutter [7]. In practice, as mentioned above, this capillary hysteresis is rarely explicitly taken into consideration in flow analysis.

    Numerically, a variation law of the storage can be chosen on basis of experimental data, and implemented in the non linear code. That can be a polynomial or an arctangent function, but the main stumbling-block consists in finding a sufficiently relaxed storage law in order to avoid any numerical overflow in the F.E.M. computations. The variation of the storage in the unsaturated zone can be described, for example, by a polynomial function of the following type (Fig. 5) :

$$S(p) = n_e \cdot \left[C_0 + C_1(p/-a) + C_2(p/-a)^2 + C_3(p/-a)^3 + C_4(p/-a)^4\right] \quad (11)$$

with the prescribed conditions: (1) $S(p) = 0$ or Cst if $p = -a$

                                (2) $S(p) = n_e$ if $p = 0$

$$(3)\ dS(p)/dp = 0 \qquad\qquad \text{if } p = -a$$
$$(4)\ dS(p)/dp = 0 \ \text{ or } \ S_s/\rho.g \ \text{ if } p = 0$$
$$(5)\ d^2 S(p)/dp^2 = 0 \qquad\qquad \text{if } p = -2a/3$$

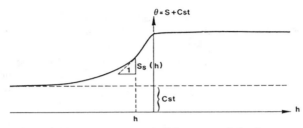

Fig. 3 Evolution of the water content and of the storage in both unsaturated and saturated zones, in function of h.

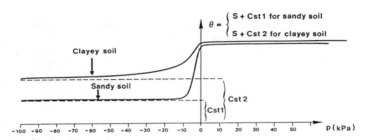

Fig. 4 Evolution of the water content and of the storage in function of p, for sandy and clayey soils.

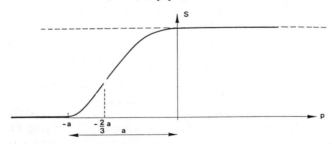

Fig. 5 Polynomial storage law in the unsaturated zone, the location of the inflexion point can be prescribed.

The conditions (1) and (3) express that at a given negative pressure $(p=-a)$, we approximate the storage value by a constant (or zero) and its variation in function of the pressure (its derivative) by zero values. Similarly the conditions (2) and (4) express that at the atmospheric pressure $(p=0)$, we consider that the storage has reached a constant value equal to the effective porosity and its derivative is equal to zero (as we neglect the specific storage coefficient of saturated conditions in front of the effective porosity, cfr above). The condition (5) prescribes the location of the inflexion point in the polynomial curve that we try to fit to the experimental data. In the case of the Fig. 5 , this location has been chosen at $p = -2a/3$. The five constants of the equation (11) are calculated using the five equations provided by the five prescribed conditions. The expression of the storage law in function of the pore pressure becomes in our case:

$$S(p) = 0 \qquad \text{for} \qquad p < -a$$

$$S(p) = n_e \cdot \left[1 - 4(p/-a)^3 + (p/-a)^4 \right] \qquad \text{for} \quad -a \le p \le 0 \qquad (12)$$

$$S(p) = n_e \qquad \text{for} \qquad p > 0$$

The degree of the polynomial function and the different conditions are found on basis of experimental data about the water content in the unsaturated porous medium.

APPLICATIONS AND PROSPECT FOR FUTURE WORKS

Our non-linear code, called LAGAMINE [2,10], has been already used to model in 3D different regional water table aquifers with a high level of accuracy: (a) the groundwater model of a regional water table aquifer, called "Hesbaye aquifer", in Belgium [10]; (b) the regional groundwater model of an alluvial water table aquifer in the valley of the Meuse River downstream to the city of Liège (Belgium) [11]: For these studies, the complexity of the geological conditions, the 3D discretization, the required accuracy added to the transient conditions, have justified fully the use of the Finite Element Method with a fixed meshing network and using a non linear storage law. Unfortunately, no accurate data were available concerning the water content or storage variation in the unsaturated porous media of both cases (the fissured chalk in the "Hesbaye aquifer" and the fluviatile deposits in the River Meuse alluvial aquifer). As mentioned previously by the author [12], an arctangent storage law has been used to approximate the variation of the storage in function of the pore pressure:

$$S = n_e \cdot \left(\frac{1}{\pi} \cdot arctg \left[\frac{p + Cst}{\alpha_r} \right] + \frac{1}{2} \right) + \frac{S_s}{\rho.g} \langle p \rangle \qquad (13)$$

where $\quad \langle p \rangle = p \quad$ if $p > 0$
$\qquad \langle p \rangle = 0 \quad$ if $p \le 0$

$\qquad \alpha_r$ = relaxation coefficient influencing the shape of the function (Fig. 6).
$\qquad Cst$ = constant allowing to translate the arctangent function (Fig. 6).

The storage arctangent function has been applied with $Cst=0$ and $\alpha_r = 1 \ 10^4$ Pa. As the arctangent function is here a purely theoretical function, neither based on actual data, nor verified, the unsaturated flows have been excluded from the computations. After many 1D, 2D and 3D simple tests (comparisons with analytical and other numerical solutions)[10], the accuracy of the computations has been verified and the two case studies mentioned above have been completed [10,11].

In a future prospect, it would be very useful to adjust actual data on the polynomial law of the 4th degree (see above) which should be convenient to describe the storage evolution. A better approximation in the changeover zone where the medium passes from the saturated to the unsaturated state will be obtained, considering that the unsaturated flow has an influence on the saturated flow. It should be convenient in order to simulate unconfined aquifers with accuracy using F.E.M. models.

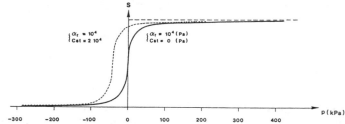

Fig. 6 Arctangent storage law in the unsaturated zone, the parameter a influences the relaxation of the curve and the constant (Cst) can translate the curve.

ACKNOWLEDGEMENTS

The numerical developments have been introduced in the Finite Element code "Lagamine" which is the research code of M.S.M. and L.G.I.H. departments of the University of Liège. Thanks to Mr J.P. Radu of the M.S.M. team for the valuable work he provided in some complex numerical situations. This research was supported by the Scientific Policy Services of the French speaking Community of Belgium. Thanks to IBM (Belgium) support, the "Lagamine" code is now running on a IBM/Risc 6000 system in the L.G.I.H. department of the University of Liège.

REFERENCES

1. Bear, J., and Verruijt, A., *Modeling groundwater flow and pollution*, Reidel, 414 p.,1987.
2. Dassargues, A., *Paramétrisation et simulation des réservoirs souterrains, Discrétisation du domaine, Préparation statistique des données, Couplages et non linéarités des paramètres*, PhD Thesis, Applied Sciences Faculty of the University of Liège,Belgium, 1991.
3. Bathe, K.J. and Khoshgoftaar, M.R. 'Finite element free surface seepage analysis without iteration', *Int. J. Num. and Anal. Meth. in Geomechanics*, Vol. 3, pp. 13-22, 1979.
4. Dagan, G., *Flow and transport in porous formations*,Springer-Verlag, 465 p.,1989.
5. Vachaud, G., *Contribution à l'étude des problèmes d'écoulement en milieu poreux non saturés*,Thèse de Doctorat, Grenoble,1968.
6. Dysli, M. and Rybisar, J. 'Coupled models and free-surface seepage analysis without mesh iteration', in ICONMIG/88 (Ed. Swoboda, G.), pp. 791-795, *Proceedings of the sixth Int.Conf.on Numerical Methods in Geomechanics*, Innsbruck, Austria, 1988.
7. Musy, A. and Soutter, M. , *Physique du sol*, Presses Polytechniques et Universitaires Romandes, Collection Gérer l'Environnement n°6, 335 p., 1991.
8. Charlier, R., Radu, J.P. and Dassargues, A. 'Numerical simulation of transient unconfined seepage problems, in Computer and Water Resources' Groundwater and aquifer modelling (Ed. Ouazar D. and Brebbia C.A.), pp. 143-155, *Proceedings of the 1st Int. Conf. in Africa on Computer Methods and Water Resources*, Vol. 1, Rabat, Morocco, 1988.
9. Comini, G.,de Guidice, S.,Lewis, R.W. and Zienkiewicz, O.C., 'Finite Element solution of non linear heat conduction problems with special reference to phase change', *Int. J. Num. Meth. in Eng.* , vol.8 , pp. 613-624, 1974.
10. Dassargues, A., Radu, J.P.and Charlier, R. 'Finite element modelling of a large water table aquifer in transient conditions', *Adv. in Water Resources*, Vol. 11, June, pp. 58-66, 1988.
11. Dassargues, A. and Lox, A. 'Modélisation mathématique de la nappe alluviale de la Meuse en aval de Liège (Belgique)', 'Le système hydrologique dans la région frontalière Liège-Maasbracht; résultats des recherches 1985-1990', *Rapport et notes* n°26 ,*CHO-TNO*, Delft, pp. 27-54.,1991.
12. Dassargues, A. 'Water table aquifers and Finite Element Method: Analysis and presentation of a case study', in Moving Boundaries/91 (Ed. Wrobel, L.C.,Brebbia, C.A.),vol.1 Fluid flow, pp.63-72, *Proceedings of the Int. Conf. on Computational Modelling of Free and Moving Boundary Problems*, Comp. Mech. Publ., 1991

Invited Paper
Location of free surface in porous media

K. Mizumura

Dept. of Civil Engineering, Kanazawa Institute of Technology, 7-1, Ogigaoka, Nonoichimachi, Ishikawa Pref. 921, Japan

Abstract

Simulating the flow among solid particles by many pipe flows which are generated by random numbers, the piezometric head (the pressure head and the potential head) is computed along each pipe. Taking the average of the piezometric heads of many pipe flows gives the free surface profile in the porous media. The free surface profile in the rectangular and the trapezoidal shapes is computed. This method is applicable to the case of arbitrary boundaries and turbulent flow.

Introduction

One of the most important problems in ground water flow is the determination of the free surface location. Generally, the location of the free surface is obtained by solving Laplace equation numerically and applying the kinematic and the dynamic boundary conditions on the free surface. In this study, the flow among solid particles is approximated by the combination of many pipe flows. The dimension and the direction of each pipe are simulated by generating many random numbers, so called Monte Carlo simulation. The locations of the free surface are determined by taking the average of piezometric heads in all pipe flows at the same position. Since the flow resistance of pipe flow is applicable to turbulent and laminar flows, this method is employed to the both flow regimes.

Method of Approach

To obtain the location of the water surface, let us consider a simple case of the rectangular porous media as shown in Fig.1. The pipe line simulated

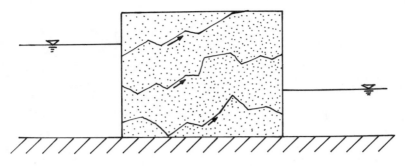

Figure 1: Definition Sketch

by Monte Carlo method is given in Fig.2. The total energy loss h_ℓ is given by

$$h_\ell = [\sum_i f_i \frac{\ell_i}{D_i^5} + \sum_j \frac{f_{bj}}{D_j^4} + \sum_k \frac{f_{sek}}{D_k^4} + \sum_\ell \frac{f_{sc\ell}}{D_\ell^4} + \frac{f_e}{D_0^4} + \frac{f_o}{D_n^4}] \frac{\Delta Q^2}{2g(\frac{\pi}{4})^2} \qquad (1)$$

in which $f_i=$ friction coefficient; $\ell_i=$ length of one pipe element; $D_i=$ diameter of one pipe element; $D_o=$ diameter of the first pipe element; $D_n=$ diameter of the last element; $f_{bj}=$ coefficient of energy loss due to pipe bend; $f_{sek}=$ coefficient of energy loss due to enlargement of pipe; $f_{sc\ell}=$ coefficient of energy loss due to contraction of pipe; $f_e=$ coefficient of energy loss due to pipe entrance from the water reservoir; $f_o=$ coefficient of energy loss due to water reservoir entrance from the pipe; $g=$ the gravitational acceleration; and $\Delta Q=$ the discharge through the pipe. When the flow regime is laminar in the pipe, the friction coefficient f_i is expressed by

$$f_i = \frac{64}{Re_i} \qquad (2)$$

in which $Re_i= v_i D_i/\nu$; $v_i=\Delta Q/(\frac{\pi}{4}D_i^2)$; $\nu =$ the dynamic viscosity of fluid. When the flow regime is turbulent in the pipe, namely, $Re_i \geq 4$, the friction coefficient f_i is expressed by

$$\frac{1}{\sqrt{f_i}} = 2\log_{10}\frac{D_i}{d_m} + 1.14 - 2\log_{10}[1 + \frac{9.28}{R_e(d_m/D_i)\sqrt{f_i}}] \qquad (3)$$

in which $d_m=$ the mean diameter of soil particles. In this study, the value of the equivalent roughness is assumed to be the mean diameter of the porous media. In the turbulent flow, the try and error iteration is used to get the value of the flow rate ΔQ through a pipe line. When the length of the porous media and the higher water level of the inlet and the outlet are L

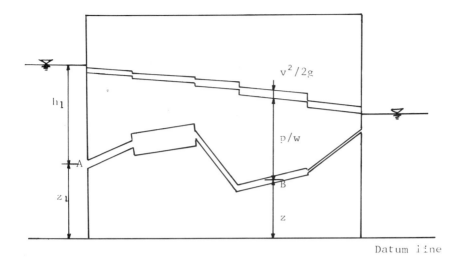

Figure 2: Simulated Pipe System

and H, respectively, the porosity of the porous media λ is defined by

$$\lambda \cong \frac{N d_m}{H} \tag{4}$$

in which $N=$ the total number of pipes per cross section and $d_m=$ average diameter of sand particles of the porous media. Let us consider two cases of pipe lines. In the case 1 (see Fig.3), the inlet and the outlet of the pipe line are under the water surface. The average hydraulic gradient $\Delta h/L$ between two points is equal to the difference of two water levels of the reservoirs over the total length of the pipe line. In case 2 (see Fig.3), the hydraulic pressure at the outlet point F is equal to zero (atmospheric pressure). The average hydraulic gradient $\Delta h/L$ between two points is the difference between the upstream water level and the vertical position of the outlet z_F over the total length of the pipe line. Since the difference of the piezometric head at the inlet and the outlet of the pipe line is Δh, the discharge ΔQ through one pipe line is computed by

$$\Delta Q = \sqrt{\frac{g\pi^2 \Delta h}{8}} / [\sum_i^n f_i \frac{\ell_i}{D_i^5} + \sum_j \frac{f_{bj}}{D_j^4} + \sum_k \frac{f_{sek}}{D_k^4} + \sum_\ell \frac{f_{sc\ell}}{D_\ell^4} + \frac{f_e}{D_0^4} + \frac{f_o}{D_n^4}]^{1/2}$$

Applying the energy equation between Point A and B, we obtain

$$h_1 + z_1 = \frac{v_B^2}{2g} + z_B + \frac{p_B}{w} + \sum_m h_{\ell m} \tag{6}$$

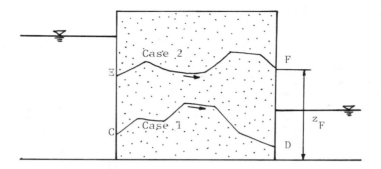

Figure 3: Computation of Hydraulic Gradient

in which $h_1=$ the water depth of the pipe at Point A; $z_1=$ the location of the pipe at Point A; $v_B=$ the velocity at Point B; $z_B=$ the location of the pipe at Point B; $p_B=$ the hydraulic pressure at Point B; $w=$ the specific weight of water; $\sum_m h_{\ell m}=$ energy loss between Point A and B. The hydraulic pressure at Point B is calculated from Eq.(6)

$$\frac{p_B}{w} = h_1 + z_1 - \frac{v_B^2}{2g} - z_B - \sum_m h_{\ell m} \qquad (7)$$

The piezometric head along the pipe line is also given by

$$\frac{p_B}{w} + z_B = h_1 + z_1 - \frac{v_B^2}{2g} - \sum_m h_{\ell m}$$

According to Forchheimer[2], the discharge and the free surface profile in the porous layer are given by ,

$$Q = \frac{k}{2L}(H^2 - h_0^2)$$

$$h = [H^2 - \frac{L-x}{L}(H^2 - h_0^2)]^{1/2}$$

in which $L=$ horizontal length of porous media layer; $h=$ location of free surface; $H=$ water depth at upstream boundary; and $h_0=$ water depth at downstream boundary.

Monte Carlo Simulation

To construct the pipe network, the length ℓ_i and the diameter D_i of each pipe element (Fig.4) and the angle of the pipe element to the horizontal

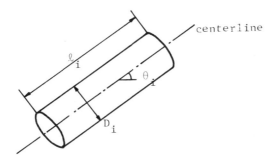

Figure 4: Pipe Element

θ_i must be determined by the generation of random numbers. Therefore, the location of the free surface is plotted as shown in Fig.5. The pipe diameter is produced from the probability density function of the Gaussian distribution of which mean is equal to the mean diameter of soil particles d_m and standard deviation is several times of d_m. The angle of the pipe bend is assumed to be uniformly distributed between $-\pi/2$ and $\pi/2$. Each pipe has three kinds of energy loss except friction loss. They are sudden enlargement of cross-sectional area (diameter), sudden contraction of cross-sectional area (diameter), and pipe bend. The energy loss due to the sudden enlargement is given by

$$h_{se} = \{1 - (\frac{D_i}{D_{i+1}})^2\}^2 \frac{v_{max}^2}{2g} \tag{8}$$

in which D_i= the smaller diameter of the pipe; D_{i+1} = the larger diameter of the pipe; and v_{max}=the flow velocity in the smaller diameter of the pipe. The energy loss coefficient f_{se} is theoretically obtained by

$$f_{se} = \{1 - (\frac{D_i}{D_{i+1}})^2\}^2 \tag{9}$$

The energy loss due to the sudden contraction of cross-sectional area is defined by

$$h_{sc} = f_{sc} \frac{v_{max}^2}{2g} \tag{10}$$

in which $f_{sc} = 0.485[1 - (\frac{D_{i+1}}{D_i})^2]$. The energy loss due to the pipe bend is also represented by

$$h_{be} = f_{be} \frac{v_{max}^2}{2g} \tag{11}$$

in which $f_{be} = 0.946 \sin^2 \frac{\alpha}{2} + 2.05 \sin^4 \frac{\alpha}{2}$;α= the angle difference between two directions at the pipe bend. The above coefficients f_{sc} and f_{be} are empirically obtained[3].

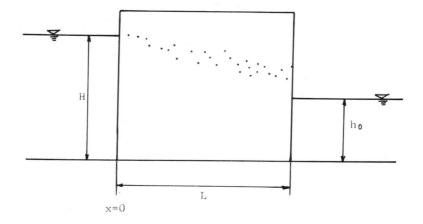

Figure 5: Location of Free Surface or $p=0$

Numerical Result

Fig.6 shows the locations of free surface for different values of mean diameter of solid particles when the effective porosity is 0.3. This gives the effect of the mean diameter of solid particles. When the mean diameter of solid particles becomes larger, the location above the downstream water surface at the downstream boundary is higher. The dotted curve represents Forchheimer's solution which is obtained under the assumption of horizontal flow. Fig.7 draws the lacations of free surface for different values of mean diameter of solid particles when the effective porosity is 0.5. This is almost the same as the previous one. Fig.8 gives the shapes of free surface for different values of mean diameter of solid particles when the effective porosity is 0.3 and the form of the porous layer is trapezoidal. The downstream water level above the bottom is 0.6 m. Fig.9 shows the shapes of free surface profile in the same condition as the previous case when the downstream water level above the bottom is zero. Fig.10 describes the comparison of the computed discharge with the theoretical result derived from Forchheimer's equation. For simplicity, the hydraulic conductivity in Forchheimer's equation is assumed to be $k=100d_{10}^2$, in which $d_{10}=$ diameter of solid particles of 10% in distribution curve of diameter.

Concluding Remarks

Through this study the following are obtained.

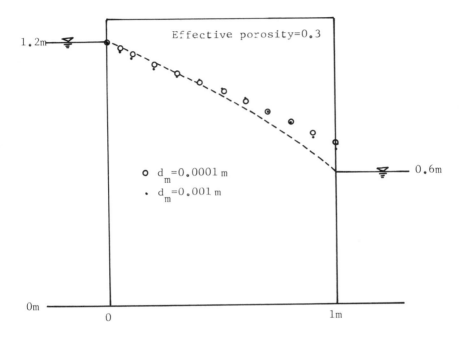

Figure 6: Location of Free Surface for $\lambda=0.3$

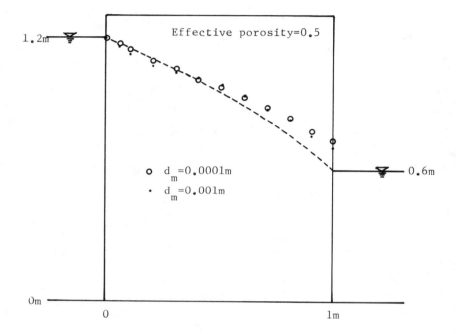

Figure 7: Location of Free Surface for $\lambda=0.5$

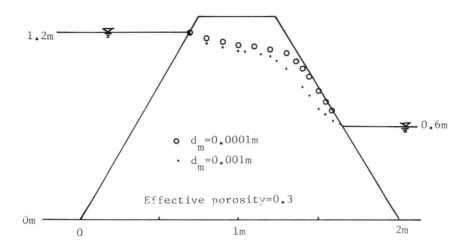

Figure 8: Location of Free Surface for λ=0.3 and Shape of Trapezoid

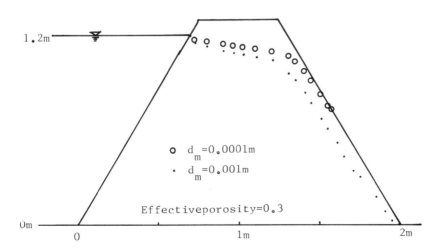

Figure 9: Location of Free Surface for λ=0.3 and Shape of Trapezoid

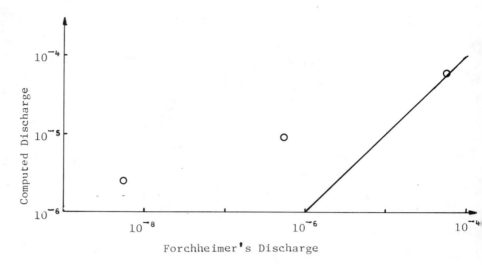

Figure 10: Comparison of Computed Discharge with Theoretical Result

1. The locations of free surface are computed although the flow regime is turbulent or laminar.

2. The mean diameter of solid particles to form the porous layer have an effect on the shape of the free surface.

3. The influence of the effective porosity on the shape of the free surface is negligible in the result of the comparison of the effective porosity of 0.3 and 0.5..

References

[1] Bear, Jacob. *Dynamics of Fluids in Porous Media*, Dover Publications, Inc., New York, 1972.

[2] Homma, M. *Hydraulics*, Maruzen Co., Ltd., Tokyo, 1967 (in Japanese).

[3] JSCE, *Hydraulics Formula*, Japan Society of Civil Engineers, 1970 (in Japanese).

A study of some unsteady free surface problems in porous media

F.H. Chaudhry, S.M.G.L. Montenegro
Department of Hydraulics and Sanitary Engineering, São Carlos School of Engineering, University of São Paulo, 13.560 São Carlos, SP, Brazil

ABSTRACT

Various simple unsteady saturated flow configurations related to drawdown and recharge in a block of soil are employed to test the accuracy of the numerical solution of these transient flow problems against experimental observations made on the corresponding Hele-Shaw model constructed for the purpose. Relative importance of procedural approximations involved in the application of boundary element method like time and boundary discretization, weighting factor for derivative approximation, coefficient matrix evaluation etc., is pointed out by comparing numerical and experimental results.

INTRODUCTION

The usefulness of the boundary element method (BEM) for the solution of the potential flow problems is now well-established [2,3,4]. It helps reduce the complexity of the numerical solution procedures by considering only the information along the boundary of the region of interest. This method is naturally indicated for dealing with free surface problems like those encountered in groundwater flow.

The application of BEM involves various tradeoffs [3,5,7] as regards the geometrical description of the boundary elements, interpolation functions used to describe the variation of potential along a boundary element, time step size, space derivative approximation in time, strategy of updating coefficients and the method of evaluating integrals. The refinements introduced in dealing

with these approximations may not always be called for in view
of the interactions that exist among them. It is the purpose of
this paper to consider the effect of some of these refinements
in the procedures for BEM numerical solution with reference to
simple flow configurations representing drainage and recharge
of a block of saturated porous medium vis-a-vis the experimental
observations on a Hele-Shaw model.

FLOW WITH MOVING BOUNDARY

The flow of an incompressible fluid in a homogeneous isotropic
porous medium is described by Laplace's equation for hydraulic
potential ϕ as,

$$\nabla^2 \phi = 0 \tag{1}$$

For steady flows, the variation of ϕ inside the flow region R is
completely determined by the boundary conditions in terms of ϕ
and/or its normal derivatives. The solution is not as straight-
forward in free surface flow because the geometry of the upper
boundary is unknown "a priori", especially so if the boundary
moves as an unsteady flow during drainage and recharge. An additional condition to be satisfied at the moving boundary for 2-
dimensional flow with recharge is [4],

$$\frac{\partial \phi}{\partial t} = - \frac{k}{n_e} \frac{1}{\cos \beta} \frac{\partial \phi}{\partial n} + \frac{N_v}{n_e} \tag{2}$$

where k is the hydraulic conductivity, n_e the effective porosity,
N_v the recharge rate and n is the direction of the outward normal at the free surface. t is time and β is the angle that free
surface makes with the horizontal.

Despite their apparent complexity, the moving boundary problems are handled well by BEM because the solution for this boundary is obtained directly without having to solve flow inside R.
Let us consider the recharge sample problem in Figure 1.

The boundary conditions for the problem are:

$$\frac{\partial \phi}{\partial n} = 0 \quad \text{at the plane of symmetry a}$$

$$\phi = z(x,t) \quad \text{at the free surface b} \tag{3}$$

ϕ = z at the seepage face c
ϕ = h at the downstream face d

$$\frac{\partial \phi}{\partial n} = 0 \text{ at the impermeable base e}$$

The condition at the free surface is expressed more precisely in Equation (2).

The boundary element method of solution of Equation (1) subject
to the boundary conditions in (2) and (3) has been presented in
detail in literature [2,3,4,6,7].

EXPERIMENTAL AND NUMERICAL SIMULATIONS

From the above brief description of BEM for solution   of   unsteady free surface flow, it is apparent that it involves a number of approximations whose effect must be considered in   the
choice of procedures, discretization parameters and tolerances.
A number of experimental and numerical simulations were   conducted to highlight their importance using the two-dimensional
drainage/recharge problem in Figure 1.

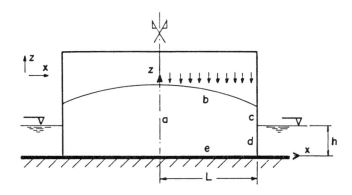

Figure 1. Sample Problem

A Hele-Shaw model, which provides solution of Equation (1)
by analogy to viscous flow between two plates, was used as   a
reference to study the factors involved in the numerical treatment. The model constructed from acrylic plates (200 cm x 70 cm)

placed 1.5 mm apart could be subjected to vertical   recharge
and also drainage at one end. The other end remained sealed to
reproduce problem symmetry (Figure 1). Three experiments   were
conducted with Shell oils Vitrea 72 and 320 at constant   temperatures. These are: (1) Drainage from an initially   horizontal free surface due to sudden drawdown on the downstream face;
(2) Recharge of initially horizontal or curved free   surface;
(3) Drainage of established phreatic surface after   cessation
of recharge. The flow parameters during each experimental condition are presented in Table 1.

Table 1. Experimental Parameters

L = 199 cm   b = 1.5 mm, n_e = 1

Experiment	N_v cm/sec.	h cm	H cm	ν cm^2/sec.	k=8 b^2/12ν cm/sec.
I	–	19.0	48	0.0588	0.313
V	–	5.3	55	0.0796	0.231
VIII	0.00608	7.2	–	0.0876	0.210
IX	0.00868	7.0	–	0.0770	0.239
X		7.2	–	0.0721	0.255

Experimental results are compared with numerical   simulations employing the experimental parameters of Table 1 without
any attempt at calibrating them. The numerical simulations were
conducted using different alternative choices for   procedures
and parameters. All the results presented graphically are   expressed in dimensionless form as:

$$(\phi', \ x', \ t') = (\frac{\phi}{L}, \ \frac{x}{L}, \ \frac{tk}{n_e L})$$

RESULTS

A comparison between experimental and numerical   results   is
made to examine the evolution in time of the position of   free
surface near the seepage face and the plane of symmetry.

Sudden Drawdown

The use of smaller time steps recommended to deal with the approximations resulting from the calculation of the coefficients of unknowns in the system of equations on the basis of solution at $k\Delta t$, is investigated in Figure (2). Numerical results   are presented for time steps of 100 sec., 50 sec. and 5 sec. along with the experimental data. It is observed that, for Δt of 100 sec. and 50 sec., the position of the point of the free   surface-seepage surface intersection calculated numerically   is wide off the experimental values although the reduction in Δt slightly improves the numerical estimates. At very small step size (5 sec.), one observes in Figure(2) that an instability arises in numerical results away from the seepage face while the seepage point continues to be overestimated   in   the   initial stages. Thus reducing the step size does not necessarily compensate for the approximation of free surface   coefficients from the known solution and does not garantee good results especially in the sudden drawdown case. The iterative   procedure which adjusts these coefficients according to the   solution at $(k+1)\Delta t$, on the other hand, produces satisfactory results all over as shown in Figure (3) and is not so sensitive to time step size.

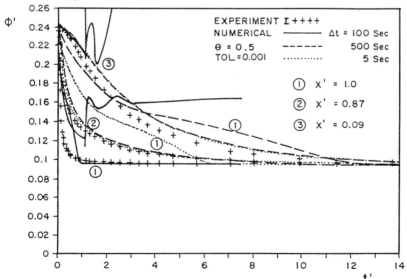

Figure 2. Sudden Drawdown Data versus Noniterative Numerical

Results for Various Time Steps

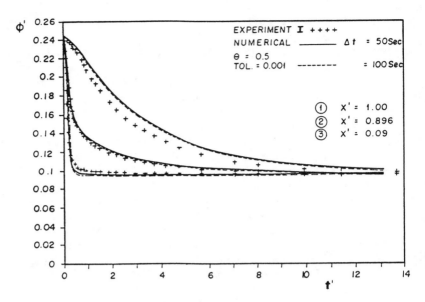

Figure 3. Sudden Drawdown Data versus Iterative Numerical
Results of Different Time Steps

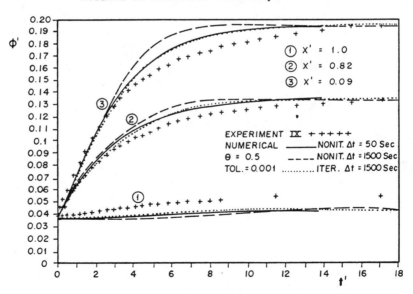

Figure 4. Effect of Time Step Size on Iterative and Noniterative
Schemes for Drainage with Recharge

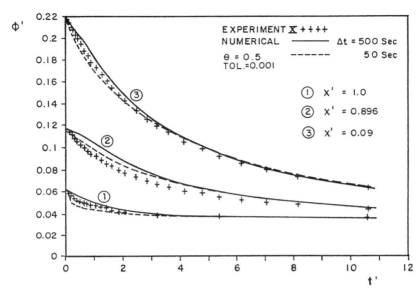

Figure 5. Noniterative Numerical Results for Drainage after
Cessation of Recharge

Vertical Recharge

Free surface numerical predictions for the vertical recharge case
are rather robust whether initialized from a horizontal or curved
surface. For recharge of an initially horizontal surface, Figure
(4) shows that the iterative procedure with extremely large time
steps (1500 sec.) produces estimates nearly as good as the noniterative one with small steps of 50 sec. However, the noniterative
method at Δt = 1500 gives unsatisfactory results. There is a certain disparity between numerical and observed values for initially
horizontal surface attributable, perhaps, to the experimental arrangement for recharge through jets descending from 24 needles.

Drainage after Recharge Cessation

Figure (5) shows experimental data for this drainage problem together with the numerical results with noniterative procedure for
two time step sizes. In view of the reasonable agreement between
observed and calculated values, this procedure appears to be satisfactory with small time steps though sensitive, prone to producing inferior results for large steps.

   Further simulations not reproduced here showed that the   use
of quadratic interpolation function for the free surface do   not
necessarily improve the solution as it requires numerical evaluation of integrals whose approximations may counterbalance   the
added accuracy of higher order interpolation.

CONCLUSIONS

It is found that the procedure which evaluates the coefficients of normal derivatives of hydraulic potential at free surface   on the basis of a known solution is prone to producing erroneous results.The use of small time steps as suggested in literature [3,4,7] can lead to numerical instability with this procedure as observed in numerical calculations for drainage from an initially horizontal free surface. It is shown that if the coefficients are iteratively calculated so that they correspond to free surface solution at the   next time interval, the numerical results are greatly improved. This iterative procedure is found to be quite robust in the face of decisions regarding time step size, the weighting factor that positions space derivatives in time, the number of boundary nodes, interpolations function order etc. This conclusion is   reached by   numerous comparisons between numerical simulations and experimental observation for various drainage/recharge cenarios.

REFERENCES

1. Bear, J. *Dynamics of Fluids in Porous Media*. Dover Publications, New York, 1982.
2. Brebbia, C.A., Telles, J.C.F. and Wrobel, L.C. *Boundary Element Techniques* Springer-Verlag, Berlin and New York, 1984.
3. Liggett, J.A. 'Location of Free Surface in Porous Media' *J. Hydraulic Division,* ASCE Vol. 103 (HY 4), pp. 353-365, 1977.
4. Liggett, J.A. and Liu, P.L.F. *The Boundary Integral Equation Method for Porous Media Flow* G. Allen and Unwin, London, 1983.
5. Liu, P.L.F. and Liggett, J.A. 'Numerical Stability and Accuracy of Implicit Integration of Free Surface Groundwater Equations' *Water Resources Research* Vol.16(5) pp.897-900, 1980.
6. Montenegro, S.M.G.L. *Estudo Experimental e Numérico de Drenagem Subterrânea - Aplicação do Método de Elementos de Contorno,* Master's Thesis, São Carlos School of Engineering - USP, São Carlos, SP, Brazil, 1989.
7. Sá, P.A.C.O. and Wrobel, L.C. 'Escoamento de Águas Subterrâneas em Aqüíferos Semi-Confinados'. *Revista Bras. de Engenharia - Caderno de Recursos Hídricos* Vol. 4(1) pp. 81-93.

Application of the boundary element method for plane and axisymmetric flows in zonal homogeneous porous media

N.N. Yas'ko, D.V. Evdokimov
Mechanical and Mathematical Faculty,
Dniepropetrovsk University, 320625
Dniepropetrovsk-10, Ukraine

ABSTRACT

The direct method of boundary elements is used for the solution of the plane and axisymmetric problems of groundwater seepage in porous media. Media may contain several zones in which the permeability coefficients are supposed to be constants. In this case the boundary integral equation contains unknown values on external and interzonal boundaries. Numerical results are given for flow through zoned dam and near the well.

INTRODUCTION

The prediction of free surface position and water pressure distribution associated with seepage through porous media is an important problem in dams and mining design. The boundary element method is perhaps the most efficient tool for solving the seepage problem [1-4] involving free surface, because the BEM requires discretization only on the boundary rather than over the whole region, as required in other methods. Usually the boundary element method is applied to problems of a flow in porous media only where the permeability can be considered constant, i.e. homogeneous medium. In case of variable permeabilities, the volume integral remains in the problem, and to perform the integration the solution domain must, in general, be descretized.

Lafe and Cheng [5] proposed a perturbation-based BEM for steady groundwater flow in heterogeneous aquifers. This technique based on expansion of the potential into a perturbation series and solution the resultant Laplace and Poisson equations using the existing BEM codes. This method is highly efficient for slow to moderately varying hydraulic permeabilities. For problems with varying hydraulic permeability over several orders of magnitude within the domain, however, this technique reduces to a diverged solution.

In groundwater problems, however, the domain is often consists of several zones, within each zone the permeability coefficient is constant value. Usually the permeability in one zone may be two or three orders of magnitude different than in an adjacent zone. In this case Laplace's equation is used separately in each zone and the compatibility conditions are matching on interzonal boundaries[3,4]. The general solution procedures for these problems have been given in Liggett and Liu [4], in which the final global matrix has a blocked structure, hence allowing the use of an efficient blocked equation solver.

In this work a new approach is applied to solution seepage problems in zonal homogeneous porous media, in which the resulting system of linear equations can be solved by the direct Gaussian elimination method for all unknowns.

GOVERNING EQUATION

The basic governing equation for incompressible flow in fully saturated porous media Ω for the general case of anisotropic soil behavior is

$$\nabla(k\nabla\Phi) = 0, \tag{1}$$

where $\Phi = \frac{p}{\rho g} + z$ is the groundwater potential; and $k = k(x, z)$ is the permeability coefficient. The discharge velocity can be expressed as $\overline{v} = -k\nabla\phi$. We assume that the region Ω consists of several zones $\Omega_i(\Omega = U\Omega_i)$, in which $k = k_i = const$. The boundary of region Ω is $S = US_i$, where S_i is the external part of boundary Ω_i. The internal boundaries between the zones Ω_i and Ω_j are S_{ij}.

A typical plane free surface problem of seepage flow through an earth dam sitting on an impermeable foundation is used as an illustration of the statement of problem. Shown in Figure 1 is an earth dam which consists of two zones Ω_1 and Ω_2 with the permeability coefficients k_1 and k_2. The free surface is initially unknown and will be a part of the problem solution.

The boundary condition (see, Polubarinova-Kochina [6]) is
$\Phi = z, \Phi_{,n} = 0$ on the free surface;
$\Phi = H_1$ on the upstream face;
$\Phi = H_2$ on the downstream face;
$\Phi_{,n} = 0$ on the bottom face;
$\Phi = z$ on the seepage face;
$\Phi_1 = \Phi_2, k_1\Phi_{1,n} = k_2\Phi_{2,n}$ on the interzonal boundary S_{12}.
The unit normal $\overline{n}$ is defined as an outward normal from Ω.

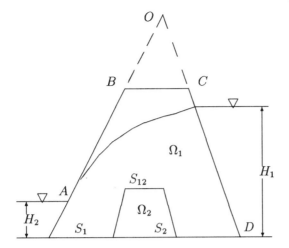

Figure 1. Definition sketch of the zoned dam problem.

BOUNDARY ELEMENT FORMULATION

Let domain Ω consists of several zones $\Omega_i(\Omega = \bigcup \Omega_i, i = 1,...N)$. The boundary of domain Ω is $S = \bigcup S_i$, where S_i is a external part of the boundary Ω_i. Interior boundaries between zones "i" and "j" are S_{ij}. We assume that in each zone permeability coefficient is constant and equal to k_i.

The integral representation of solution of the equation (1) is

$$\omega_M \Phi_M = \int_S k_P (\Phi_{P,n} G_{MP} - \Phi_P G_{MP,n}) \rho^\epsilon dS_P + \int_\Omega \Phi_P \nabla k_p \nabla G_{MP} \rho^\epsilon d\Omega \quad (2)$$

where $\epsilon = 0$ for plane case and $\epsilon = 1$ for axisymmetric case; $M(r, z)$ is any point; $P(\rho, \zeta)$ is a point on the boundary; $G_{MP} = -\frac{1}{2\pi} \ln r_{MP}$ is a fundamental solution for isotropic 2D medium; $G_{MP} = \frac{1}{\pi} \frac{1}{\sqrt{(\rho+r)^2+(\zeta-z)^2}} K(\gamma)$ is a fundamental solution for axisymmetric case; r_{MP} is the distance between points $M(r, z)$ and $P(\rho, \zeta)$; and $\gamma^2 = \frac{4r\rho}{(\rho+r)^2+(\zeta-z)^2}$. The complete elliptic integrals of the first $K(\gamma)$ and second kinds may be approximated by polynomial approximation [7].

Consider a similar problem, in which the permeability coefficient k changes from k_i to k_j in the δ-neigbourhood of the interzonal boundary S_{ij}(see, in figure $2, a$). We assume that $\delta > 0$ is a small value and k has a continuous first derivative along the direction of the normal to a boundary S_{ij}(see, fig. $2, b$). If $\delta \to 0$ then the solutions of the initial and moderated problems will

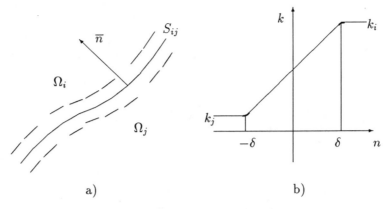

Figure 2. Fragment of the interzonal boundary.

be close.

If $\delta \to 0$, then the last integral in (2) may be represented as

$$\int_\Omega \Phi_P \nabla k_P \nabla G_{MP} \rho^\epsilon d\Omega_P = \sum_{i,j}(k_i - k_j)\int_{S_{ij}} \Phi_P G_{MP,n}\rho^\epsilon dS_P \qquad (3)$$

The coefficient ω_M in the equation (2) is

$$\omega_M = \begin{cases} \frac{\alpha_{iM}}{2\pi}k_i & M \in S_i \\ k_i & M \in \Omega_i \\ \frac{\alpha_{iM}}{2\pi}k_i + \frac{\alpha_{jM}}{2\pi}k_j & M \in S_{ij} \\ o & M \notin \Omega + S \end{cases}$$

where α_{iM} is the angle between the boundary segments at M in zone Ω_i.

If we know Φ and $\Phi_{,n}$ everywhere on external boundary S and ϕ on interzonal boundaries S_{ij}, then we can find the value of Φ at any interior point by a line integration (2). In a well posed problem, however, ϕ or $\Phi_{,n}$ are known on S_{ij} and Φ is unknown on S_{ij}. The integral equation (2) can be used to find the 'missing data'. Thus the boundary integral equation for zonal homogeneous medium contains the integrals of simple and double layer on the external boundary S and integrals of double layer on the interzonal boundaries S_{ij}.

NUMERICAL METHOD

The boundary S of the domain and interzonal boundaries S_{ij} was divided into N boundary elements. Constant elements were used in this case. The technique of this discretization and the application of direct boundary element method is well known (see, Brebbia and others [1]).

The coefficients of system of algebraic equations for Φ_i and $\Phi_{i,n}$ were calculated for plane case analytically using the following formulas

$$I_{Mj}^1 = \int_{-\frac{L_j}{2}}^{\frac{L_j}{2}} G_{MP,n} ds_P = \begin{cases} \frac{1}{2\pi}(\arctan \frac{\overline{rs}^+}{\overline{rn}} - \arctan \frac{\overline{rs}^-}{\overline{rn}}) & \overline{rn} \neq 0 \\ 0 & \overline{rn} = 0 \end{cases}$$

$$\int_{-\frac{L_j}{2}}^{-\frac{L_j}{2}} G_{MP} ds_P = \frac{1}{4\pi}\{\overline{rs}^+ \ln[(\overline{rs}^+{}^2 + \overline{rn}^2] - \overline{rs}^- \ln[(\overline{rs}^-{}^2 + \overline{rn}^2] + 2L_j\} + 2\overline{rn} I_{Mj}^1$$

where $\overline{rn} = \overline{r}_{MP_j} \overline{n}_j$; $\overline{rs}^\pm = \overline{r}_{MP_j} \overline{s}_j \pm \frac{1}{2}L_j$; $\overline{r}_{MP_j}$ is the distance between a point M and center the boundary element $< j >$; L_j is the length of the boundary element $< j >$. For axisymmetric case numerical integration was used.

An iterative process is used for prediction of the free boundary. This procedure can be summarized as follows:
- assume initial position for unknowns free boundary;
- for known $\phi_{,n}$ on free boundary Φ is calculated;
- new position of free boundary is calculated as

$$z^N = \Phi,$$

$$x^N = x + \frac{x - x_o}{z - z_o}(z^N - z),$$

where $O(x_o, z_o)$ is the point of intersection of the lines AB and CD (fig.1).
- iterative process repeats until convergence.

NUMERICAL RESULTS

The original numerical algorithm adopted was program SEEPAGE which computes a plane and axisymmetric problems of groundwater seepage in zonal homogeneous porous media and runs on IBM $PC(MS$ DOS). This program contains graphic editor for input boundary of the region and allows one to receive isolines of pressure, velocity vectors and other results. In order to verify computational results several linear numerical examples were run using this program for flow through a rectangular region. The analytical solutions of these problems were

$$\Phi = x, \qquad \Phi = x^2 - z^2, \qquad \Phi = \ln(1 + x^2 + z^2)$$

The boundary and interior solutions of these problems for 40 boundary elements demonstrated a high accuracy of the solution linear boundary problem in each case.

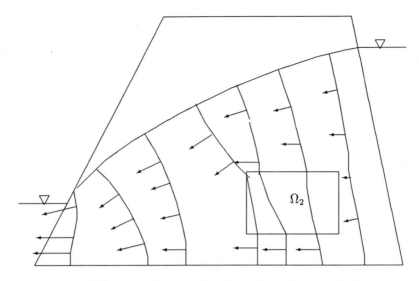

Figure 3. Free surface flow through a zoned dam.

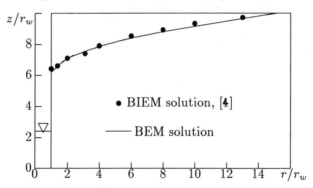

Figure 4. Free surface near the well in the finite aquifer.

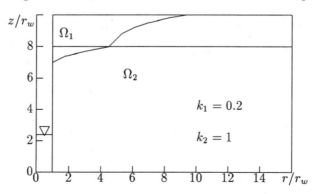

Figure 5. Free surface flow near the well in two zoned aquifer.

The seepage flow through an earth dam is used here as a successful example to illustrate the computational iterative procedure for unknown free surface. Computed results are presented for flows through a dam which consists of the two zones with permeability coefficients $k_1 = 10 k_2$ (fig.3). These results considered the location of free surface and the isolines of groundwater potential and velocity vectors into the domain.

To verify the present computation data with other numerical solutions, a problem for a pumping well in a finite aquifer is presented. In figure 4, the numerical results of Ligget and Liu [4] are plotted with numerical curve obtained by the present program. The agreement between these data is excellent. Figure 5 shows the BEM solutions for a pumping well, assuming a well is being pumped at a constant rate. The finite aquifer consists of the two stratums constant thickness with the permeability coefficients $k_1 = 0.2$ and $k_2 = 1$ accordingly.

CONCLUSIONS

In groundwater modeling, even more then in other scientific activities, there are never enough data. The numerical algorithm can be used to fill in the gaps. The proposed boundary integral formulation for zonal homogeneous media seems to be very effective and efficient. Many practical problems of groundwater modelling may be solved to underline this.

REFERENCES

1. Brebbia, C.A., Telles, J.C.F. and Wrobel, L.C. *Boundary Element Techniques* Springer-Verlag, Berlin and New York, 1984.
2. Lafe, O.E., Montes, J.S., Cheng, A.H.-D., Liggett, J.A., and Liu, P.L.-F. 'Singularities in Darsy Flow Through Porous Media' *J. Hud. Div.*, ASCE, v.106, p.977-997, 1980.
3. Lennon, G.P., P.L.-F. Liu and J.A.Liggett. 'Boundary Integral Equation Solution to Axisymmetric Potential Flows. 2. Recharge and Well Problems in Porous Media' *Water Resources Res.*, v.15, $N5$, pp.1107-1115, 1979.
4. Liggett, J.A. and Liu, P.L.-F. *The Boundary Integral Equation Method for Porous Media Flow* George Allen & Unvwin Ltd.,Winchester, Mass., 1983.
5. Lafe, O.E. and Cheng, A.H.-D. ' A Perturbation Boundary Element Code for Groundwater Flow in Heterogeneous Aquifers' *Water Resources Res.* v.23, $N6$, pp.1079-1084, 1987.
6. Polubarinova-Kochina, P.Ya. *Theory of Groundwater Movement* Princeton University Press, 1962.
7. Abramovitz, M. and Stegun, I.A. *Handbook of Mathematical Functions* New York: Dover, 1974.

Invited Paper

An efficient fully parallel finite difference SOR algorithm for the solution of a free boundary seepage problem

K.P. Wang, J.C. Bruch, Jr.

Department of Mechanical and Environmental Engineering, University of California, Santa Barbara, CA 93106

ABSTRACT

A fully parallel SOR algorithm is presented for the finite difference method. Also, techniques for domain decomposition are discussed. This parallel SOR iterative algorithm requires no overlapping blocks and no coloring scheme. By using domain decomposition and reordering the computation sequence, the inherently sequential SOR scheme is altered into a fully parallel iterative scheme. With this parallel SOR iterative scheme, not only computations for the mesh points in the subdomain but also computations for the mesh points on the interface are carried out parallelly. In addition, implementations of this scheme on an iPSC/2 D5 Hypercube concurrent Computer are presented.

INTRODUCTION

The SOR (successive over-relaxation) iterative algorithm is an inherently sequential iterative scheme. However, it is possible to convert this sequential scheme into a parallel scheme. To bring parallelism to the SOR algorithm, coloring, domain decomposition and overlapping block techniques are often used.

The ordering techniques change the order of the computing sequence to make it possible to update data concurrently. Several Jacobi type passes are performed using the ordering technique. On the other hand, domain decomposition techniques are used to subdivide the computation domain into subdomains. Then these subdomains could share the computation tasks and perform them at the same time. Similar to domain decomposition, overlapping block techniques subdivide the computation domain into overlapping blocks. With these overlapping blocks, computation tasks for the internal points of blocks can be executed concurrently with the data transferred and updated in the common area of two adjacent blocks.

For the past decade, parallel algorithms based on these three aforementioned techniques have been studied intensively. For example, Evans [1] presented several parallel SOR iterative methods using the red and black ordering scheme. Red and black colors were mapped into computation points or computation blocks. Also, Adams [2] used multi-color mapping which reorders the SOR computation sequence and maintains the same asymptotic rate of convergence to obtain parallelism at different computation levels. In addition, White [4] proposed parallel iterative methods using a reordering scheme given by coloring and domain decomposition and an overlapping block (multisplitting) method. Moreover, Rodrigue and Shah [4] imposed pseudo boundary conditions to accelerate the Parallel Schwarz method. Neumann and Dirichlet boundary conditions were imposed on each subdomain to ensure the continuities of the solutions. Wang and Bruch [5] used SOR and Jacobi iteration on overlapped blocks. Convergence checking was performed at certain iterations. On the other hand, Funaro et al. [6] proposed domain decomposition ideas without using coloring and overlapping blocks. During the iterative process, an interface relaxation factor θ was introduced. Continuity of the solution and continuity of normal gradient conditions were imposed in pairs on two sides of an interface. In addition, similar to Funaro et al. [6], Papadopoulos et al. [7] suggested a technique for domain decomposition on a problem involving a free surface which did not require an overlap region.

Herein, a simple and effective parallel SOR iterative scheme based on the domain decomposition technique is proposed. No coloring, no overlapping and no interface relaxation factor are needed. The basic concept will be illustrated on a one dimensional case first. Then ways are discussed for formulations on different domain decomposition patterns in two dimensional cases. Finally, implementations of this parallel SOR iterative scheme with appropriate modifications will be presented for a free boundary seepage problem.

BASIC CONCEPT

When developing parallel algorithms, many studies (see [1]-[3]) concentrated on the discrete relations that exist in the difference equations derived from the partial differential equations using the finite difference method. That makes implementations of these algorithms much more complicated than the sequential algorithm. However, the actual purpose of parallel algorithms is to solve sets of equations simultaneously. Therefore, studies of parallel algorithms should focus on finding parallelism that exists among these sets of equations instead. Accordingly, a parallel SOR iterative algorithm is developed for the finite difference method. This parallel SOR iterative algorithm uses the parallelism found among sets of difference equations derived from the differential form. By altering the order of the computing sequence, the inherent sequential SOR iterative algorithm is turned into a fully parallel SOR iterative scheme. Thus, efforts for implementing this parallel algorithm are eliminated; no special ordering and no complicated data structure are needed.

The basic idea of this parallel SOR iterative scheme is based on the domain decomposition method and the reordering of the computation sequence. With domain decomposition, the computation domain is partitioned into a certain number of subdomains. Separated by the interfaces, all subdomains can be solved independently. The values of the dependent variable at interior mesh points of a subdomain are computed independently from the others. In addition, all interfaces are isolated from each other. Thus, values at interface mesh points can also be solved parallelly. Accordingly, the computations for the interior mesh point data are uncoupled from the interface data which are treated as boundary conditions. In addition, the interface mesh points are weakly coupled with the interior mesh points. With contributions from related interior mesh points, computations of all interface values are also uncoupled. Thus, computations on interfaces can be carried out parallelly.

To show the basic concept of this parallel SOR iterative scheme, consider the one dimensional example:

$$\frac{d^2\phi}{dx^2} = 1.$$

(1)

Using the finite difference method, Equation (1) can be discretized into

$$\phi_{i+1} - 2\phi_i + \phi_{i-1} = c_1 \, ,$$

(2)

where $c_1 = \Delta x^2$ and i is the mesh point number. If i =2, ..., 4, the following difference equations are obtained:

$$\phi_3 - 2\phi_2 + \phi_1 = c_1 , \tag{3}$$

$$\phi_4 - 2\phi_3 + \phi_2 = c_1 , \tag{4}$$

and

$$\phi_5 - 2\phi_4 + \phi_3 = c_1 . \tag{5}$$

Equations (3)-(5) can then be solved by the SOR iterative scheme:

$$\phi_2^{(n+1/2)} = \left(\phi_3^{(n)} + \phi_1^{(n+1)} - c_1\right)/2 ,$$
$$\phi_2^{(n+1)} = (1 - \alpha)\, \phi_2^{(n)} + \alpha\phi_2^{(n+1/2)} ; \tag{6}$$

$$\phi_3^{(n+1/2)} = \left(\phi_4^{(n)} + \phi_2^{(n+1)} - c_1\right)/2 ,$$
$$\phi_3^{(n+1)} = (1 - \alpha)\, \phi_3^{(n)} + \alpha\phi_3^{(n+1/2)}; \tag{7}$$

and

$$\phi_4^{(n+1/2)} = \left(\phi_5^{(n)} + \phi_3^{(n+1)} - c_1\right)/2 ,$$
$$\phi_4^{(n+1)} = (1 - \alpha)\, \phi_4^{(n)} + \alpha\phi_4^{(n+1/2)} ; \tag{8}$$

where n is the iteration number and α is the relaxation factor. If ϕ_1 and ϕ_5 are known, this example has Dirichlet boundary conditions. Iterations performed through Equations (6)-(8) is a sequential process. However, by changing the order of the equations this sequential process can be altered to be a parallel process.

As shown in Equations (3) and (5), ϕ_2 and ϕ_4 are independent of each other. In addition, changing the order of the equations would not affect the final solution. Thus, Equations (3) and (5) could be solved first, then Equation (4). Therefore, the SOR iterative process becomes:

$$\phi_2^{(n+1/2)} = \left(\phi_3^{(n)} + \phi_1 - c_1\right)/2 ,$$
$$\phi_2^{(n+1)} = (1 - \alpha)\, \phi_2^{(n)} + \alpha\phi_2^{(n+1/2)} ; \tag{9}$$

$$\phi_4^{(n+1/2)} = \left(\phi_5 + \phi_3^{(n)} - c_1\right)/2 ,$$
$$\phi_4^{(n+1)} = (1 - \alpha)\, \phi_4^{(n)} + \alpha\phi_4^{(n+1/2)} ; \tag{10}$$

and

$$\phi_3^{(n+1/2)} = \left(\phi_4^{(n+1)} + \phi_2^{(n+1)} - c_1\right)/2 ,$$
$$\phi_3^{(n+1)} = (1 - \alpha)\, \phi_3^{(n)} + \alpha\phi_3^{(n+1/2)} ; \tag{11}$$

Equations (9) and (10) can be executed at the same time since there is no dependency between ϕ_2 and ϕ_4. In addition, in Equation (11), contributions from ϕ_2 and ϕ_4 can also be obtained simultaneously. Therefore, consider points 1, 2 and 3 to be subdomain 1, points 3, 4, and 5 to be subdomain 2, and point 3 to be the interface between subdomain 1 and subdomain 2. Thus, for every iteration, computations for subdomain 1 and for subdomain 2 and their contributions to the interface are executed concurrently on two different processors. Then the interface point is updated on one (or both) of the processors. The new interface data is used as the new boundary condition for both of the subdomains. This process will be repeated until convergence of the values for both the subdomain and the interface mesh points.

Applying the concept mentioned above to p subdomain ($p \geq 2$) cases, there will be p subdomains and p - 1 interfaces. Thus, these p subdomains can be assigned to p processors. Therefore, all p subdomains are solved concurrently and then p - 1 interface mesh point values are also solved concurrently. The new interface values are then used as the new boundary conditions for the next iteration for each subdomain. This procedure will be repeated until convergence is obtained for all interior and interface values. This strategem, therefore, is said to be a fully parallel SOR iterative method in the sense that all interior values of the p subdomains are evaluated parallelly in p processors, and all p - 1 interface values are evaluated parallelly in p - 1 processors.

FORMULATIONS FOR TWO-DIMENSIONAL CASES

Similar to the formulation in the one-dimensional case, parallel SOR iterative formulations for the two-dimensional case are based on the domain decomposition and the reordering of the computing sequence method. Take, as an example, the following two dimensional differential equation in a square domain, with Dirichlet boundary conditions imposed on the boundaries:

$$\frac{\partial^2 \phi}{\partial x^2} + \frac{\partial^2 \phi}{\partial y^2} = 1 . \tag{12}$$

Using the finite difference method, Equation (12) can be discretized into:

$$\bar{c}_1\left(\phi_{i+1,j} - 2\phi_{i,j} + \phi_{i-1,j}\right) + c_2\left(\phi_{i,j+1} - 2\phi_{i,j} + \phi_{i,j-1}\right) = 1 , \tag{13}$$

where $\bar{c}_1 = 1/\Delta x^2$ and $c_2 = 1/\Delta y^2$. The subscript i stands for the horizontal location, and the subscript j denotes the vertical location. Thus, i =1, ..., nc (number of columns) and j =1, ..., nr (number of rows). Moreover, values for points located along i = 1, i = nc, j = 1, and j = nr are known since they are boundary points. Rearranging Equation (13), yields

$$\phi_{i,j} = \frac{\bar{c}_1}{c_3}\left(\phi_{i+1,j} + \phi_{i-1,j}\right) + \frac{c_2}{c_3}\left(\phi_{i,j+1} + \phi_{i,j-1}\right) - \frac{1}{c_3} , \tag{14}$$

where $c_3 = (2/\Delta x^2) + (2/\Delta y^2)$.

Using the SOR iterative method on one processor, the following iterative relation is computed at all points within the computation domain (i = 2, ..., nc - 1 and j = 2, ..., nr - 1):

$$\phi_{i,j}^{(n+1/2)} = \frac{\bar{c}_1}{c_2}\left(\phi_{i+1,j}^{(n)} + \phi_{i-1,j}^{(n+1)}\right) + \frac{c_2}{c_3}\left(\phi_{i,j+1}^{(n)} + \phi_{i,j-1}^{(n+1)}\right) - \frac{1}{c_3} , \tag{15a}$$

and

$$\phi_{i,j}^{(n+1)} = (1 - \alpha)\,\phi_{i,j}^{(n)} + \alpha\phi_{i,j}^{(n+1/2)} . \tag{15b}$$

Since i and j are varied from 2 continuously to nc - 1 and nr - 1, respectively, this process is a sequential process. However, as in the one-dimensional case, by reordering the computing a sequential process. However, as in the one-dimensional case, by reordering the computing sequence, the SOR iterative procedure could be altered into a fully parallel process.

As with the one-dimensional case, domain decompositions are needed to transform the sequential SOR iteration scheme into a parallel SOR iteration scheme. The computation domain could be subdivided into columns, rows, or blocks of subdomains. For column type subdomains, the computation domain is split vertically. The row type subdomains, on the other hand, are obtained from subdividing the computation domain horizontally. When the computation domain is subdivided both in vertical and horizontal directions, there will be blocks of subdomains.

<u>Formulation for Vertical Splitting</u>
By vertical splitting (see Fig. 1), the computation domain will be subdivided into columns of subdomains. In addition, each subdomain will have at most two interfaces, one on the left and one on the right. A subdomain shares one interface with the right hand neighboring subdomain, and another interface with the left hand neighboring subdomain. Similar to the one dimensional case, if the computation domain is subdivided into p subdomains, there will be p - 1 interfaces. Thus, there will be nr rows and $subnc$ columns of mesh points in a subdomain, where $subnc$ is the number of columns of mesh points. Accordingly, points along column $subnc$ of a subdomain will be the same as points along column 1 of its right hand neighboring subdomain. Using the domain decomposition technique, a subdomain is assigned to a processor. Thus, SOR iteration can be performed parallelly by all processors at the same time with data transferred between two adjacent subdomains.

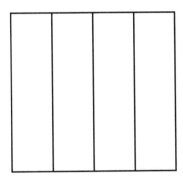

Figure 1. Columns of subdomains (vertical splitting).

To perform the parallel SOR iterative procedure, each processor computes the values of interior points of the subdomain assigned to it using Equations (15) with i = 2, ..., $subnc$ - 1 and j = 2, ..., nr - 1. Then the values at the interface points are updated concurrently by

$$\phi_{Int,j}^{(n+1/2)} = \frac{\overline{c_1}}{c_3}\left(\phi_{Int+1,j}^{(n+1)} + \phi_{Int-1,j}^{(n+1)}\right) + \frac{c_2}{c_3}\left(\phi_{Int,j+1}^{(n)} + \phi_{Int,j-1}^{(n+1)}\right) - \frac{1}{c_3}, \qquad (16a)$$

and

$$\phi_{Int,j}^{(n+1)} = (1-\alpha)\,\phi_{Int,j}^{(n)} + \alpha\phi_{Int,j}^{(n+1/2)}, \qquad (16b)$$

where Int is the interface column of a subdomain. Int = 1 for the left hand interface, and Int = $subnc$ for the right interface; and j = 2, ..., nr.

Note that, if Int = 1, then column Int - 1 will be column *subnc* - 1 of a subdomain's left neighboring subdomain. Also, if Int = *subnc*, column Int + 1 will be column 2 of a subdomain's right neighboring subdomain. Therefore, if there are p subdomains assigned to p processors, only p - 1 processors are needed to compute the data on p - 1 interfaces. Thus a processor needs only to compute values at points on one of its two interfaces (the left one or the right one) with contributions sent from the corresponding subdomain. In addition, only one processor of the p processors used will be idling while the others are computing values on the interfaces. However, for problems requiring the computation power of a parallel computer, there are always many more computation points within a subdomain than on the interface. Thus, the most time used by a processor will be the time needed for the computations for the interior points, the time needed for synchronizing, and the time for data transferring overhead. Therefore, the idling of a processor during the computations at the interface points will have no significant effect on the overall performance of this parallel SOR iterative scheme.

Formulation for Horizontal Splitting

Having all the properties of the vertical splitting, horizontal splitting is the transpose of the vertical splitting (see Fig. 2). However, now there are *subnr* rows and *nc* columns of mesh points in a subdomain, where *subnr* is the number of rows of mesh points. Accordingly, points along row *subnr* of a subdomain will be points along row 1 of the upper neighboring subdomain. As with the vertical splitting, the subdomain and the processor is a one to one mapping.

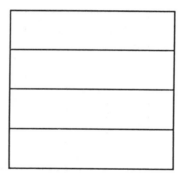

Figure 2. Rows of subdomains (horizontal splitting).

To perform parallel SOR using the horizontal splitting, Equations (15) are used again with i = 2, ..., nc-1 and j = 2, ..., subnr-1. After completing one iteration at the interior points, the interface values are updated by:

$$\phi_{i,\text{Int}}^{(n+1/2)} = \frac{\bar{c}_1}{c_3}\left(\phi_{i+1,\text{Int}}^{(n)} + \phi_{i-1,\text{Int}}^{(n+1)}\right) + \frac{c_2}{c_3}\left(\phi_{i,\text{Int}-1}^{(n+1)} + \phi_{i,\text{Int}+1}^{(n+1)}\right) - \frac{1}{c_3}, \qquad (17a)$$

and

$$\phi_{i,\text{Int}}^{(n+1)} = (1-\alpha)\,\phi_{i,\text{Int}}^{(n)} + \alpha\phi_{i,\text{Int}}^{(n+1/2)}, \qquad (17b)$$

where Int is the interface row of a subdomain. Int = 1 for the lower interface; Int = *subnr* for the upper interface; and i = 2, ..., nc-1.

Similar to the vertical splitting, if Int = 1 for a subdomain, then row Int - 1 will be row *subnr* - 1 of the lower neighboring subdomain. In addition, for a subdomain, if Int = *subnr*, row Int + 1 will be row 2 of the upper neighboring subdomain. The parallel SOR iterative scheme is carried out in the same fashion as it is in the vertical splitting case.

Formulation for Block Splitting

Block splitting (see Fig. 3) is the combination of the vertical splitting and the horizontal splitting. The computation domain is subdivided into blocks of subdomains. For each subdomain there are four interfaces, two horizontal interfaces and two vertical interfaces. In addition, there are *subnr* rows and *subnc* columns of mesh points in a subdomain, where *subnr* and *subnc* are the same as defined previously. However, there are intersection points for the block splitting since the vertical interface and the horizontal interface will intersect each other. Thus, there will be a special formulation for the intersection points.

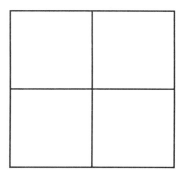

Figure 3. Blocks of subdomains (vertical and horizontal splitting).

For the interior and interface mesh point computations excluding the intersection points, Equations (15)-(17) are used as before. Only the ranges of i and j need to be changed to the corresponding values. The range of i is 2 to *subnc* - 1, and the range of j is 2 to *subnr* - 1. An extra equation is needed for an intersection point:

$$\phi_{Inti,Intj}^{(n+1/2)} = \frac{\bar{c}_1}{c_3}\left(\phi_{Inti,Intj+1}^{(n+1)} + \phi_{Inti,Intj-1}^{(n+1)}\right) + \frac{c_2}{c_3}\left(\phi_{Inti-1,Intj}^{(n+1)} + \phi_{Inti+1,Intj}^{(n+1)}\right) - \frac{1}{c_3} \, , \quad (18a)$$

and

$$\phi_{Inti,Intj}^{(n+1)} = (1-\alpha)\,\phi_{Inti,Intj}^{(n)} + \alpha\phi_{Inti,Intj}^{(n+1/2)} \, , \quad (18b)$$

where Inti and Intj is the location of the intersection point. In addition, Inti is defined as the Int in Equations (16) and Intj is defined as Int in Equations (17). Accordingly, using Equations (18), subdomains sharing the same intersection point can update the intersection at the same time with extra data transferred from neighboring subdomains.

In performing the parallel iterative SOR scheme using the block splitting, the processors are arranged in a pattern of a two-dimensional array. Extra communication among neighboring processors for a processor are needed since there are more interfaces and intersection points. However, the length of the interface data transferred is shorter than it is in the vertical splitting and the horizontal splitting. It can be expected that the time required for the interface mesh point computations and communication could compete with the vertical splitting and the horizontal splitting. On the other hand, since the computation time needed for the interface points and the intersection points are negligible, the most time consumed still is the time for computing at the interior points of a subdomain.

NUMERICAL IMPLEMENTATION

As a numerical implementation, the free surface seepage problem shown in Fig. 4 is studied. The relevant dimensions are taken to be: $a = 20$, $y_1 = 20$, and $y_2 = 5$. The free surface seepage problem in a fixed domain formulation is modeled by the governing equations and boundary conditions given in Fig. 4. In Fig. 4, D is the region ABEF and Ω (the seepage region) is the region $ABC_{\bar{f}}F$. The location of the curve $FC_{\bar{f}}$ is not known *a priori* but comes out as part of the solution. The variable ω is the dependent variable obtained using the Baiocchi integral transformation of the extended potential function. The detailed derivations of these equations and the SOR numerical iteration solution scheme with projection are given in [8]. It should be noted that the projection operator in the numerical scheme must be applied during the iteration process. It can not be applied after the iteration process has been completed since if it were, an incorrect solution would be obtained. The stopping error criterion was 10^{-2} for the maximum absolute difference between iterates at a mesh point.

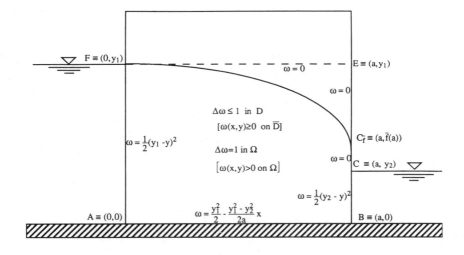

Figure 4. Free boundary seepage problem.

To solve this seepage problem using a finite difference formulation, computation grids within the computation domain are created. The computation domain is subdivided into different types of subdomains. The number of mesh points within a subdomain is about the same for all the subdomains such that the computation load is balanced among processors. Then the free boundary seepage problem is solved on a Hypercube Concurrent computer using the following procedure:

1. Each subdomain is assigned to a processor of the parallel computer.
2. Each processor initializes the computation information.

3. Each processor solves parallelly, using the SOR iteration scheme, for the values at the interior mesh points of the subdomain assigned.
4. Each processor transfers the contributions of the interior mesh points to the interface mesh points to the neighboring subdomains.
5. Each processor receives contributions of the interior mesh points from the neighboring subdomains and updates the interface's data by the interface SOR iterative formulations stated previously. In addition to the algorithmic ideas discussed in the previous section a projection operation must be added to the process.
6. Each processor checks the convergence of the values at the mesh points of the subdomains. If all mesh point values in a subdomain (interior and interfaces) converge, the convergence flag is set to 0. Otherwise, the convergence flag is set to 1. Then a global summation of all convergence flags will indicate the convergency of that iteration. More specifically, if the summation is greater than 0, then that iteration does not converge. Otherwise it converges.
7. Each processor repeats Step 3. to Step 6. until the convergence of the values at all mesh points in the computation domain are achieved.
8. Each processor outputs results.

Steps 1-6 can be executed parallelly. Communication occurs at Steps 4-6. Synchronizing and waiting are required by the communication processes. Thus, the communication is the only place that slows down the parallel computation.

The measurement of the speedup adopts the convention:

$$S_p = \frac{T_1}{T_p},\qquad(19)$$

where T_p is the time required to execute the algorithm using p processors and T_1 is the time required to execute the same program on a single processor. It should be noted that when the computations are performed on the p processors their sequence has been changed in that the computations on the interfaces are performed after those in the subdomains. Also, T_p is selected from the processor that takes the longest time. On the other hand, to measure the effectiveness of how the algorithm executes on a parallel computer, the efficiency e_p is defined by

$$e_p = \frac{S_p}{p}.\qquad(20)$$

RESULTS AND DISCUSSION

Solutions obtained using the proposed parallel SOR iterative schemes on three different computation grid sizes are studied. The fastest solutions for a sequential SOR iterative scheme on one processor were found by changing the relaxation factor α. Then the parallel SOR iterative process uses the α that yielded the fastest sequential solution to solve the problem. These α's were: 1.92 for grid size (101,101), 1.94 for grid size (141,141), and 1.96 for grid size (201,201).

Using these α's, Tables 1-3 show the speedup and the efficiency using different types of subdomains and different number of processors for grid sizes (101,101), (141,141), and (201,201), respectively. In these Tables, c denotes the number of the column type subdomains, and r denotes the number of the row type subdomains. For vertical splitting, $r = 1$ and for horizontal splitting $c = 1$. In addition, for combinations of vertical splitting and horizontal splitting there will be $r \times c$ subdomains. As shown in Table 3 the best speedup is 26.83 using 32 processors ($c = 16$, $r = 2$) on grid size (201,201).

The goal of a parallel algorithm is to distribute the computation load to processors such that a processor shares one part of the computation task and all processors perform the computations concurrently and independently. As discussed previously, this parallel SOR iteration is a fully parallel iterative scheme. Although the computation tasks can be subdivided and executed parallelly, there are factors that will affect the performance of the parallel algorithm. The communication overhead, the synchronization and the number of iterations needed to obtain the solution are three important factors.

As shown in Tables 1-3, the communication overhead and the synchronization delay are factors that affect the efficiencies of using multiple processors. The communication overhead and synchronization delay will degrade the efficiency of the parallel computation. Both degradings are due to the use of the multiple processors. When more processors are used, there will be less computation load assigned to a processor. In addition, when multiple processors are used and if the computation loads are not well balanced, some processors will be idle while other processors are computing. Unless the computation loads are distributed fairly evenly among processors, the more processors used the less synchronization there is. Therefore, the time needed for communication and synchronization becomes important when the computation load is small in a processor. For example, in Table 1 the efficiency is 97% using 2 processors ($c = 2, r = 1$), but is 55% using 32 ($c = 32, r = 1$) processors. When more computation grids are used, the efficiencies will be improved. After increasing the computation load, the computation time then becomes dominant and the time for communication and synchronization becomes less significant. For example, for the mesh cases (141,141) and (201,201), the efficiencies vary from 97% to 67% and from 97 to 81% ($c = 2, 4, ..., 32, r = 1$), respectively. As shown, the efficiencies have been improved by increasing the computation load.

no. proc.	c	r	no. ite.	time(sec)	S_p	e_p
1	1	1	95	63.73	1	1
2	2	1	94	32.74	1.95	0.97
2	1	2	95	33.03	1.93	0.96
4	4	1	93	17.31	3.68	0.92
4	2	2	94	17.39	3.66	0.92
4	1	4	96	17.36	3.67	0.92
8	8	1	91	9.18	6.94	0.88
8	4	2	93	9.56	6.67	0.83
8	2	4	96	9.82	6.49	0.81
8	1	8	97	9.82	6.49	0.81
16	16	1	95	5.6	11.38	0.71
16	8	2	91	5.26	12.12	0.76
16	4	4	94	5.48	11.63	0.73
16	2	8	97	5.9	10.80	0.68
16	1	16	101	6.13	10.40	0.65
32	32	1	94	3.63	17.56	0.55
32	16	2	95	3.43	18.58	0.58
32	8	4	91	3.07	20.76	0.65
32	4	8	95	3.25	19.61	0.61
32	2	16	100	3.73	17.09	0.53
32	1	32	116	4.65	13.71	0.43

Table 1.   Results for (101,101) grids, α=1.92.

no. proc.	c	r	no. ite.	time(sec)	S_p	e_p
1	1	1	113	175.86	1	1
2	2	1	133	90.79	1.94	0.97
2	1	2	133	90.98	1.93	0.97
4	4	1	132	47.68	3.69	0.92
4	2	2	132	47.29	3.72	0.93
4	1	4	134	46.99	3.74	0.94
8	8	1	131	25.12	7.00	0.87
8	4	2	131	25.60	6.87	0.86
8	2	4	133	26.18	6.72	0.84
8	1	8	134	25.96	6.78	0.85
16	16	1	129	13.42	13.11	0.82
16	8	2	130	13.74	12.80	0.80
16	4	4	132	14.64	12.01	0.75
16	2	8	124	14.85	11.84	0.74
16	1	16	137	14.58	12.06	0.75
32	32	1	132	8.22	21.41	0.67
32	16	2	130	7.94	22.15	0.69
32	8	4	131	7.92	22.22	0.69
32	4	8	133	8.14	21.59	0.67
32	2	16	136	8.69	20.25	0.63
32	1	32	144	9.30	18.92	0.59

Table 2. Results for (141,141) grids, α=1.94.

no. proc.	c	r	no. ite.	time(sec)	S_p	e_p
1	1	1	180	494.49	1	1
2	2	1	179	255.97	1.93	0.97
2	1	2	181	254.54	1.94	0.97
4	4	1	177	132.42	3.73	0.93
4	2	2	180	133.46	3.71	0.93
4	1	4	183	130.48	3.79	0.95
8	8	1	166	64.18	7.70	0.96
8	4	2	178	70.07	7.06	0.88
8	2	4	182	71.35	6.93	0.87
8	1	8	189	75.25	6.57	0.82
16	16	1	163	33.10	14.94	0.93
16	8	2	167	34.50	14.33	0.90
16	4	4	180	39.02	12.67	0.79
16	2	8	188	41.62	11.88	0.74
16	1	16	194	41.15	12.02	0.75
32	32	1	166	19.07	25.93	0.81
32	16	2	163	18.43	26.83	0.84
32	8	4	169	19.31	25.61	0.80
32	4	8	186	21.68	22.81	0.71
32	2	16	193	22.54	21.94	0.69
32	1	32	207	25.19	19.63	0.61

Table 3. Results for (201,201) grids, α=1.96.

Another factor that affects the efficiencies is the number of iterations. Note that, from Tables 1-3, the number of iterations vary using different types of subdomains. This is caused by the reordering of the equations. It was found that, in this study of the free surface seepage problem, the number of iterations tends to be less than the number obtained using a single processor when the column type and block type subdomains are used. The reason for this is that the boundary data is fed into the solution region faster in the parallel computations. Also, when the row type subdomains are used, the number of iterations tends to be larger than the one obtained using a single processor. It is intuitive that the higher the number of iterations needed the higher the computation load will be, and vice versa. Also, the more iterations needed the more time needed for the synchronization, since the synchronization is processed at every iteration. Therefore, if the number of iterations is decreased using the parallel computation then the efficiency will be increased. Moreover, if the number of iterations is increased the efficiency will be degraded when parallel computation is used.

ACKNOWLEDGEMENTS

This material is based upon work supported by the National Science Foundation under Award No. ECS-9006516. The authors would also like to thank the Cornell Theory Center's Advanced Computing Research Institute for providing time on their Hypercube Concurrent Computer (iPSC/2).

REFERENCES

1.   D.J. Evans, 'Parallel S.O.R. Iterative Methods,' *Parallel Computing*, Vol. 1, pp. 3-8, 1984.

2.   L. Adams, 'Reordering Computations for Parallel Execution,' *Commun. Appl. Numer. methods*, Vol. 2, pp. 263-271, 1985.

3.   R.E. White, 'Multisplittings and Parallel Iterative Methods,' *Comp. Meth. Appl. Mech. Engng.*, Vol. 64, pp. 567-577, 1987.

4.   G. Rodrigue and S. Shah, *Parallel Supercomputing: Method, Algorithms and Applications*, Wiley, pp. 77-88, 1989.

5.   K.P. Wang and J.C. Bruch, Jr., 'Solutions of a Steady State Free Surface Seepage Problem on a Hypercube Concurrent Computer,' *Eng. Comput.*, Vol. 6, pp. 225-236, 1989.

6.   D. Funaro, A. Quarteroni, and P. Zanolli, 'An Iterative Procedure with Interface Relaxation for Domain Decomposition Methods,' *SIAM J. Numer. Anal.*, Vol. 25, pp. 1213-1236, 1988.

7.   C.A. Papadopoulos, K.P. Wang, J.M. Sloss, and J.C. Bruch, Jr., 'Domain Decomposition for Free Boundary Seepage,' *Computational Modelling of Free and Moving Boundary Problems*, Proc. of the First Int. Conf., (Ed. L.C. Wrobel and C.A. Brebbia), Southampton, United Kingdom, July 2-4, 1991, Vol. 1, Fluid Flow, pp. 37-48, 1991.

8.   J.C. Bruch, Jr., 'A Survey of Free Boundary Value Problems in the Theory of Flow through Porous Media: Variational Inequality Approach,' *Advances in Water Resources*, Part I, Vol. 3, pp. 65-80, 1980.

Numerical finite element model for 3-d phreatic flow in porous media

A. Larabi, F. De Smedt

Laboratory of Hydrology, Vrije Universiteit Brussel Pleinlaan 2, B-1050, Brussels, Belgium

ABSTRACT

A numerical procedure is developed for solving steady state three dimensional phreatic groundwater flow with the finite element technique. The problem is solved with a fixed element mesh by iteratively adjusting the water table position and neglecting flow in the unsaturated zone. This is achieved without explicitly changing the coefficient matrix of the finite element equations, which makes the method computationally fast. Test problems demonstrate that the technique is accurate when compared with Polubarinova-Kochina's analytical solution, and efficient when compared with the moving finite element mesh technique.

INTRODUCTION

In many practical situations groundwater flow through porous media involves a 3-D free surface and seepage face. Analytical solutions can only be obtained when simplifying assumptions are introduced as the Dupuit-Forchheimer horizontal flow approximation. Comprehensive and standard references for background information on the subject, mainly in the context of saturated unconfined porous flows, and their solutions are given by several authors as Polubarinova-Kochina [1], Bear [2] and Cranks [3], which formulated mathematically several free-boundary problems, and discussed various methods to obtain exact and numerical solutions. It is very often difficult to use such analytical solutions, because of complexities as heterogeneity of the domain properties, significant vertical flow component, etc. Hence, practical approaches are based on numerical techniques as finite element, finite difference and boundary element methods. Several numerical solutions and techniques pertaining to the posed problem have been published within the last 20 years. In these techniques the difficulties arise essentially from the requirement to satisfy the boundary condition of zero pressure at a free surface, for which the position is unknown a priori. There are two alternatives, either the flow domain is fixed, including the unsaturated zone and the flow in the saturated and unsaturated part is solved simultaneously [4], or the unsaturated zone is neglected and only the flow in the saturated part is solved by locating iteratively the position of the water table [5]. Most simulations reported in the literature are limited to 2-D flow situations, and only few 3-D numerical models have been developed. Cooley [6] presented some procedures for numerical solution of variably saturated flow problems, using 2-D fixed FE technique. Cabral and Wrobel [7] applied B-spline boundary elements to 2-D fully saturated flow problems, including seepage through an earth dam. Huyakorn et al. [4] developed a 3-D finite element model for simulating water flow in variably saturated porous media. Baseghi and Desai [8] solved 3-D free surface flow using the residual flow procedure in conjunction with fixed FE technique.

In this study we try to combine the best of these approaches. The finite element technique is used to discretize the whole space domain, but the flow is only considered to occur in the saturated zone below the water table. The equations remain basically non linear, but there is no longer a moving boundary as in the classical approach. Nevertheless the position of the free surface needs to be determined. A numerical procedure is developed for solving this problem iteratively by adjusting successively the water table position. The main novelty is that this is achieved without explicitly changing the coefficient matrix of the finite element equations, by splitting of the geometric and hydraulic conductive part of the coefficient matrix. Examples are presented to demonstrate that the technique is accurate and efficient.

THEORY

The general form of the equation describing the flow in an isotropic porous medium is

$$\nabla (K \nabla h) = 0 \qquad (1)$$

where K is the hydraulic conductivity, which depends upon position and the pressure or saturation degree, h is the hydraulic head and $\nabla = (\partial/\partial x, \partial/\partial y, \partial/\partial z)$ is the del-operator. Boundary conditions need to be specified in order to have a unique solution in the flow domain D. Generally, two types of conditions are considered on the boundary, namely flux and potential conditions. In case the water table is considered as a domain boundary, both boundary conditions are needed or a mixed condition [2]. For instance, the boundary conditions with respect to the academical problem of flow through a vertical dam as shown in Figure 1 are :

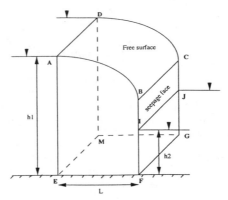

Figure 1 : Problem definition of flow through a dam

- face ABFE $q_n = 0$
- face FGIJ $h = h_2$
- face BCJI $h = z$ (seepage face)
- face ABCD $q_n = 0$ and $h = z$ (free surface)
- face ADME $h = h_1$

where h_1 and h_2 are respectively the left and right reservoir levels and q_n is the normal flux. This simple problem, has stimulated many attempts to find analytical solutions. A popular approximation was given by Dupuit and Forchheimer assuming saturated horizontal flow and neglecting the seepage face. The expression for steady unconfined flow is

$$q = K \frac{(h_1^2 - h_2^2)}{2L} \qquad (2)$$

where L is the length of the dam foundation. The free surface is obtained by the so-called Dupuit parabola :

$$h^2 = h_1^2 + \frac{(h_1^2 - h_2^2)}{L} x \qquad (3)$$

It was already established long ago [1], that Dupuit's formula (2) is accurate for steady flow through dams. However, the shape of the free surface has been shown to be less accurate, mainly because it ignores the existence of the seepage face. A more accurate solution to equation (1) has been presented by Polubarinova-Kochina [1] with the results of complex integral calculations, given in a series of graphs for dams of various dimensions.

In the present approach a fixed finite element mesh is used to discretize the whole domain, including both saturated and unsaturated zones. The numerical solution is given as a linear combination of nodal heads times basis functions. This approximation results in residuals when introduced in the flow equation, which are minimized by the Galerkin procedure. A system of nonlinear equations results

$$\mathbf{G(h)\ h = Q} \qquad (4)$$

where **h** is the vector of unknown nodal heads, **G** is the conductance matrix and **Q** a vector containing the boundary conditions. The coefficients of the conductance matrix are given by

$$G_{ij} = \int_D K \nabla b_i \nabla b_j dxdydz \qquad (5)$$

where b_i and b_j are basis functions respectively related to nodes i and j. The following properties are satisfied

- Matrix **G** is symmetric and positive definite

- and
$$\sum_{j} G_{ij} = 0 \quad \text{or} \quad G_{ii} = - \sum_{j \neq i} G_{ij} \tag{6}$$

Two contributions can be recognised in these coefficients : the gradients of the basis functions refer to the geometry of the finite elements, while the K-factor refers to the hydraulic properties of the medium. Whatever approach is chosen it follows that the G_{ij} coefficients depend upon the position of the water table. In case the elements remain fixed, the conductivity will depend upon the pressure or saturation degree, as some elements will fall in the unsaturated zone. In case the mesh is iteratively adapted to the water table position, the basis function will vary with each step. Hence, the algebraic system is nonlinear and can only be solved iteratively until a satisfactory accuracy is obtained. The key point is to choose a method such that calculations are kept to a minimum. Making use of Equation (6) the finite element equation can be written as

$$\sum_{j \neq i} G_{ij}(h_j - h_i) = Q_j \tag{7}$$

which can be considered as a numerical equivalent of Darcy's law. Now, for $i \neq j$, G_{ij} can be approximated as

$$G_{ij} \simeq k_{ij} \int_D K_s \nabla b_i \nabla b_j \, dxdydz = k_{ij} G_{ij}^* \tag{8}$$

where K_s is the saturated hydraulic conductivity and k_{ij} a relative conductivity ($0 < k_{ij} < 1$), which expresses the saturation degree of the region between nodes i and j. The diagonal terms G_{ii} are calculated with Equation (6)

$$G_{ii} = - \sum_{j \neq i} k_{ij} G_{ij}^* \tag{9}$$

Notice that the saturated conductance coefficients G_{ij}^* remain fixed during the solution procedure, and only the relative conductivities have to be adapted each iteration. This is achieved at the end of each iteration by calculating the nodal pressure potential $\Psi_i = h_i - z_i$. If the the pressures at nodes i and j are positive, the zone between node i and j is saturated and the corresponding relative hydraulic conductivity equals 1. In case one of the pressures is negative k_{ij} has to be updated. This updating must be done in a smooth way, especially when passing from the unsaturated to the saturated flow domain. The following method was chosen to achieve this :

$$k_{ij} = 1 \qquad\qquad \text{if } \Psi_i > 0 \text{ and } \Psi_j > 0$$

$$k_{ij} = \varepsilon \qquad\qquad \text{if } \Psi_i < 0 \text{ and } \Psi_j < 0$$

$$k_{ij} = (1 - \varepsilon) \left(\frac{\Psi_i}{\Psi_i - \Psi_j}\right) + \varepsilon \qquad \text{if } \Psi_i \geq 0 \text{ and } \Psi_j < 0 \qquad (10)$$

$$k_{ij} = (1 - \varepsilon) \left(\frac{\Psi_j}{\Psi_j - \Psi_i}\right) + \varepsilon \qquad \text{if } \Psi_i < 0 \text{ and } \Psi_j \geq 0$$

where ε is theoretically zero, but chosen here as a small number in order to allow for the finite element equations corresponding to nodes in the unsaturated zone to remain in the equation system, without obstructing the numerical solution procedure. The iteration process is repeated until there is no more significant change in the potential values over the whole domain.

For the boundary conditions, only the seepage face poses a problem. The position of this seepage face is initially unknown and constitutes another non-linearity of the problem. The objective is to satisfy the condition of zero pressure at the nodes on the seepage face and outflowing fluxes. Therefore, all the nodes expected to be part of the seepage face are treated as prescribed potential boundaries, with the potential equal to the elevation. After every iteration step, the flux values on the seepage face are checked. If an inflowing flux is encountered, this is set equal to zero and in the next iteration step the node is treated as a prescribed flux boundary. On the other hand, if a positive value of pressure is encountered at a boundary node in the unsaturated zone, in the next iteration step this node is treated as a seepage face node boundary.

APPLICATIONS AND RESULTS

To test the validation of the numerical model described in the previous section, two examples are considered, for which analytical solutions, are considered. Both problems involve flow through a homogeneous and isotropic vertical dam of length L as depicted in Fig.1 and are essentially only 2-D flow situations. These cases were chosen because they have been used by many authors as a model problem for assessing new methods for solving unconfined flow. The geometrical dimensions with respect to the first problem are $h_1 = 1m$, $h_2 = 0.5m$ and $L = 0.5m$; $h_1 = 1m$, $h_2 = 0$ m and $L = 1m$ for the second case. The Polubarinova-Kochina 2-D analytical solutions for both problems, evaluated numerically by [9], are used for comparison with our model. The flow domains are discretized with cubic elements of size 0.025m. This yields grids with respectively 20 and 40 elements in the x-direction for problems 1 and 2, and 40 elements in the z-direction and 1 element in the y-direction. Hence, problems 1 and 2 were discretized respectively into 1722 nodes and 800 elements and 3362 nodes and 1600 elements. Figures 2(a) and 3(a) illustrate these meshes. A tolerance for the potentials of 10^{-6} was chosen as stop criterion for the iteration. The results are illustrated in figures 2(b) and 3(b) and show a good agreement with the Polubarinova-Kochina solution. Table 1 compares the flow rates obtained from the analytical solution (6) and the present model. The agreement is perfect. Also the seepage face heights are compared. The numerical results give the elevation of the nodes which are closest to the actual seepage height. Hence, the predicted seepage height is not as accurate, because the nodes are spaced at distances of 0.025m.

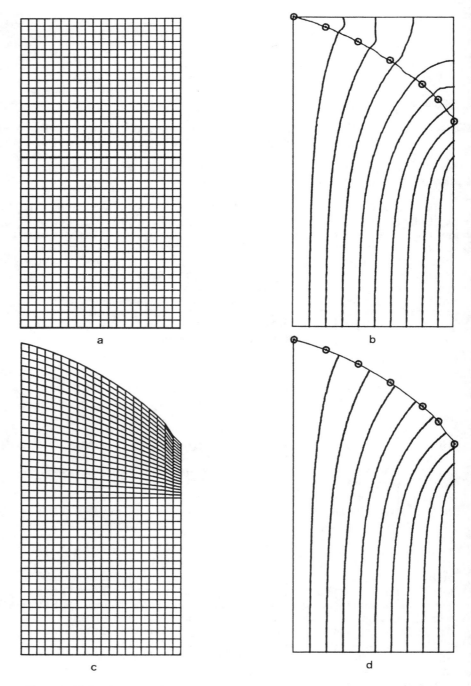

Figure 2 : Finite element mesh and distribution of the potentials (0.05m of interval) for
problem 1, (a) and (b) Fixed mesh method, (c) and (d) Moving mesh method. The water table
position is given by circled points (analytical) and continuous line (numerical).

	Flow Rate (m3/day)		Seepage face height (m)	
	Numerical	Analytical	Numerical	Analytical
Problem 1	0.01879	.0.01875	0.675	0.662
Problem 2	0.02559	0.02500	0.375	0.368

Table 1 : Comparison of the outflow rates and the heights of the seepage face

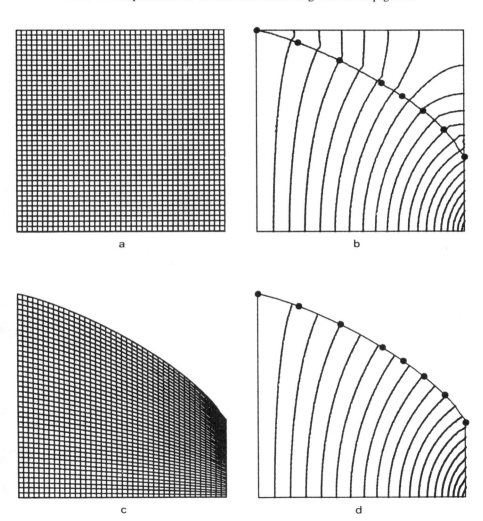

a

b

c

d

Figure 3 : Finite element mesh and distribution of the potentials (0.05m of interval) for problem 2, (a) and (b) Fixed mesh method, (c) and (d) Moving mesh method. The water table position is given by circled points (analytical) and continuous line (numerical).

It is also interesting to compare the efficiency of the present model with the finite element technique based on a variable mesh. Using this approach, only saturated flow is considered and the phreatic surface is adjusted by moving the element mesh each iteration. Fig.2(c) and Fig.3(c) show the final meshes, and Fig.2(d) and 3(d) show the distribution of the potentials in a vertical section. Table 2 compares the efficiency of both techniques for a SUN workstation. The fixed element approach performs the best, since it requires less iteration steps and less CPU time. Notice that the finite elements (fig.2(c) and 3(c)) of the moving mesh become very flat; especially for the elements close to the seepage face, this will make the numerical system more difficult to solve.

		Fixed Mesh Method		Variable Mesh Method	
	No. nodes	Iterations	CPU	Iterations	CPU
Problem 1	1722	10	70	14	205
problem 2	3362	19	349	28	1131

Table 2 : Comparison of the convergence efficiency, CPU is in seconds

CONCLUSION

A numerical procedure solution is developed using a fixed finite element mesh technique to simulate unconfined groundwater flow. The accuracy of the model was tested with the Polubarinova-Kochina's analytical solution. The efficiency of the model was tested by comparison with the variable mesh technique and shows that the present model is more efficient because it requires less computational efforts and less CPU time.

References

[1] Polubarinova-Kochina, P.Y., *Theory of Groundwater Movement*, translated from russian by J.N.R. de Wiest, Princeton University Press, Princeton, New Jersy, 1962.
[2] Bear, J., *Hydraulics of Groundwater*, McGraw-Hill, New York, 1979.
[3] Cranks, J., *Free and Moving Boundaries Problems*, Clarendon Press, Oxford, 1984.
[4] Huyakorn, P.S., Springer, E.P., Guvanasen, V. and Wadaworth,T.D., A three-dimensional finite-element model for simulating water flow in variably saturated porous media,*Water Resources Research*, Vol.22(13), pp. 1790-1808, 1986.
[5] Bear, J. and Verruijt, A., *Modeling groundwater flow and pollution*, Reidel, Dordrecht, 1987.
[6] Cooley, R.L., Some new procedures for numerical solution of variably saturated flow problems, *Water Resources Research*, Vol.19(5), pp. 1271-1285, 1983.
[7] Cabral, J.J.S.P. and Wrobel, L.C., Application of B-spline boundary elements to groundwater flow problems, *Computational Modelling of Free and Moving Boundary Problems*, Computational Mechanics Publications, Boston, Vol.1, pp. 21-36, 1991.
[8] Baseghi, B. and Desai, C.S., Laboratory verification of the residual procedure for three-dimensional free surface flow, *Water Resources Research*, Vol.26(2), pp. 259-272, 1990.
[9] Hornung, U. and Krueger, T., Evaluation of the Polubarinova-Kochina formula for the dam problem, *Water Resources Research*, Vol.21, pp. 395-398, 1985.
[10] Larabi, A. and de Smedt, F., Comparison of some conjugate gradient preconditioners applied to 3-D finite element groundwater modeling, *Hydrocomp'92*, Budapest, pp.15-23,1992.

SECTION 2: WAVE PROPAGATION

Flow calculations for a ship travelling in the vicinity of a pycnocline

L.H. Wong, S.M. Calisal

Department of Mechanical Engineering, University of British Columbia, 2324 Main Mall, Vancouver, B.C., Canada, V6T 1Z4

ABSTRACT

This paper reports on a numerical procedure for the potential flow, time domain computation of waves generated by a body advancing slowly in the vicinity of a shallow pycnocline, a region in a fluid where density variation over depth is significant. The problem is simplified in that the fluid is assumed to consist of two distinct layers of slightly different densities with a discontinuity of the Brunt-Väisälä number at their interface. Slender body theory is used to convert the three dimensional moving ship problem into a series of two dimensional time domain wavemaker problems in the plane of the stations, and marching from bow towards aft. The boundary element method is used to compute flow around each section.

While velocities and pressures are taken to be unique at the interface, the velocity potentials go through a discontinuity across that interface. The kinematic and dynamic conditions at the interface are obtained by equating velocity and pressure at the 'double nodes', one belonging to the upper and the other to the lower layer, on the common boundary. The thickness of the upper layer is of the order of the ship draught. Results for cases where the upper layer thickness is greater and less than the draught are presented. These results are compared to experimental values obtained by other researchers.

INTRODUCTION

The variation of the density with water depth is due to changes in the salinity and/or temperature over a region called a pycnocline. Such density stratification is a common phenomenon occuring both in the oceans and inland waters.   Although the density differences are small, ships moving very slowly in a shallow upper layer experience what is known as deadwater effects.   Near a given critical speed, the slope of the drag curve gets very steep and the vessel may lose manouevrability.   The available power from ship's engines may not be sufficient to push her beyond that critical speed. This is due to energy being expended in the creation of internal waves below the free surface and the disturbance of the flow around the ship due to these internal waves.   In naval applications, fully or partially submerged vessels could produce undesirable internal wave signatures.

Stratified flow analysis has been a topic of interest for a long time. Sabuncu [1] used source distributions to calculate the wave resistance and moment on a Rankine body in the presence of interfacial and surface waves in a stratified fluid.   Recent resurgence of interest in the problem is due to attempts to explain the long narrow V-wake left behind a ship advancing in stratified seas sensed by radar. Tulin and Miloh [2] obtained a solution in terms of a Green's function.   In connection to this, Ma and Tulin [3] measured experimentally the interfacial waves excited by a prolate spheroid.

The work described in the following sections is applicable to a slender body moving in a two layer fluid.   The three dimensional problem can be converted into a series of two dimensional 'wavemaker' problems using slender body theory, see for example Calisal and Chan [5].

FORMULATION

The frame of reference has the origin on the ship centreline at amidships and on the undisturbed free surface as given in Figure 1, where x is taken as positive in the direction of the bow.   The computational domains, one for the upper layer with density $\rho^{(1)}$ and one for the lower domain with density $\rho^{(2)}$, have a common boundary at the interface.   This simplification is justifiable only if the depth of the pycnocline is small.   Consequently,the Brunt-Väisälä number ($N^2 = -g\frac{\partial \rho}{\partial z}$) behaves like a δ function, being infinite at the interface.   The lower layer has a higher density than that in the upper layer.   This is necessary for overall gravitational stability.   The fluid is taken to be immiscible, inviscid and incompressible and the flow is assumed irrotational.   With these assumptions, flow in each layer is governed, within the realms of slender body theory, by the 2D Laplace equation (the superscripts in brackets refer to the domain considered):

$$\frac{\partial^2 \phi^{(i)}}{\partial y^2} + \frac{\partial^2 \phi^{(i)}}{\partial z^2} = 0 \qquad (1)$$

where ϕ is the velocity potential and $i = 1, 2$.

The solution can be obtained by solving a series of 2D 'wavemaker' problems, marching in small steps from the bow in the negative x-direction.   The 'wavemaker' is represented by the hull section and has a velocity distribu-

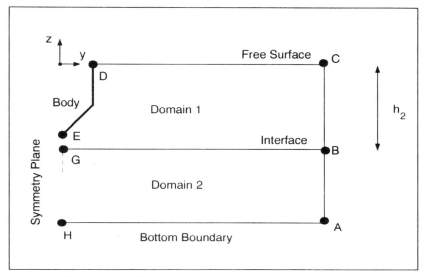

Figure 1: Definition of the computational domains.

tion given by the rate of change of the section with respect to x. This is given by:

$$\pm U Y_x - \phi_y \pm \phi_z Y_z = 0 \tag{2}$$

where subscripted variables are understood to be derivatives with respect to the subscript. The hull is represented by $y = \pm Y(x, z)$.

The boundary (H-A-B-C) in Figure 1 is taken to be impermeable. This condition is used to represent a towing tank so that calculated results can be compared to the experimental results in [3]. The following conditions thus apply at the bottom and far wall:

$$\phi_n = 0 \tag{3}$$

Due to the low speed of the body, the free surface amplitudes are expected to be small compared to the wavelength. Hence the linearized form of the free surface conditions are used. Although the nonlinear free surface conditions can be deployed, it is uncertain whether the increase in the already heavy computational requirements (two domains with a common boundary) is worthwhile.

$$U \phi_x^{(1)} + g \eta^{(1)} = 0 \qquad\qquad at\ z = 0 \tag{4}$$

$$U \eta_x^{(1)} - \phi_z^{(1)} = 0 \qquad\qquad at\ z = 0 \tag{5}$$

where $\eta^{(1)}$ is the surface wave elevation and g is the gravitational acceleration. Ignoring shear effects and equating pressures at the interface, the following two conditions can be written for an upper layer of thickness h_2:

$$U\eta_x^{(2)} = -\phi_n^{(1)} = \phi_n^{(2)} \qquad\qquad at\ z = -h_2 \qquad (6)$$

$$\phi_x^{(1)}\rho^{(1)} = \phi_x^{(2)}\rho^{(2)} + \frac{g\eta^{(2)}}{U}[\rho^{(2)} - \rho^{(1)}] \qquad at\ z = -h_2 \qquad (7)$$

where $\eta^{(2)}$ is the internal wave elevation with respect to the undisturbed level at the interface. Here normal velocities are taken to be positive pointing out of a domain.

NUMERICAL PROCEDURE

At the plane of symmetry, there should be no flow in the y-direction, that is $\phi_n = 0$. A prolate spheroid is used as a disturber and its geometry is defined by:

$$Y(x, z) = \pm[(1 - \frac{4x^2}{L^2})(\frac{B}{2})^2 - z^2]^{0.5} \qquad (8)$$

where B and L are the beam and length of the spheroid respectively. The normal velocity to be used for the 2D problem is then given by:

$$V_n = V.n = \frac{-UY_x}{\sqrt{1 + (Y_z)^2}} \qquad (9)$$

The simulation starts by considering Domain 2, which consists of three sides where the normal velocities are zero and a fourth (the interface) where the potential needs to be predicted. The first order Adam-Moulton-Bashforth (ABM) predictor is used where:

$$\phi(x + \delta x) = \phi(x) + [3\phi_x(x) - \phi_x(x - \delta x)]\frac{\delta x}{2} \qquad (10)$$

where δx is the step size. The problem is then solved using quadratic boundary elements. Emerging from the solution are normal velocities at nodes where the potentials are specified (B-G). Normal velocities found at the interface are then used as input for Domain 1. Nodes on the interface can hence be viewed as 'double nodes' where the velocities and pressures are taken to be unique and the potential has a discontinuity across the interface.

For the upper domain, normal velocities are specified at all nodes except at the free surface. The ABM predictor given in Equation 10 is again used. After solving Domain 1, required derivatives at $(x+\delta x)$ are to be calculated. On the free surface, the rate of change η can be found using Equation 5. Wave elevations at all nodes for (C-D) are calculated using:

$$\eta(x + \delta x) = \eta(x) + [\eta_x(x) + \eta_x(x + \delta x)]\frac{\delta x}{2} \qquad (11)$$

and Equation 4 can then be used to find ϕ_x.

At the interface, Equation 6 gives the rate of change of the interfacial wave elevation. The wave elevations for the next step $(x + \delta x)$ are found using Equation 11. For the boundary (B-G) belonging to Domain 1, the spatial derivative of the potential is found using a three point difference formula of the form:

$$\phi_x^{(1)}(x + \delta x) = \frac{3\phi^{(1)}(x + \delta x) - 4\phi^{(1)}(x) + \phi^{(1)}(x - \delta x)}{2\delta x} \qquad (12)$$

From this, Equation 7 is used to determine values of $\phi_x^{(2)}$. This completes the predictor part of the computations. The ABM corrector is then used on potential values on the interface and free surface as before using:

$$\phi(x + \delta x) = \phi(x) + [\phi_x(x + \delta x) + \phi_x(x)]\frac{\delta x}{2} \qquad (13)$$

Using the same equations as before, derivatives are again determined at the end of the corrector part. The above predictor-corrector pair is repeated for all subsequent steps. Each domain is therefore solved twice per δx.

NUMERICAL RESULTS

A prolate spheroid of $L = 45.70$ cm and $B = 8.90$ cm is used in the calculations. The densimetric Froude number, a parameter related to internal wave generation, is defined as:

$$F_i = \frac{U}{\sqrt{(\delta\rho/\rho)gh_2}} \qquad (14)$$

where $\delta\rho$ is the positive difference in density between the two layers and h_2 is the thickness of the upper layer. Results for two upper layer depths (h_2) at approximately the same F_i are presented in this paper:

1. Case 1 : $U = 12.86$ cm/s, $F_i = 3.00$, $h_2 = 6.70$ cm, $\delta\rho = 0.0028$.

2. Case 2 : $U = 11.43$ cm/s, $F_i = 2.95$, $h_2 = 4.25$ cm, $\delta\rho = 0.0036$.

The interfacial displacement for Case 1 $(h_2 > \frac{B}{2})$ is plotted in perspective view in Figure 2. Three interfacial crest lines are clearly visible for the length of x plotted. Crest lines for Case 1 are non-dimensionalized and plotted in Figure 3 for comparison with the results in [3]. The present method generally predicts earlier formation of the interfacial crest lines. A similar effect was observed for Case 2.

On the other hand, decay characteristics of the first interfacial crest is in excellent agreement with the measured results in [3], see Figure 4. Fitting

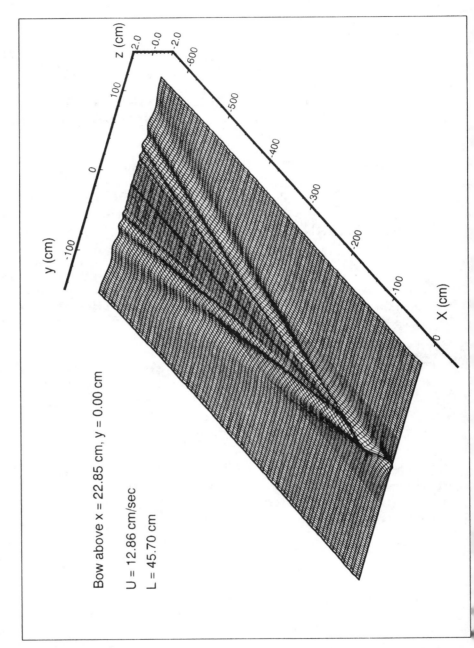

Figure 2: Interfacial displacement for prolate spheroid (Case 1).

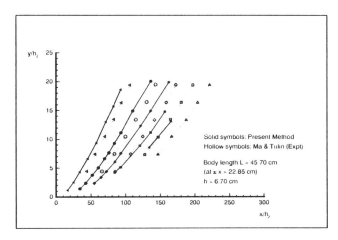

Figure 3: Interfacial crest lines in the wake, Case 1: $h_2 > \frac{B}{2}$.

a straight line through the calculated points gives a value of $\alpha \approx 0.80$, if $(\eta/h_2) \approx (x/h_2)^{-\alpha}$. Ma and Tulin [3] obtained a value of $\alpha \approx 1.0$ for this case.

CONCLUSION

A boundary element procedure for the calculation of the waves generated by a body advancing slowly in a two layer fluid is presented. The computed wave field in Figure 2, with a characteristic deep depression below the bow and the subsequent upsurge and oscillations giving rise to at least six crests in the far wake, compared well to those in [2] and [3]. Calculated crest lines (Figure 3) are in fairly good agreement with experimental values [3] except for a phase shift. The discrepancies are believed to be due to a number of contributing factors. These include the assumption of zero pycnocline depth, disregard of the trim and sinkage of the body as well as the lack of initial conditions at the bow in the computations. However, the interfacial wave amplitudes are very well predicted by the present method.

ACKNOWLEDGEMENT

The above work was made possible by the financial support of the Natural Sciences and Engineering Research Council of Canada (NSERC). Also, the authors gratefully acknowledge the kindness of Professor Marshall Tulin and Dr Huamin Ma (both of University of California, Santa Barbara) in granting permision for the use of their experimental results.

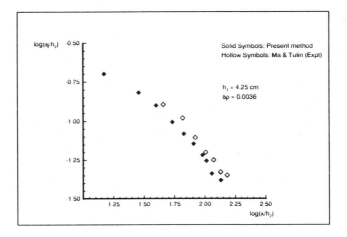

Figure 4: Decay of first interfacial crest, Case 2: $h_2 < \frac{B}{2}$.

References

[1] Sabuncu T., 'Some Predictions of the Values of the Wave Resistance and Moment concerning the Rankine solid under Interfacial Wave Conditions', Norwegian Ship Model Experiment Tank, *Technical University of Norway, Publication No.65*, 1962.

[2] Tulin M.P. and Miloh T., 'Dead-Water Effects of a Ship Moving in Stratified Seas', *Proc 11th Int Conf Offshore Mech and Arctic Engg*, Vol 1(A), pp 59-67, 1992.

[3] Ma H. and Tulin M.P., 'Experimental Study of Ship Internal Waves: The Supersonic Case', *Proc 11th Int Conf Offshore Mech and Arctic Engg*, Vol 1(A), pp 51-57, 1992.

[4] Brebbia C.A. and Dominguez J., *Boundary Elements: An Introductory Course*, Computational Mechanics Publications, Southampton, 1989.

[5] Calisal S.M. and Chan J.L.K., 'A numerical modelling of ship bow waves', *Journal of Ship Research*, Vol 33(1), pp 21-28, 1989.

Stem waves along breakwater with arbitrary reflection coefficient

K. Mizumura

Dept. Civil Engineering, Kanazawa Institute of Technology, 7-1, Ogigaoka, Nonoichimachi, Ishikawa Pref. 921, Japan

Abstract

The phenomenon of stem waves which propagate along a straight breakwater are studied by solving the shallow water equations. The numerical result shows that the flat region of high wave height is formed in front of the breakwater and the influence of reflection coefficient reduction causes the wave height reduction. But stem waves are produced along a straight breakwater for any values of reflection coefficient.

Introduction

When the incident wave propagates almost parallel to the breakwater, its wave height increases and it induces overtopping and erosion along the breakwater. This wave is called a "stem wave". In order to decrease wave reflection from the breakwater, concrete blocks are generally constructed along the breakwater. This study investigates wave transformation along the breakwater with different value of reflection coefficient. Fig.1 shows the definition sketch of stem wave. The region of high wave height expands and its value is less than the wave height obtained from the linear theory.

Governing Equations

The continuity equation is given by

$$\frac{\partial h}{\partial t} + \frac{\partial hu}{\partial x} + \frac{\partial hv}{\partial y} = 0 \tag{1}$$

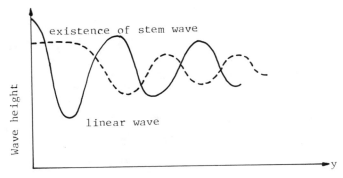

Figure 1: Characteristics of Stem Waves

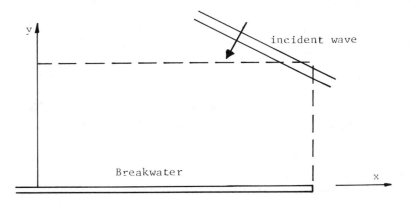

Figure 2: Coordinate System

in which $h=$ the water depth; $u=$ the flow velocity in x direction; $v=$ the flow velocity in the y direction; x and $y =$ the orthogonal coordinate system shown in Fig.2 ; and $t=$ time. Fig.3 represents the relationship between the incident wave and coordinate system. The momentum equations are also written by

$$\frac{\partial u}{\partial t} + u\frac{\partial u}{\partial x} + v\frac{\partial u}{\partial y} + g\frac{\partial h}{\partial x} = g(S_{ox} - S_{fx}) \qquad (2)$$

$$\frac{\partial v}{\partial t} + u\frac{\partial v}{\partial x} + v\frac{\partial v}{\partial y} + g\frac{\partial h}{\partial y} = g(S_{oy} - S_{fy}) \qquad (3)$$

in which $g=$ the gravitational acceleration; S_{ox} and $S_{oy} =$ the bottom slopes in the x and y directions; and S_{fx} and $S_{fy}=$ the friction slopes in the x and y directions. Eqs.(1), (2), and (3) are expressed in the finite difference forms as follows:

$$\frac{h_{i,j}^{m+1} - h_{i,j}^m}{\Delta t} + h_{i,j}^m \frac{u_{i,j}^m - u_{i-1,j}^m}{\Delta x} + \frac{u_{i,j}^m + \mid u_{i,j}^m \mid}{2} \frac{h_{i,j}^m - h_{i-1,j}^m}{\Delta x}$$

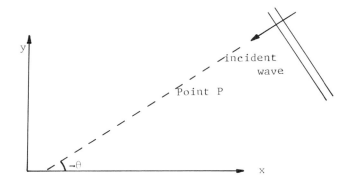

Figure 3: Relation between Incident Wave and Coordinate

$$+\frac{u_{i,j}^m - \mid u_{i,j}^m \mid}{2}\frac{h_{i+1,j}^m - h_{i,j}^m}{\Delta x} + h_{i,j}^m\frac{v_{i,j}^m - v_{i-1,j}^m}{\Delta y} + \frac{v_{i,j}^m + \mid v_{i,j}^m \mid}{2}\frac{h_{i,j}^m - h_{i-1,j}^m}{\Delta y}$$

$$+\frac{v_{i,j}^m - \mid v_{i,j}^m \mid}{2}\frac{h_{i+1,j}^m - h_{i,j}^m}{\Delta y} = 0 \tag{4}$$

$$\frac{u_{i,j}^{m+1} - u_{i,j}^m}{\Delta t} + \frac{u_{i,j}^m + \mid u_{i,j}^m \mid}{2}\frac{u_{i,j}^m - u_{i-1,j}^m}{\Delta x} + \frac{u_{i,j}^m - \mid u_{i,j}^m \mid}{2}\frac{u_{i+1,j}^m - u_{i,j}^m}{\Delta x}$$

$$+\frac{v_{i,j}^m + \mid v_{i,j}^m \mid}{2}\frac{u_{i,j}^m - u_{i-1,j}^m}{\Delta y} + \frac{v_{i,j}^m - \mid v_{i,j}^m \mid}{2}\frac{u_{i+1,j}^m - u_{i,j}^m}{\Delta y}$$

$$+g\frac{h_{i+1,j}^m - h_{i-1,j}^m}{2\Delta x} = g(S_{ox_{ij}} - S_{fx_{ij}}) \tag{5}$$

$$\frac{v_{i,j}^{m+1} - v_{i,j}^m}{\Delta t} + \frac{u_{i,j}^m + \mid u_{i,j}^m \mid}{2}\frac{v_{i,j}^m - v_{i-1,j}^m}{\Delta x} + \frac{u_{i,j}^m - \mid u_{i,j}^m \mid}{2}\frac{v_{i+1,j}^m - v_{i,j}^m}{\Delta x}$$

$$+\frac{v_{i,j}^m - \mid v_{i,j}^m \mid}{2}\frac{v_{i,j}^m - v_{i-1,j}^m}{\Delta y} + \frac{v_{i,j}^m - \mid v_{i,j}^m \mid}{2}\frac{v_{i+1,j}^m - v_{i,j}^m}{\Delta y}$$

$$+g\frac{h_{i+1,j}^m - h_{i-1,j}^m}{2\Delta y} = g(S_{oy_{ij}} - S_{fy_{ij}}) \tag{6}$$

Initial and Boundary Conditions

When we compute Eqs.(4), (5), and (6), the water depth and velocity at the initial time must be known. They are

$$h = h_o(x) \qquad \text{at} \quad t = 0 \tag{7}$$

$$u = v = 0 \qquad \text{at} \quad t = 0 \tag{8}$$

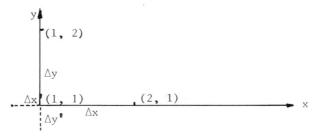

Figure 4: Selection of $\Delta x'$ and $\Delta y'$

In this study, there are three kinds of boundary conditions exist. They are impermeable boundary, an open boundary, and a boundary of which reflection coefficient is K_r. On the impermeable boundary the velocity normal to it is zero. On the open boundary, the wave height is approximately equal to a half which is computed by assuming that there is the impermeable wall on the boundary. Assuming the velocity in x direction or y direction at the point P is zero, the water surface deviation from the still water level is obtained as η_p. If the boundary is open, the wave height η_p is as twice as the normal wave height. Therefore,

$$\eta = \frac{\eta_p}{2} \qquad (9)$$

If the incident wave height outside the computational domain is η_i, the wave height at the point P is given by

$$\eta = \eta_i + \frac{\eta_p}{2} \qquad (10)$$

When the reflection coefficient of the boundary is K_r, the wave height at the point P is written by

$$\eta = \frac{1 + K_r}{2}\eta_p \qquad (11)$$

To apply this technique, the following relation between the spatial and the time increment must be satisfied.

$$\Delta x' = \sqrt{gh_o}\Delta t \mid \cos\theta \mid \qquad (12a)$$

$$\Delta y' = \sqrt{gh_o}\Delta t \mid \sin\theta \mid \qquad (12b)$$

in which $\theta=$ an angle between x axis and incident wave direction. Figs.4 and 5 show the expression of $\Delta x'$ and $\Delta y'$. At the corner of $x=0$ and $y=0$ (subscript(1,1)), the water depth is given by

$$h' = h_{1,1}^m - \Delta t[\frac{u_{1,1}^m h_{1,1}^m}{\Delta x'} + \frac{u_{1,1}^m h_{1,1}^m}{\Delta y'}] \qquad (13a)$$

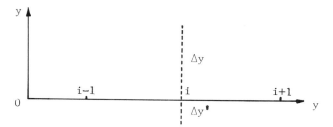

Figure 5: Selection of $\Delta y'$

$$h_{1,1}^{m+1} = \frac{h' - h_o}{4}(1 + K_r) + \eta_i \tag{13b}$$

in which $h_o=$ still water depth; $K_r=$the reflection coefficient; $\eta_i=$ the incident wave height. The flow velocities are derived as:

$$u_{1,1}^{m+1} = u_{1,1}^m - \Delta t [u_{1,1}^m \frac{u_{2,1}^m - u_{1,1}^m}{\Delta x} + v_{1,1}^m \frac{u_{1,2}^m - u_{1,1}^m}{\Delta y}$$

$$+ g \frac{h_{2,1}^m - h_{1,1}^m}{\Delta x} - g\{S_{ox_{1,1}} - S_{fx_{1,1}}\}] \tag{14}$$

$$v_{1,1}^{m+1} = v_{1,1}^m - \Delta t [u_{1,1}^m \frac{v_{2,1}^m - v_{1,1}^m}{\Delta x} + v_{1,1}^m \frac{v_{1,2}^m - v_{1,1}^m}{\Delta y}$$

$$+ g \frac{h_{1,2}^m - h_{1,1}^m}{\Delta y} - g\{S_{oy_{1,1}} - S_{fy_{1,1}}\}] \tag{15}$$

Along the breakwater $y = 0$, the water depth is given by

$$h' = h_{i,1}^m - \Delta t [\frac{u_{i+1,1}^m h_{i+1,1}^m - u_{i-1,1}^m h_{i-1,1}^m}{2\Delta x} + \frac{u_{i,1}^m h_{i,1}^m}{\Delta y'}] \tag{16}$$

The flow velocities are derived as:

$$u_{i,1}^{m+1} = u_{i,1}^m - \Delta t [u_{i,1}^m \frac{u_{i+1,1}^m - u_{i-1,1}^m}{2\Delta x} + v_{i,1}^m \frac{v_{i,2}^m - v_{i,1}^m}{\Delta y}$$

$$+ g \frac{h_{i+1,1}^m - h_{i-1,1}^m}{2\Delta x} - g\{S_{ox_{i,1}} - S_{fx_{i,1}}\}] \tag{17}$$

$$v_{i,1}^{m+1} = v_{i,1}^m - \Delta t [u_{i,1}^m \frac{v_{i+1,1}^m - v_{i-1,1}^m}{2\Delta x} + v_{i,1}^m \frac{v_{i,2}^m - v_{i,1}^m}{\Delta y}$$

$$+ g \frac{h_{i,2}^m - h_{i,1}^m}{\Delta y} - g\{S_{oy_{i,1}} - S_{fy_{i,1}}\}] \tag{18}$$

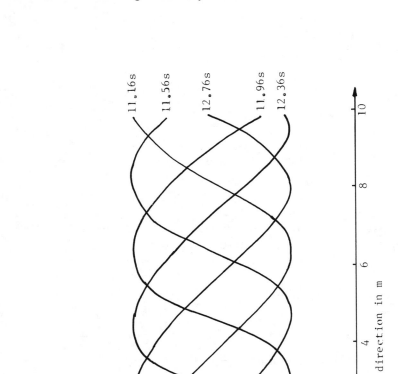

Figure 6: Water Surface Profile Normal to Breakwater at $x=0$ in case of $K_r=0$ when Incident Wave Angle is $\pi/4$

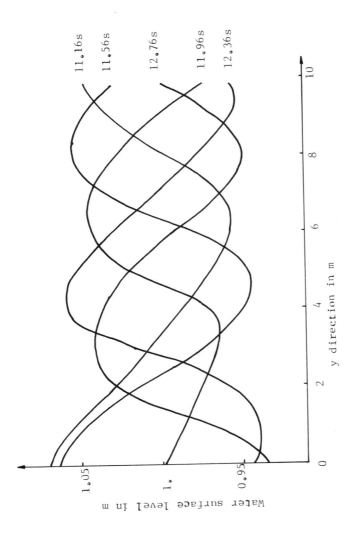

Figure 7: Water Surface Profile Normal to Breakwater at $x=0$ in case of $K_r=0.5$ when Incident Wave Angle is $\pi/4$

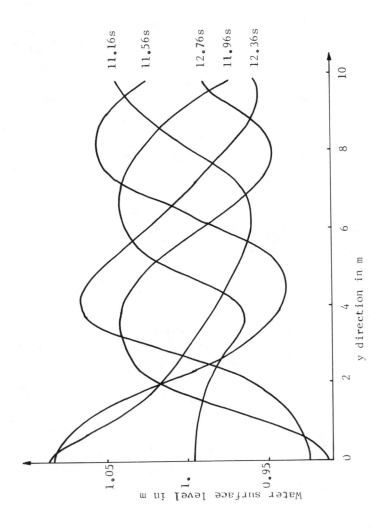

Figure 8: Water Surface Profile Normal to Breakwater at $x=0$ in case of $K_r=1.0$ when Incident Wave Angle is $\pi/4$

Numerical Result

Figs.6, 7, 8 show the water surface profile in front of the breakwater at $x=0$. In this case the incident wave angle is $\pi/4$ and the reflection coefficients are 0, 0.5, and 1.0. The water surface profile is regular and there is not sign of stem waves. Stillmore, when the incident wave angle becomes $5\pi/12$, the water surface profile for the reflection coefficients of 0.5 and 1.0 are represented in Figs. 9 and 10. The region of the high wave height expands and it shows the existence of stem waves. Fig.11 shows the wave height variation as the function of y when the incident wave angle approaches to $\pi/2$. As the incident wave angle approaches to $\pi/2$, the existence of stem waves is remarkable.

Concluding Remarks

When the direction of the incident wave is almost parallel to the breakwater, by solving nonlinear shallow water equations numerically, the existence of stem wave is proved. This is caused for any value of reflection coefficient and the region of high wave height expands. As the incident wave direction approaches to parallel to the breakwater, the wave height decreases.

References

[1] Yoon, S. B. and Liu, P. L.-F. Stem Waves along Breakwater. *Jour. of Waterway, Port, Coastal, and Ocean Engineering*, ASCE, Vol.115, No.5, Sept., 1989, pp.635-648.

[2] Melville, W. K. On the Mach reflection of a solitary wave. *Jour. of Fluid Mech.*, Vol.98, part 2, 1980, pp.285-297.

[3] Kirby, J. T. and Dalrymple. A parabolic equation for the combined reflection-diffraction of Stokes waves by mildly varying topography. *Jour. of Fluid Mech.*, Vol.136, 1980, pp.453-466.

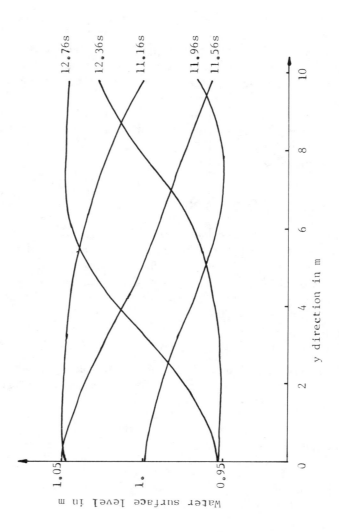

Figure 9: Water Surface Profile Normal to Breakwater at $x=0$ in case of $K_r=0.5$ when Incident Wave Angle is $5\pi/12$

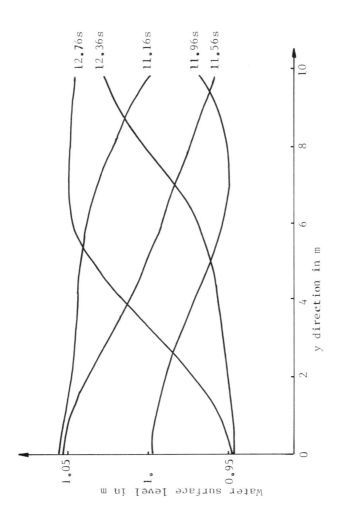

Figure 10: Water Surface Profile Normal to Breakwater at $x=0$ in case of $K_r=1.0$ when Incident Wave Angle is $5\pi/12$

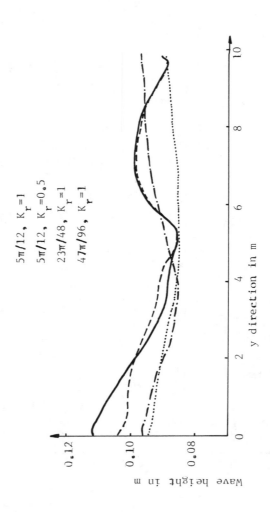

Figure 11: Water Surface Profile in front of Breakwater for different Incident wave angle

Application of a numerical wave channel (NWC) for the analysis of free floating body dynamics

C. Haack, O. Mahrenholtz, V. Schlegel

Ocean Engineering Section II, Technical University Hamburg-Harburg, D-2100 Hamburg 90, Germany

ABSTRACT

For the analysis of fluid-structure-interaction experiments with floating bodies are typically carried out in wave channels. Beside measurement equipment and test objects experiments require free capacities of laboratory facilities. In order to reduce costs and to allow the analysis of various different test configurations, the application of reliable NWC's is indispensable. The paper presents the results of simulations carried out with a NWC. The two-dimensional boundary element approach uses cubic spline approximations for the free surface discretization and a double node concept for the modeling of contact points between structures and fluid. The unknown time-dependent nonlinear boundary conditions on the free surface are evaluated by a time-stepping procedure. In order to avoid reflections at the end of the NWC an artificial boundary condition has to be formulated. A numerical damping approach is applied by adding a Rayleigh-damping term to the dynamical boundary condition of the free surface in order to simulate the physical damping facilities (e.g. sloping beaches, meshes, etc.) of the experimental set up.

PROBLEM FORMULATION

In order to solve the fluid flow problem the following usual assumptions of an incompressible fluid and an irrotational flow are made. This allows to introduce a potential flow, described by the Laplace equation:

$$\operatorname{div} \mathbf{u} = \operatorname{div} \operatorname{grad} \Phi = \nabla^2 \Phi = 0 , \tag{1}$$

where $\mathbf{u}$ is the fluid velocity and Φ the corresponding velocity potential.

Beyond this, the equation of motion of the fluid particles can be reduced to the Bernoulli equation. Written in the general form it states

$$\frac{d\,\Phi}{d\,t} = \frac{\partial \Phi}{\partial t} + \mathbf{v}\,\mathrm{grad}\,\Phi \,,$$

$$= -g\,y - \frac{1}{\rho}\,p - \frac{|\mathbf{u}|^2}{2} + \mathbf{v}\,\mathbf{u}\,, \tag{2}$$

with g the gravitational acceleration, y the vertical position of the considered point, ρ the density of the fluid and p the pressure. In this general form one has to distinguish between

> $\mathbf{u}$: the velocity vector of a fluid particle in the flow (Lagrangian description) and

> $\mathbf{v}$: the velocity vector of a point moved arbitrarily through the fluid (Eulerian description).

As mentioned before the fluid flow problem is solved by transforming the Laplace equation (1) with a direct method into an integral equation of the form

$$C(\mathbf{x})\,\Phi(\mathbf{x}) = \int_{\Gamma} \mathbf{u}_n(\xi)\,G(\mathbf{x},\xi) - \Phi(\xi)\,\frac{\partial\,G(\mathbf{x},\xi)}{\partial\,\mathbf{n}(\xi)}\,d\,\gamma(\xi) \,. \tag{3}$$

Field and source points are denoted by $\mathbf{x}$ and ξ, the fundamental solution of the problem by G and C is a constant with the property $C(\mathbf{x}) = 1/2$, if Γ is smooth and $\mathbf{x} \in \Gamma$.

This formulation is discretized by a BE approach and results in the typical approximation (ref. [3])

$$(\mathbf{C} + \mathbf{H})\,\tilde{\Phi}(\mathbf{x}) = \mathbf{F}\,\tilde{\mathbf{u}}_n(\mathbf{x}) \,, \tag{4}$$

where the vectors $\tilde{\Phi}$ and $\tilde{\mathbf{u}}_n$ consist of the ansatz-functions with regard to the different types of elements (e.g. linear, quadratic, splines, etc.).

Considering a mixed boundary value problem the known and unknown boundary conditions in equation (4) have to be rearranged to get them in the form

$$\mathbf{A}\,\mathbf{y} = \mathbf{b} \,, \tag{5}$$

as a set of linear equations, where $\mathbf{A}$ is in general a dense and unsymmetric matrix. The right hand sides $\mathbf{b}$ are given by the boundary conditions:

> Φ : on the free surfaces of the fluid and
>
> $\mathbf{u}_n = \mathbf{v}_n$: on all other boudaries.

NUMERICAL IMPLEMENTATION

As mentioned before the two-dimensional fluid flow problem is solved by a direct BEM. The considered domain is discretized by one-dimensional elements. A double-node concept allows to have both, arbitrary shaped boundaries as well as the transitions of different kinds of boundary conditions. In order to analyze even time-dependent, transient problems the equations of motion of the fluid particles on the free surface and of the floating body with in general nonlinear r.h.s. have to be taken into account. These two sub-problems are condensed to an initial value problem (e.g. [2], [4])

$$\frac{d\mathbf{x}}{dt} = f(\mathbf{x}, t), \quad \mathbf{x}(t=0) = \mathbf{x}_0.$$ (6)

This system is solved by an explicit predictor-corrector scheme, starting with a higher order Runge-Kutta method. The motion of the fluid particles at the free surfaces is described by a Lagrangian formulation, with $\mathbf{v} = \mathbf{u}$ in equation (2). So the equations of motion for the fluid particles yield in fully nonlinear form:

$$\frac{D\mathbf{x}}{Dt} = \nabla\Phi = \mathbf{u},$$
$$\frac{D\Phi}{Dt} = -gy - \frac{1}{\rho}p + \frac{|\mathbf{u}|^2}{2}.$$ (7)

Here, the position of the fluid particles on the free surfaces is described by the vector $\mathbf{x} = [x_{fl}\ y_{fl}]^T$. The initial condition is given by $\Phi(t=0) = \Phi_0$. The unknown time-dependent pressure on the submerged surface of a floating body is gained by transforming equation (2) into the form

$$p(t) = \rho\left(-gy - \frac{|\mathbf{u}|^2}{2} - \frac{d\Phi}{dt} + \mathbf{v}\mathbf{u}\right).$$ (8)

The evaluation of the pressure distribution (8) requires an approximation of the time derivative of the potential $d\Phi/dt$ and of $\mathbf{v}$, the absolute velocity of a single grid point. This is evaluated by a second order polynomial approximation and achieves best agreement for the considered applications. The main feature of a NWC is a controlled excitation of the free surface. Such a wave generator is numerically implemented by a given function at a Neumann-type boundary. If a sinusoidal flap excitation is assumed the time-dependent position vector $\mathbf{x}(t)$ and the boundary conditions $v_n(t)$ are described by:

$$\alpha(t) = \alpha_0 + A\,sin(\omega t + \psi)$$

$$\mathbf{x}(t) = r\left[\begin{array}{c} sin(\alpha(t)) \\ cos(\alpha(t)) \end{array}\right]$$

$$v_n(t) = r\,\dot{\alpha}(t) = r\,\omega\,A\,cos(\omega t + \psi)$$

(9)

with amplitude A, angular velocity $\omega = 2\pi/T = $ const., phase shift ψ and distance r to the hinge of the flap.

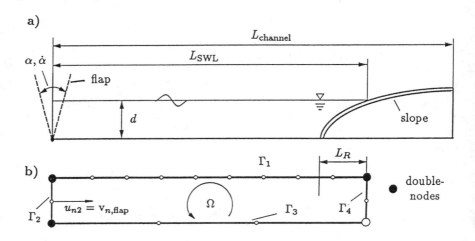

Figure 1: Sketch of the experimental wave channel (a)
and its discretization in the NWC model (b)

The boundary conditions of the boundaries Γ_1 to Γ_4 in the wave channel are now given by (ref. Fig. 1):

$$\begin{aligned}
\Phi_1 &= \Phi_1(t)\,, \\
u_{n2} &= \mathrm{v}_{n,\text{flap}}\,, \\
u_{n3} &= 0\,, \\
u_{n4} &= 0\,.
\end{aligned}$$

(10)

The physical damping of the slope is modeled by a modified dynamic boundary condition at the free surface Γ_1. The wave absorption is introduced by assuming Rayleigh-damping on the free surface in the region of the slope (see Betts and Mohamad [1]):

$$\frac{D\Phi_1}{Dt} = -g\,y - \frac{1}{\rho}p + \frac{1}{2}u^2 - \mu_R\Phi_1\,, \quad \text{if } \Gamma_1 \in L_R\,,$$

(11)

where $\mu_R = f(x)$ gives the Rayleigh-damping coefficient as a function of the fluid particle's position. The additional term $\mu_R\,\Phi_1$ in the Bernoulli equation represents a force in opposite direction of the velocity and results therefore in dissipation of energy.

RESULTS

The main feature of an experimental wave channel is a damping facility like sloping beaches, meshes, etc., that prevent reflections of incoming waves at the end of the wave channel. The mathematical modeling of such damping facilities is essential in order to carry out simulations with a NWC. In this section both, the effect of wave reflections due to fixed walls at the end of the channel and the adaptation of the physical and numerical damping behavior are shown. Figure 2 depicts a typical test configuration for the analysis of free floating body dynamics, with: a = 4.5 m, b = 5 m, d = 1 m, L = 10 m, the mass of the body M = 240 kg and an initial vertical upward displacement $y_0 = 0.04$ m at time $t = 0$. The vertical walls at the end of the channel are considered to be fixed, i.e. $v_n = 0$. The typical heave response of the centre of mass versus time is given in Figure 3. An undisturbed damped oscillation is observed for $t < 5$ s, whereas for longer times $t > 5$ s obviously reflections occur.

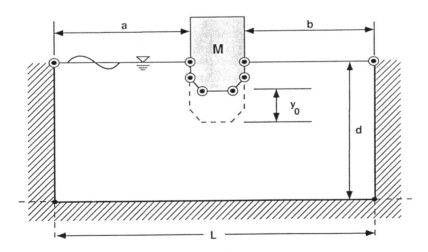

Figure 2: NWC with free floating body (initial condition)

In order to adapt the damping parameters for the Rayleigh-damping term in (11) experiments were carried out in a wave channel with a flap-type wave generator. At different positions in the wave tank the wave elevations were measured for the case where the flap excitation stops at time $t \geq t_{stop}$. The damped oscillation of the free surface was recorded and gives the character- istics of the physical damping in the experimental set up. Figure 4 shows

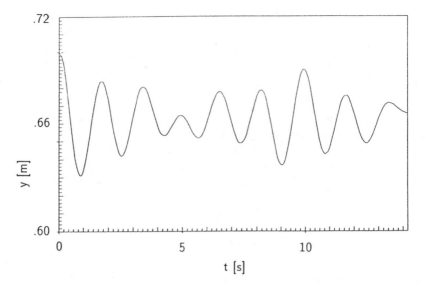

Figure 3: Heave motion of the centre of mass versus time

the result of the experiment compared with numerical results. Here, the difference between computations with and without numerical damping is obvious. In the case of no damping again intense reflections occur. Against that, the simple Rayleigh-damping approach suppresses these reflections nearly completely and shows good agreement with the damping behavior of the experimental results.

A deeper insight into the numerical damping is achieved by monitoring the kinetic energy

$$E_{kin} = \frac{\rho}{2} \int_{\Gamma} \Phi \frac{\partial \Phi}{\partial n} \, d\Gamma \ . \tag{12}$$

For computations with and without numerical damping this is compared in Figure 5. Several experiments for different frequencies of the flap excitation were carried out. Even here, the Rayleigh-damping approach with a linear distribution $\mu(x) = d_{max} \, (L_R - x)$, for $0 < x < L_R$, starting with a maximum value d_{max}, shows good results. But in this case both, the length of the damping zone L_R and the maximum value d_{max} have to be adjusted depending on the wave frequency. The length of the damping zone is approximated by the expected wave length (ref. [1]) and, as an additional condition, we use the relation

$$\int_{0}^{L_R} = \mu(x) \, dx = \text{const.} \ . \tag{13}$$

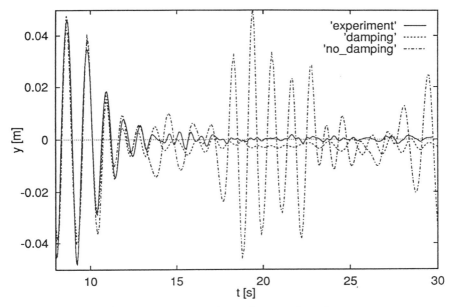

Figure 4: Wave absorption, comparison of wave elevations
(solid line: experiment, dashed lines: computations)

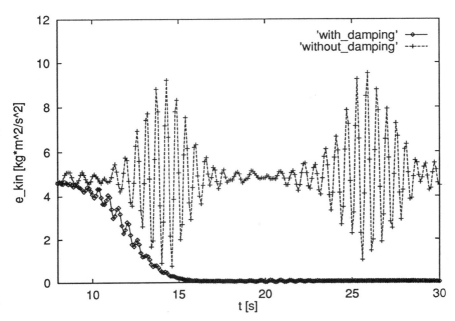

Figure 5: Wave absorption, comparison of kinetic energy
(computations with and without numerical damping)

CONCLUSIONS

The paper presents a boundary element formulation to simulate fluid-structure-interaction problems with nonlinear gravity waves. Because all quantities of interest are located on the boundary itself this is a most efficient approach with minimal discretization expenses. A time-stepping procedure allows the treatment of time-dependent and nonlinear conditions. In particular this proposal provides the extension to a numerical wave channel (NWC) in order to simulate typical laboratory wave channel experiments. The major drawback of this fully nonlinear approach is the mathematical formulation of open boundary or damping conditions to avoid reflections at the vertical boundaries. The comparison of experimental and numerical results shows good agreements of the damping behavior in the case of a simple Rayleigh-damping, introduced at the dynamical boundary condition of the free surface. The disadvantage of the Rayleigh-model is the fact, that the damping parameters of the mathematical model depend on the frequency of the incoming waves. Therefore, a modified adaptive model has to be formulated in the case of free floating body analysis.

ACKNOWLEDGEMENTS

These investigations were partly supported by the German Research Foundation (DFG) under Grant No. Ma 358/48-2.

REFERENCES

[1] P.L. Betts and T.T. Mohamad. 'Water waves: A time-varying unlinearized boundary element approach'. In: Finite Element Flow Analysis (T. Kawai, ed.), Univ. of Tokyo Press, pp. 923–929, 1982.

[2] E.F.G. van Daalen. *Numerical and theoretical studies of water waves and floating bodies.* PhD thesis, University of Twente, Enschede, 1993.

[3] C. Haack, P. Gravert and V. Schlegel. 'The modelling of extreme gravity waves: An approach towards a numerical wave channel'. In: Computational Modelling of Free and Moving Boundary Problems, Vol. 1, pp. 91–104, de Gruyter, Berlin, 1991.

[4] P.J. Zandbergen, J. Broeze and E.F.G. van Daalen. 'A panel method for the simulation of nonlinear gravity waves and ship motions'. In: Advances in Boundary Element Techniques, Springer-Verlag, Berlin,..., 1992.

[3] Bayada, G. Chambat, M.: "Sur Quelques Modelizations de la Zone de Cavitation en Lubrification Hydrodynamique".*J. of Theor. and Appl. Mech.*, Vol. 5, N. 5, pp. 703–729, 1986.

[4] Bayada, G. Durany, J. Vázquez, C.: "Existence of Solution for a Lubrication Problem in Elastic Journal Bearing Devices with Thin Bearing". (to appear).

[5] Bermudez, A. Durany, J.: "Numerical Solution of Cavitation Problems in Lubrication." *Comp. Meth. in Appl. Mech. and Eng.*, 68, pp. 55–65, 1988.

[6] Bermudez, A. Moreno, C.: "Duality Methods for Solving Variational Inequalities." *Comput. Math. Appl.*, 7, pp. 43–58, 1981.

[7] Brezis, H. Kinderlehrer, Stampacchia, G.: "Sur une Nouvelle Formulation du Probléme de l'Écoulement á travers une Digue".*C.R.Acad.Sci. Paris*. Sér. A-B, 187, pp. 711–714, 1978.

[8] Cimatti, G.: "Existence and Uniqueness for Nonlinear Reynolds Equations". *Int. J. Eng. Sci.* Vol 24, N. 5, pp. 827–834, 1986.

[9] Durany, J. Vázquez, C.: "Numerical Approach of Lubrication Problems in Journal Bearing Devices with Axial Supply." in *Numerical Methods in engineering '92, (Eds: Ch. Hirsch et al.)*, Elsevier Science Publishers, pp. 839–844, 1992.

[10] Durany, J. García, G. Vázquez, C.: "Finite Element Approximation of Lubrication Problems with Cavitation in Elastic Journal-Bearings." *Proceedings of VIII International Conference on Finite Elements in Fluids*, Barcelona (Spain), 1993 (to appear).

[11] Glowinski, R. Pironneau, O.: "Sur la Résolution Numérique du Probleéme de Dirichlet pour l'Opérateur Biharmonique par une Méthode Quasi-directe". *C.R.Acad.Sci. Paris*. Sér. 282 A, pp. 223–226, 1976.

[12] Rektoris, K.: *"Variational Methods in Mathematics Science and Engineering"*. Reidel, 1977.

[13] Reynolds, O.: "On the Theory of Lubrication and its Applications to M.Beauchamp Tower's Experiments". *Phil. Trans. Roy. Soc.* , London A117, pp. 157-234, 1886.

[14] Vázquez, C.: *"Análisis Matemático y Resolución Numérica de Problemas de Lubricación con Cavitación"*. Ph.D. Thesis, Publications of University of Santiago de Compostela (Spain), 1992.

Fast computation of the Green function for steady ship wave resistance

B. Ponizy[a], M. Ba[a], M. Guilbaud[b], F. Noblesse[c]

[a]*E.N.S.M.A., L.E.A URA CNRS 191, Rue Guillaume VII 86034 Poitiers, France*
[b]*C.E.A.T., Université de Poitiers, 43 Route de l'Aérodrome 86036 Poitiers, France*
[c]*David Taylor Model Basin, Bethesda MD, USA*

ABSTRACT

A very efficient method for computing the non oscillatory near-field term in the Green function, and its gradient, for steady ship waves is presented. The method employs linear interpolation of tabulated values of the near-field term N and its derivatives N_X, N_Y, N_Z with respect to the coordinates X, Y, Z. The interpolation tables are determined using transformations of both coordinates and functions. The coordinate transformation maps the infinite space of coordinates into a unit cube of interpolation variables, and the function transformation defines the singular terms N_X, N_Y, N_Z in terms of continuous and slowly-varying interpolation functions. The efficiency of the method is illustrated in an example application to the steady flow due to a submerged spheroid.

INTRODUCTION

One of main difficulties of the computations of the free-surface effect is due to the complexity of the corresponding Green functions. This complexity has led to several studies, the subject of which being for one part, the development of computations of the most important Green functions, and for the other one, the development of numerical methods based on the fundamental Rankine singularity, much simpler. These "Rankine" methods are very popular for the ship wave resistance computations. Nevertheless, the use of Green functions satisfying the free-surface boundary conditions presents well-known important advantages.

The most studied Green functions are the ones associated with the diffraction-radiation problems whithout forward speed, and with the steady ship wave resistance. Various strategies have been employed, particularly fast and precise computation methods based on the use of series developments, e.g. Telste and Noblesse[1], approximations by Chebyshev polynomials, e.g. Newman[2,3] and tabulation-interpolation, e.g. Ba,Ponizy and Noblesse[4], Telste and Noblesse[5], Masson,De Bayser and Martin[6], and Hendrix and Noblesse[7]. The main object of this paper is the computation of the non oscillatory term representing a local perturbation. The simplest and most efficient way to compute this term is to use a linear interpolation from one or several tables. Several interpolation tables have been used [5,6] associated with series developments close to and far from the origin; this method has been recently modified [4,7] to use a unique interpolation table over the definition domain of the Green function. This method is here extended to the computation of the non oscillatory term and its gradient for the wave resistance problem with tables of the same dimension. To illustrate the efficiency of the method, a potential based panel method is developed to compute the steady flow around a spheroid below the free-surface.

THE GREEN FUNCTION AND ITS GRADIENT

Non dimensional coordinates (x,y,z) are defined with respect to a reference length $L = U^2/g$ (U forward speed and g gravitational constant). The potential is referred to U^3/g. The plane z=0 is the undisturbed free-surface, and the water fills the lower half space $z < 0$. If we consider a field point M(x,y,z), a source point M'(x',y',z') and its image with respect to the free-surface $M_1'(x', y', -z')$ the Green function G can be expressed as the sum of three terms:

$$4\pi G = -\frac{1}{r} + \frac{1}{r'} - 4N(X, Y, Z) + W(X, Y, Z) \tag{1}$$

where

$$X = x - x', \ Y = y - y', \ Z = z + z'.$$
$$r = \sqrt{(x - x')^2 + (y - y')^2 + (z - z')^2}, \ r' = \sqrt{X^2 + Y^2 + Z^2}$$

are the distances from the field point to the source point and its image, respectively. Convenient expressions to evaluate the non oscillatory term N and its derivatives N_X, N_Y and N_Z have been given by Noblesse[8]. These expressions are defined in the domain:

$$-\infty < X < \infty, \ -\infty < Y < \infty, \ -\infty < Z \leq 0.$$

This infinite domain can be reduced to a unit cube by a transformation proposed in [7] :

$$\rho = \frac{\sqrt{r'}}{(1 + \sqrt{r'})}, \ \alpha = \frac{|X|}{(|X| + \sqrt{Y^2 + Z^2})}, \ \beta = \frac{-Z}{\sqrt{Y^2 + Z^2}}$$

so that $0 \leq \rho \leq 1$, $0 \leq \alpha \leq 1$ and $0 \leq \beta \leq 1$. Furthermore, $\vec{\nabla}N = (N_X, N_Y, N_Z)$ is singular at the origin. To remove the singularity of $\vec{\nabla}N$ at the origin and to obtain tables with moderate dimensions, instead of N and $\vec{\nabla}N$, we will use the regular functions defined by :

$$N' = (1+r')N, \; N'_X = (1+r')r'N_X, \; N'_Y = \frac{(1+r')r'}{\sqrt{1-\beta^2}} N_Y \; and N'_Z = (1+r')r'N_Z.$$

The variations of these four functions are depicted in Fig.1. It can be seen that N' and $\vec{\nabla}N'$ are regular everywhere.

Linear interpolation

Let us assume a table $F(N', N'_X, N'_Y, N'_Z)$ representing the values $F_{i,j,k} = F(\rho_i, \alpha_j, \beta_k)$ computed with a constant step. To compute a value $F(\rho, \alpha, \beta)$ by interpolation, we have to determine the intervals $(i \rightarrow i+1, j \rightarrow j+1, k \rightarrow k+1)$ surrounding the coordinates ρ, α, β. Linear interpolation of F gives :

$$F(\rho, \alpha, \beta) \simeq \lambda[\mu(\nu F_{i+1,j+1,k+1} + \tilde{\nu} F_{i+1,j+1,k}) + (1-\mu)(\nu F_{i+1,j,k+1} + \tilde{\nu} F_{i+1,j,k})]$$

$$+(1-\lambda)[\mu(\nu F_{i,j+1,k+1} + \tilde{\nu} F_{i,j+1,k}) + (1-\mu)(\nu F_{i,j,k+1} + \tilde{\nu} F_{i,j,k})] \quad (2)$$

with

$$\lambda = \rho(N_\rho - 1) - Int[\rho(N_\rho - 1)], \; \mu = \alpha(N_\alpha - 1) - Int[\alpha(N_\alpha - 1)],$$

$$\nu = \beta(N_\beta - 1) - Int[\beta(N_\beta - 1)], \; \tilde{\nu} = 1 - \nu,$$

where N_ρ, N_α, and N_β are the number of equally-spaced values $\rho_i(i = 1, .., N_\rho), \alpha_j(j = 1, .., N_\alpha), \beta_k(k = 1, .., N_\beta)$.

Interpolation error and table size

The upper bound ϵ_{max} of the error resulting from the previous interpolation (Equation (2)) is given in [7]:

$$8\epsilon_{max} = (\Delta\rho)^2 \Big|\frac{\partial^2 F}{\partial \rho^2}\Big|_{max} + (\Delta\alpha)^2 \Big|\frac{\partial^2 F}{\partial \alpha^2}\Big|_{max} + (\Delta\beta)^2 \Big|\frac{\partial^2 F}{\partial \beta^2}\Big|_{max} + ... \quad (3)$$

If we assume that when one of the second derivatives is maximum, the two others are zero, the steps to use can be obtained :

$$\Delta\rho = \sqrt{\frac{8\epsilon_{max}}{\big|\frac{\partial^2 F}{\partial \rho^2}\big|_{max}}}, \; \Delta\alpha = \sqrt{\frac{8\epsilon_{max}}{\big|\frac{\partial^2 F}{\partial \alpha^2}\big|_{max}}}, \; \Delta\beta = \sqrt{\frac{8\epsilon_{max}}{\big|\frac{\partial^2 F}{\partial \beta^2}\big|_{max}}}. \quad (4)$$

Here we choose $\epsilon_{max} \leq 0.1\%|N'|$ for the non oscillatory term of the Green function and $\epsilon'_{max} \leq 0.1\%|\vec{\nabla}N'|$ for its gradients , where $|\vec{\nabla}N'| = (N'^2_X + N'^2_Y + N'^2_Z)^{\frac{1}{2}}$. The dimensions of the table for N' were already obtained in [7] as $N_\rho = 83$, $N_\alpha = 24$ and $N_\beta = 14$ but with a slightly different method.

The absolute values of the maxima of the second derivatives with respect to the transformed coordinates are:

$$\frac{1}{|\nabla \vec{N'}|}|\frac{\partial^2 N'_i}{\partial \rho^2}|_{max} = 120; \quad \frac{1}{|\nabla \vec{N'}|}|\frac{\partial^2 N'_i}{\partial \alpha^2}|_{max} = 6; \quad and \quad \frac{1}{|\nabla \vec{N'}|}|\frac{\partial^2 N'_i}{\partial \beta^2}|_{max} = 2.1,$$

where $i = X, Y, Z$. By using these values in Equation (4) we compute the table size ($N'_\rho = 124$; $N'_\alpha = 29$ and $N'_\beta = 18$), and the maximum interpolation error have been shown to be $\epsilon_{max}^{'int} = 0.243\%|\nabla \vec{N'}|$. To correct this problem, we have assumed that the correct table size is given by $N'_\rho = C \times 124$; $N'_\alpha = C \times 29$ and $N'_\beta = C \times 18$, where $C = \sqrt{\frac{\epsilon_{max}^{'int}}{\epsilon_{max}^{'}}} = \sqrt{\frac{0.243}{0.1}} = 1.56$. Consequently we obtain $N'_\rho = 193$; $N'_\alpha = 45$ and $N'_\beta = 28$. The errors, computed at the center of each interpolation cell, with the new tables are shown in Fig.2 and it can be seen that everywhere the error is less than 0.1%. The same dimensions have been choosen too for the table of N', for simplicity sake, and the error, depicted also in Fig.2 is much less than 0.1%. To compute 1000 terms, CPU time was $2.6 \times 10^{-6}s$ instead of $10^{-2}s$ by classical integration.

Computation of the oscillatory term

The wavelike disturbance term has been computed, for $|Z| > .3$ by the procedure proposed in [9]. For small or moderate values of r', converging series using Bessel functions J and K (following Abramowitz and Stegun [10]) are used, whereas asymptotic series using Bessel functions Y and I are used for large values of r'. For lower depth of immersion, better precision has been achieved by numerical integration of complete expression for W and its gradient in spite of the larger CPU time required.

FORMULATION AND DISCRETIZATION OF THE PROBLEM

The flow around a body S_B located under but close to a free-surface is studied (Fig.3). A frame of reference fixed to the body is used. The flow is assumed to be steady and irrotational; the fluid is considered as incompressible and non viscous. The velocity can be derived from the perturbation velocity potential φ, satisfying the Laplace equation under the free-surface, the body condition on S_B and the Kelvin linearized free-surface condition on the undisturbed plane z=0. Application of Green's identity to the potential φ and the Green funtion G yields:

$$\frac{\varphi(M)}{2} + \int_{S_B} \varphi(M')\frac{\partial G(M, M')}{\partial n_{M'}}dS(M') = -\int_{S_B} n_x(M')G(M, M')dS(M')$$

(5)

where $\vec{n}_{M'} = (n_x, n_y, n_z)$ is the outer normal vector to the body S_B. For the resolution, the body S_B is divided into NT panels. By writing Equation

(5) at each centroid of panels we obtain NT equations for NT unknowns (doublet intensities).

NUMERICAL RESULTS

This method has been used to check the results for a spheroid (cf. Fig.3) defined by the ratio of length to midsection diameter a/b=5 located at a depth of immersion h=0.5c where $c = \sqrt{a^2 - b^2}$. Fig.4 shows the distribution of potential versus the abscissa at Froude number $F_r = \frac{U}{\sqrt{2gc}} = 0$; the numerical solutions for various numbers of panels are compared to the analytical solution. A great number of panels is needed to achieve small errors. The convergence of solutions for various Froude numbers is illustrated in Fig.5 where the wave resistance coefficient $C_W = \frac{R}{\pi \rho g c^3}$ is plotted versus the panel number on the spheroid. It can be seen that for NT/2 greater than 300, the variation of C_W is very weak. Finally Fig.6 shows the variation of C_W versus Froude number obtained by the present method, with the results of Farell[11] and the results of Kim[12]. The comparaison is quite satisfactory.

Computations have been done on a ALLIANT FX40 computer; and with 700 panels on the half of the spheroid we need a CPU time of 80 minutes.

CONCLUSION

We have presented a method for computing the non oscillatory term of the Green function and its gradient. These functions have been transformed into regular functions and are evaluated by means of table interpolation . The dimensions of tables have been choosen to yield errors smaller than 0.1% of the regular functions. These tables have been used in a potential based panel method to compute the hydrodynamic flow around a body under a free-surface, showing a very efficient computing time. This last method has to be improved for surface piercing bodies and for lifting flows by taking into account the shape the vortex sheet extending from the trailing edge and by computing more rapidly the wave term of the Green function.

AKNOWLEDGMENTS

B. Ponizy is granted by the "Région Poitou-Charentes" for this work. The authors thank the Region for the support.

References

1. Telste, J.G. & F. Noblesse (1986) *Numerical evaluation of the Green function of water-wave radiation and diffraction*, Jl Ship Research,Vol. 30, pp. 69-84.
2. Newman, J.N. (1985) *Algorithms for the free-surface Green function*, Jl Engg Math., Vol. 19, pp. 57-67.
3. Newman, J.N. (1987) *Evaluation of the Wave Resistance Green function*, Part 1, Jl Ship Research,Vol. 31, pp. 79-90.
4. Ba, M., B. Ponizy & F. Noblesse (1992) *Calculation of the Green function of water-wave diffraction and radiation*, 2nd Intl Offshore and Polar Engg Conf., San Francisco, USA.
5. Telste, J.G. & F. Noblesse (1988) *The nonoscillatory near-field term in the Green function for steady flow about a ship*, 17th Symp on Naval Hydro., The Hague, Netherlands, pp. 39-52.
6. Masson, E., DeBayser, O. & Martin, D. (1991) *Evaluation de la resistance de vagues d'un sous-marin en immersion totale*, 3e Journées de l'Hydro., pp. 31-43, Grenoble, France.
7. Hendrix, D. & F. Noblesse (1992) *Recipes for computing the steady free-surface flow due to a source distribution*, Jl Ship Research, Vol. 36, pp. 346-359.
8. Noblesse, F. (1981) *Alternative Integral Representations for the Green Function of the Theory of Ship Wave Resistance*, Jl of Eng. Math., Vol. 15, pp. 241-265.
9. Baar, J.J.M. & Price, W.G. (1988) *Evaluation of the wavelike disturbance in the Kelvin wave source potential*, Jl Ship Research, Vol. 32, pp. 44-53.
10. Abramowitz, M. & Stegun, A. (1965) *Handbook of Mathematical Functions*, Dover Publications, INC, New York.
11. Farell, C. (1973) *On the Wave Resistance of a Submerged Spheroid*, Jl of Ship Research, Vol. 17, No.1 , pp. 1-11.
12. Kim, B.K. (1992) *Computation of Hydrodinamic Forces on a Submerged Lifting Body*, 2nd Int. Offshore and Polar Engg Conf., San Francisco, USA.

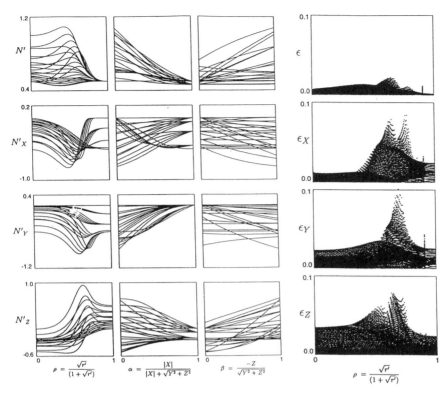

Fig.1   Regular functions N', N'_X, N'_Y, N'_Z

Fig.2   Interpolation errors on N', N'_X, N'_Y , N'_Z for the table $193 \times 45 \times 28$

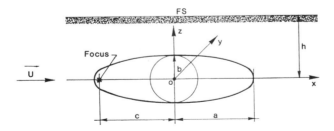

Fig.3   Position of the spheroid with respect to the free-surface

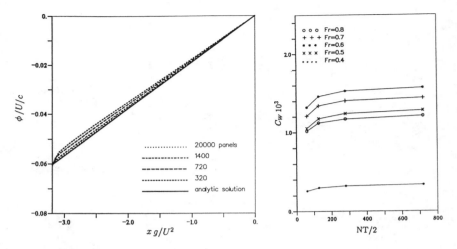

Fig.4   Potential on the spheroid (Fr=0.)

Fig.5   Wave resistance coefficient C_W with respect
to the number of panels

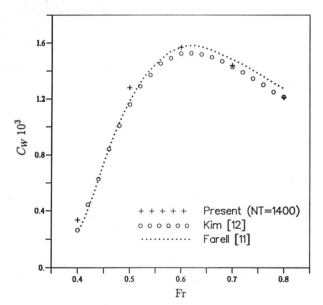

Fig.6   Evolution of the wave
resistance C_W with re-
spect to the Froude
number Fr

Electromechanical waves of deformation in soft biological shells

R. Miftakhov[a], D. Wingate[a], D. Ghista[b]

[a] *Gastrointestinal Science Research Unit, The Royal London Hospital Medical College, University of London, London E1 2AJ, England*
[b] *Department of Biophysics, UAE University, PO Box 17666, Al Ain, UAE*

ABSTRACT

A biomechanical model and mathematical formulation of the problem of propagation of the electromechanical waves of deformation along the small intestine are presented. The organ is modelled on a soft orthotropic cylindrical biological shell reinforced by incompressible, transversely isotropic muscle elements of orthogonal type of weaving and embedded in a connective tissue network. The mechanical properties of the wall are assumed to be nonlinear. Deformations of the bioshell are finite. The model describes the dynamics of propagation of the electrical wave of depolarization along the muscle layers, active force generation and the development of the electromechanical wave of deformation. The governing system of equations has been derived and solved numerically. The finite-difference method of the second order accuracy over the time and space variables has been used. The dynamics of stress-strain distribution in the shell and shape changes are analyzed. It has been shown that there is no axial symmetry in the organ's deformation during the first stage of dynamical reaction. Only with the development of contractions in the circular muscle layer is symmetry observed.

INTRODUCTION

Electromechanical wave processes form the basis of many physiological phenomena. They are inherent in the function of nonlinear biological systems which possess the properties of excitability and motor activity. Because of their internal features and specific conditions, the transmission from an initial steady state to an excitable state can occur and this may result in the formation of a propagating peristaltic wave. For example, the coordinated action of muscular elements, with myogenic, humoral and nervous mechanisms of regulation determines the existence of these waves in visceral abdominal organs.

The study of peristaltic events from the point of view of biomechanics, has only recently become the subject of scientific interest. Only a few reports have been dedicated to the analysis of mechanical events in the small intestine during peristaltic contraction. These concentrate on the depiction of the organ's shape change under artificial symmetric deformation, e.g. Bertuzzi *et al.* [1,2], Macagno *et al.* [5], and the construction of an imitation mechanical model of the intestine, e.g. Umetani and Inou [10,11]. Existing models do not describe the real processes of electromechanical conjugation, peristaltic wave formation and propagation, contraction-relaxation in the smooth muscle layers and this severely limits the applications of these types of model in physiological investigations.

The aim of this study was to simulate the processes of electromechanical coupling in a soft biological shell - an analogue of the small intestine, and to analyse changes of strain-states in the organ during its mechanical reaction.

FOUNDATION OF THE MODEL

Basic assumptions
The following assumptions are made in model construction:
(i). The small bowel is modelled on a soft orthotropic cylindrical tube. The wall is composed of two muscle layers, covered by a connective tissue network. Muscle fibres in the outer layer are orientated in a longitudinal direction of the organ and muscle fibres of the inner layer are arranged in an orthogonal, circular, direction. Mechanical properties are different for the two layers but are assumed to be uniform along the wall.
(ii). The tubular segment of a length, l, and radius, r_0, undergoes isometric contractions throughout. The intraluminal pressure, p, changes during the mechanical reaction according to the adiabatic law.
(iii). The muscle layers contract independently but in a coordinated way with the generation of active forces (T^a). Reciprocal relationships exist in their work. The first contractions start in the longitudinal muscle layer. When the contractile force reaches a maximum an activation of the circular muscle layer starts, e.g. Kottegoda [4].
(iv). Both muscle layers are assumed to be a syncytium with cable electrical properties. The longitudinal layer has anisotropic and the circular layer isotropic electrical properties.
(v). The mechanical activity of the tube is under the control of a pacemaker cell located at the left boundary which generates the excitatory stimulus of given intensity.

Mathematical formulation of the problem
The governing system of equations consists of:
(i). The small intestinal segment dynamics [6]:

$$\gamma_0 V_t = (T_1 e_{ij} \sqrt{g_{22}})_{s_1} + (T_2 e_{ij} \sqrt{g_{11}})_{s_2} + p \sqrt{g} \, n_j \qquad (1)$$

where:

$$T_{1(2)} = k \frac{\partial \varepsilon_{c(l)}}{\partial t} + \varphi_{c(l)} T^a (\lambda_{c(l)}) + T^P (\lambda_c, \lambda_l)$$

Here the following notations are used: γ_0 - the linear density of a biomaterial in undeformed state; λ_c, λ_l - the rate of elongation (hereafter the subscripts l and c are related to the longitudinal and circular muscle layers, respectively); ε_c, ε_l - deformations of the longitudinal and circular muscle layers: $\varepsilon_{c,l} = \lambda_{c,l} + 1$; e_{ij} - the direction cosines of the outward normal n_j, to the surface with respect to the cylindrical j - axis ($i = 1, 2; j = r,s,z$); g_{ij}, g -the components and determinant of the fundamental tensor; V (v_r,v_s,v_z) - the velocity vector and its radial, circumferential and longitudinal components; $T_{1,2}$ - the components of the tensor of membrane forces; Tp, T^a - the passive and active components, respectively, of the total force ($T_{c,l}$); k - the rheological parameter; p - intraluminal pressure; s_1, s_2 - the lagrangian coordinates of the bioshell.

The passive ($Tp_{c,l}$) components are calculated from:

$$T^p_{(c,l)} = \frac{\partial \, \gamma_o W}{\partial \, (\lambda_{(c,l)} - 1)} \tag{2}$$

where: W - the strain energy density function has the form [3]:

$$\gamma_o W = \frac{1}{2}\left[c_1(\lambda_l - 1)^2 + 2c_3(\lambda_l - 1)(\lambda_c - 1) + \right.$$
$$\left. + c_2(\lambda_c - 1)^2\right] + c_{10}\exp(c_4(\lambda_l - 1)^2 + $$
$$+ c_5(\lambda_c - 1)^2 + 2c_6(\lambda_l - 1)(\lambda_c - 1))$$

For the active force ($T^a_{c,l}$) components we have [6]:

$$T^a_{(c,l)} = c_{7(c,l)}\lambda^2_{(c,l)} + c_{8(c,l)}\lambda_{(c,l)} + c_{9(c,l)} \tag{3}$$

Here c_{1-10} are the mechanical constants of a biocomposite.

The characteristic feature of soft shells is the possibility of simultaneous co-existence of unstressed, uniaxial and biaxial stress-strained zones. The creaseless form occurs at: $\lambda_{l,c} > 1.0$; in a case of the development of creases, when $\lambda_l \leq 1.0$ or $\lambda_c \leq 1.0$, the wrinkled area is modelled by a "smooth zone" made up by the system of unbound filaments. This is determined by requirements which are geometrical relating to the conservation of smoothness of the surface of the bioshell, and force conditions relating to the continuity of membrane forces. Thus for $Tp_{c,l}$ at the uniaxial stress-strained state of the bioshell we assume:

$$T^p_{c,l} = \begin{cases} 0, & \lambda_{c,l} \leq 1.0 \\ c_{10}(\exp c_{11}(\lambda_{c,l} - 1) - 1), & \lambda_{c,l} > 1.0 \end{cases} \tag{4}$$

(ii). The dynamics of propagation of the electrical waves of depolarization along the anisotropic longitudinal muscle layer (φ_l) is defined as:

$$C_m(\varphi_l)_t = I_{m1}(s_1, s_2) + I_{m2}(s_1 - s_1', s_2 - s_2') - I_{ion} \tag{5}$$

where I_{m1}, I_{m2} are the transmembrane ion currents per unit volume:

$$I_{m1}(s_1, s_2) = M_{VS} \left\{ \frac{-2(\mu_{s_1} - \mu_{s_2})}{(1 + \mu_{s_1})(1 + \mu_{s_2})} \arctan\left(\frac{ds_2}{ds_1}\sqrt{\frac{G_{s_2}}{G_{s_1}}}\right) + \right.$$

$$\left. + \frac{g_{0s_2}}{G_{s_2}} \right\} \times \left(\left(\frac{g_{0s_1}}{\lambda_c}(\varphi_l)_{s_1}\right)_{s_1} + \left(\frac{g_{0s_2}}{\lambda_l}(\varphi_l)_{s_2}\right)_{s_2} \right)$$

$$I_{m2}(s_1 - s_1', s_2 - s_2') = M_{VS} \iint_S \frac{(\mu_{s_1} - \mu_{s_2})}{2\pi(1 + \mu_{s_1})(1 + \mu_{s_2})G} \times$$

$$x \frac{(s_1 - s_1')^2/G_{s_1} - (s_2 - s_2')^2/G_{s_2}}{[(s_1 - s_1')^2/G_{s_1} + (s_2 - s_2')^2/G_{s_2}]^2} \times$$

$$x \left(\left(\frac{g_{0s_1}}{\lambda_c}(\varphi_l)_{s_1}\right)_{s_1} + \left(\frac{g_{0s_2}}{\lambda_l}(\varphi_l)_{s_2}\right)_{s_2} \right) ds_1' ds_2'$$

Here:

$$\mu_{s_1} = g_{0s_1}/g_{is_1}, \qquad \mu_{s_2} = g_{0s_2}/g_{is_2}$$

$$G_{s_1} = \frac{g_{0s_1} + g_{is_1}}{\lambda_c}, \qquad G_{s_2} = \frac{g_{0s_2} + g_{is_2}}{\lambda_l}, \qquad G = \sqrt{G_{s_1}G_{s_2}}$$

and the following notations are accepted: C_m - the capacitance of smooth muscle; $g_{is1}, g_{is2}, g_{os1}, g_{os2}$ - the maximal intracellular (the subscript (i)) and interstitial space (the subscript (o)) conductivity of the longitudinal and circular muscle layers in the longitudinal and circumferential directions, respectively; M_{VS} - the membrane characteristic; I_{ion} - the total ionic current, see [8,9].

In the case of propagation along the isotropic circular muscle layer (φ_c):

$$C_m(\varphi_c)_t = \frac{M_{VS}}{(1+\mu_{s_1})}\left(\frac{g_{0s1}}{\lambda_c}(\varphi_c)_{s_1}\right)_{s_1} + \left(\frac{g_{0s2}}{\lambda_c}(\varphi_c)_{s_2}\right)_{s_2} - I_{ion} \quad (6)$$

where the above-mentioned abbreviations are used.

At the initial moment of time the whole system is in the resting state. The left and right boundaries of the tube are supposed to be rigidly fixed. The discharge of the pacemaker cell causes the development of the wave of depolarization in the longitudinal smooth muscle. When the maximum of the total force in the longitudinal muscle layer is achieved activation of the circular muscle layer is started. The right boundary of the tubular segment remains in the resting state throughout: $\varphi_{c,l} = 0$.

An explicit hybrid finite - difference scheme of the second order approximation over the space and time for the solution of (1) - (6) is used. The set of mechanical and electrical parameters and constants used in calculations is given [6,7].

RESULTS

In response to electrostimulation a positive short-term wave of deformation of an amplitude of $6.2 \cdot 10^{-3}$ $\varepsilon^+{}_l$ (figure 1) occurred in the intestinal segment. Its anterior front had the form of an ellipse and propagated at a velocity of 2.5 cm/s along the surface of the bioshell. At $t = 0.35$ s the deformation of elongation $\varepsilon^+{}_l = 2 \cdot 10^{-2}$, of the longitudinal muscle components was recorded in the vicinity of the left boundary.

The wave of relaxation, $\varepsilon^+{}_c$, of the circular muscle layer was clearly observed in the middle part of the segment at $t = 0.23$ s. It had an amplitude of $6.8 \cdot 10^{-3}$ and propagated at a velocity of 1.9 cm/s. At $t = 0.35$ s the circular muscle layer of the distal part of the bioshell was relaxed with maximum $\varepsilon^+{}_c = 1 \cdot 10^{-2}$.

The negative wave of deformation had an amplitude of $\varepsilon^-{}_l = 5 \cdot 10^{-3}$ at $t = 0.038$ s and gradually increased to $2.1 \cdot 10^{-2}$ at $t = 0.35$ s. With the development of tonic contractions at $0.58 < t < 0.8$ s the amplitude of the wave $\varepsilon^-{}_l$ increased to $3 \cdot 10^{-2}$ while in the circular muscle layer the lower amplitude $\varepsilon^-{}_c = 3.8 \cdot 10^{-3}$ was observed. At $t = 2.7$ s the segmentation of an amplitude of $1 \cdot 10^{-2}$ developed in the distal part of the intestinal segment. At the same time the proximal part was underwent relaxation where the $\max \varepsilon^+{}_c = 1.8 \cdot 10^{-2}$ was seen. At $t = 4$ s the anterior front of the wave of peristalsis reached the right boundary. The longitudinal muscle layer in the middle part of the segment were relaxed with the max $\varepsilon^+{}_l = 3.8 \cdot 10^{-2}$, and the circular muscle components were maximally contracted $\varepsilon^-{}_c = 2 \cdot 10^{-2}$. At the same time both layers in the left part of the intestinal segment underwent contraction: the maximal contraction of an

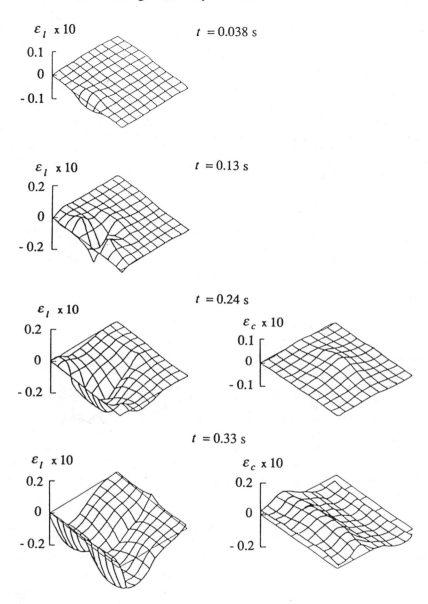

Figure 1. Dynamics of propagation of the electromechanical wave of deformation along the bioshell.

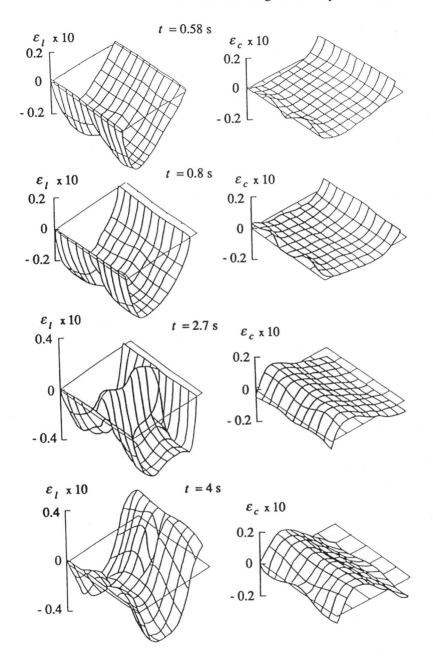

Figure 1 (continued). Dynamics of propagation of the electromechanical wave of deformation along the bioshell.

amplitude of $3.2 \cdot 10^{-2}$ was observed in the longitudinal muscle layer and $\varepsilon^+_c = 2 \cdot 10^{-2}$ was registered in the circular muscle layer.

The development of tonic contractions in the bioshell were accompanied by the increase in flexure along the length of the bioshell. The tonic wave of contraction transformed into the symmetric ring contraction ($t > 1.45$ s) that gradually shifted in the distal direction. The maximum axial displacement of the wall was $1 \cdot 10^{-3}$ cm, and the displacement in the radial direction was $-2 \cdot 10^{-3}$ cm. At $t = 4.8$ s the bioshell returned into its initial undeformed state.

CONCLUSION

Analysis of the dynamical reaction showed that there was no axial symmetry of the intestinal segment deformation for $t < 0.4$ s. Only with the development of ring contractions of the circular smooth muscle layer ($t > 0.4$ s) the symmetry in deformation was observed. This could be of physiological importance, e.g. to provide mixing and grinding of the intraluminal content at the first stage of motor activity and squeezing it into the adjacent intestinal segment during the second propulsive stage.

REFERENCES

1. Bertuzzi, A., Mancinelli, R., Ronzoni, G. and Salinari, S. 'An Analysis of the Peristaltic Reflex' *Biol. Cybern.,* Vol. 35, pp. 205-221, 1979
2. Bertuzzi, A., Mancinelli, R., Ronzoni, G. and Salinari, S. 'A Mathematical Model of Intestinal Motor Activity' *J. Biomechanics,* Vol. 11, pp. 41-473, 1978
3. Fung, Y.C. 'Perspectives of Soft Tissue Mechanics' *In: Biomechanics. Its Principles and Applications,* pp. 94-114, Pergamon Press, N.Y., 1982
4. Kottegoda, S. 'An Analysis of Possible Nervous Mechanisms Involved in the Peristaltic Reflex' *J. Physiology ,* Vol. 200, pp. 687-712, 1969
5. Macagno, E.O., Christensen, J. and Lee, C.L. 'Modelling the Effects of Wall Movement on Absorbtion in the Intestine' *American J. Physiology,* Vol. 243, pp. G541 - G550, 1982
6. Miftakhov, R.N. 'Nonlinear Electromechanical Waves in Cylindrical Shells' *Biomechanics of Soft Tissues,* pp. 40-72, 1986 (in Russian)
7. Miftakhov, R.N. and Wingate, D.L. 'A Biomechanical Model of Small Bowel Motility', Vol. 14, part. 4, pp. 1637-1639, *Proceedings of the 14th Ann. Int. Conf. of the IEEE/EBMS,* Paris, France, 1992 (Ed. Morucci, J.P., Plonsey, R., Coatieux, J.L. and Laxminarayan, S.), Paris, France, 1992
8. Plonsey, R.L. and Barr, R.G. 'Current Flow Patterns in Two-Dimensional Anisotropic Bisyncytia with Normal and Extreme Conductivities' *Biophysical J.* Vol. 43, pp. 557-571, 1984
9. Ramon, F., Anderson, N.C., Joyner, R.W. and Moore, J.W. 'A Model for Propagation of Action Potentials in Smooth Muscle' *J. Theoretical Biology,* Vol. 59, pp. 381-408, 1976.
10. Umetani, Y. and Inou, N. 'Biomechanical study of peristalsis' . *Soc. of Instrum. and Control Eng.,* Vol. 21, pp. 172-176,1985
11. Umetani, Y. and Inou, N. 'Biomechanical investigation of peristalsis II' *J. Soc. of Instrum. and Control Eng.,* Vol. 22, pp. 1081-1086, 1986.

SECTION 3: STOKES FLOW

Three-dimensional finite element simulation of multi-fluid flows

V. Legat[a], J-M. Marchal[b]

[a] *Applied Mechanics, Université Catholique de Louvain, Place du Levant 2, 1348 Louvain-la-Neuve, Belgium. (on leave from TICOM, University of Texas, 3500 West Balcones Center Dr., Austin 78759, Texas, USA)*

[b] *Polyflow SA, Place de l'Université 16, 1348 Louvain-la-Neuve, Belgium*

1. INTRODUCTION

Implicit Finite Element techniques for solving three-dimensional free surface problems in complex geometries have recently been proposed by Legat and Marchal. Direct and Inverse Extrusion Problems have been addressed (ref. 1,2), and an original method is proposed to predict the shape of the die from a prescribed extrudate geometry. Power law as well as Newtonian fluids have been considered. Surface tension has been introduced in order to analyze its effect upon the extrudate shape for the Direct and Inverse Problems. In particular, the effect of surface tension upon the presence of corners is considered in (ref. 3).

In this paper, we use the method presented in (ref. 1,2,3) to predict the interface position in multi-material problems where a contact line problem occurs. In such a flow, taking the surface tension effects into is essential since one wishes to predict accurately the position of the static contact line. We describe how to apply natural angle conditions in the three-dimensional case. This procedure is the generalization of previous results obtained for two-dimensional calculations (ref. 4,5)

2. BASIC EQUATIONS - DISCRETIZATION.

Let us consider the flow of a Generalized Newtonian fluid in a three-dimensional domain Ω. The steady-state creeping flow problem is formulated as:

- Find $(v, p, h) \in V \times P \times H$ such that :

$$\nabla.(\eta \bar{\nabla} v) - \nabla p = 0, \quad \text{in } \Omega, \qquad (1)$$

$$\nabla.v = 0, \quad \text{in } \Omega, \qquad (2)$$

$$(\eta \bar{\nabla} v - pI).n = g, \quad \text{on } \partial\Omega_{\text{Neumann}}, \qquad (3)$$

$$v = f, \quad \text{on } \partial\Omega_{\text{Dirichlet}}. \qquad (4)$$

In these equations, $\bar{\nabla}v$ stands for the symmetric part of the velocity gradient, v and p being respectively the fluid velocity and pressure. The shear viscosity η may be a function of the second invariant of the velocity gradient for Generalized Newtonian fluids. The vector n denotes the outwards normal along the boundaries. V and P are velocity and pressure function spaces.

For multifluid flows, Ω is divided into subdomains Ω_i for each fluid. Distinct velocity and pressure fields v_i and p_i are defined on each subdomain. Equations (1-2) are used in each Ω_i, and Neumann and Dirichlet conditions (3-4) apply on the boundaries of each subdomain.   Further, on the interface $\partial\Omega_{ij}$ between inviscible fluids "i" and fluid "j", we impose the following conditions :

$$v_i.n_i = 0, \qquad \text{on } \partial\Omega_{ij}, \qquad (5)$$

$$v_i = v_j, \qquad \text{on } \partial\Omega_{ij}, \qquad (6)$$

$$(\eta_i\bar{\nabla}v_i - p_i I).n_i - (\eta_j\bar{\nabla}v_j - p_j I).n_j = \gamma\,\chi, \qquad \text{on } \partial\Omega_{ij}. \quad (7)$$

where χ is the mean curvature (its sign being positive where Ω_i is locally convex) and γ is the surface tension coefficient.   Along the curve $\partial\partial\Omega_{ij}$ (i.e. along the boundary of the interface), we impose either a given traction contact vector (angle condition) or we prescribe the location for the interface. In 3-D, we found it easier to use directors rather than angles, so that the direction of traction is described by a vector in the Cartesian space.

Such boundary conditions lead to a well-posed problem only if the position of the boundary or of the interface is a *variable* of the problem. A variable h, called the geometrical degree of freedom is then introduced on the interface.   It describes the motion of the interface in the given direction d.

We define the direction d on the interface and the displacement of the interface is linked to the variable h by the relationship :

$$\delta x = h\ d. \qquad (8)$$

It must be noted that the vector d remains fixed when the interface position is updated : d is calculated as the normal direction to the initial fixed mesh by means of a least square formulation.

The finite element discretization of system (1-7) follows a classical procedure: traction terms are introduced by means of the Green's theorem applied to second order terms, and a weighted residual Galerkin formulation is used for the momentum, mass conservation and kinematic equations. The "angle" conditions along the interface boundary are automatically introduced by the use of Green's theorem applied on Rieman's surfaces for the surface tension term. (ref. 6)

Moving interface nodes without updating interior nodes will lead to unacceptable element deformation. We have to propagate the motion of the interface into the domain interior according to a remeshing rule. In our calculations, we use a Euclidean distance rule described in (ref. 1). The linearity of such rule allows us to derive a full Newton-Raphson at a reasonable cost and to reach quadratic convergence.

Quadratic functions are used as interpolation-weight functions for the velocity field, linear functions for the pressure field. For the geometrical degree of freedom, quadratic shape and weight functions are defined on the interface.

Solutions are presented as a function of the capillary number Ca defined as :

$$Ca^{-1} = \gamma \, (\eta V)^{-1}, \tag{9}$$

where η is the fluid viscosity and V is a typical velocity.

3.   PROBLEM OF THE CONTACT LINE.

Locating the intersection between the interface and a solid boundary is however a difficulty, which has been extensively analyzed (see ref. 4,5,7). In order to explain the problem, let us consider the point A of a typical two-dimensional T-geometry (Fig. 1.) where a zero velocity is imposed along the upper boundary.

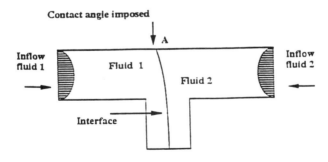

Fig.1 Schematic view of a T-geometry.

Because at point A the velocity components vanish, the coefficients of the discrete kinematic condition for A tend to be very small. In fact, the kinematic condition does not allow us to calculate the position of A (unless a very coarse mesh size is used). Coefficients of the kinematic condition will vanish at point A

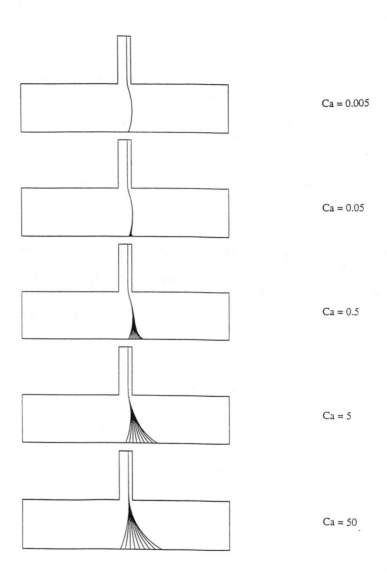

Fig. 2 Contact angles (70,80,90,100,110,120,130,140,150 degrees) in the T-
geometry.
The influence of the natural condition decreases when the capillary forces
decrease.

if the mesh is refined. Also imposing a vanishing velocity along the solid boundary prevents us from applying a natural "angle" condition at the point A.

In a first approach, it has been proposed to impose the angle condition as an essential condition. However in this case the momentum balance is in general not respected at point A. And for small capillary forces, this procedure becomes inaccurate, because the influence of the angle condition must become very small.

In order to avoid this incompatibility, we replace the discrete kinematic condition associated to node A by the projection of momentum equations along the direction **d**. This procedure has been proposed by Kistler-Scriven (ref. 4) for two-dimensional calculations, and allows us to impose a natural contact angle. Here, we extend this method to 3-D.

The robustness of this procedure is demonstrated by the results of Fig. 3 and Fig. 4. We calculate the interface position between two Newtonian fluids of different viscosity's into a T-geometry. In order to analyze the influence of the capillary number and the contact angle conditions, we superpose interface profiles at different angle values.

Capillary number is also increased and we show that the influence of contact angle decrease as a function of the surface tension coefficient. Such results are clearly in agreement with the physics, and the solution without capillary is a singular perturbation of the problem with surface tension.

4.   THREE-DIMENSIONAL RESULTS

Fig. 3 illustrates a problem involving a moving interface between two Newtonian fluids. The viscosity ratio η_1/η_2 and the surface tension parameters are modified in order to analyze their influence of the interface position.

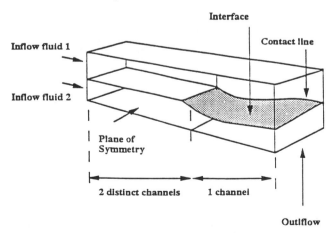

Fig. 3   Three-dimensional stratified flow.

The tangent matrix of the system has been evaluated leading to a full Newton-Raphson scheme for all variables. It should be noted that convergence is always

Fig. 4   Perspective view of the interface position and the full mesh.
Viscosity ratio = 7/4, flow rate ratio = 1; contact vector at the rigid boundary = (-2,1,0); Ca = 1.

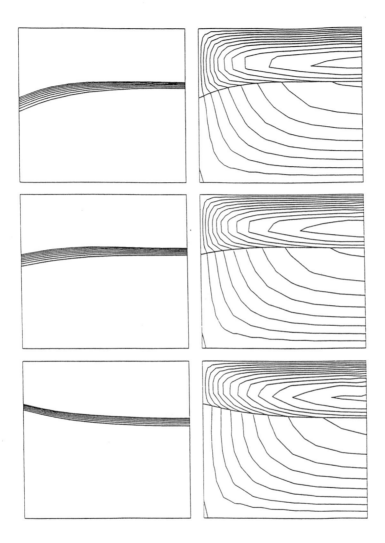

Fig. 5 Interface positions and contour lines of the axial velocity at the outflow plane.
Three contact vectors at the rigid boundary are applied : (-2,1,0) (-4,1,0) (4,-1,0).
Flow rate ratio = 1, viscosity ratio = 3 (highly viscous fluid on top); $Ca^{-1} = 1$.
Interface positions are also given on the left side for the viscosity ratios : 5/4, 6/4, 7/4, 8/4, 9/4, 10/4, 11/4.

fast, except when Ca^{-1} vanishes. Convergence of this problem to a relative precision of 10^{-6} is obtained in 5 iterations. In order to remain in the convergence radius of the iterative scheme, the viscosity ratio, the capillary number and the contact vectors have to be carefully selected. A bad choice of contact vectors can also lead to divergence or very slow convergence of the iterative scheme and also to poor results.

Fig. 4 presents a perspective plot of the deformed mesh (where the domain boundary and the interface are visible), and Fig. 5 compares the interface profiles at the exit of the domain for several values of the contact angle and some viscosity ratios. We also present contours lines of the axial velocity at the same plane.

4.   CONCLUSIONS

We have considered the effects of angle contact conditions and surface tension upon multi-fluid flows. Critical influence of the contact angle for stratified flows has been demonstrated. The technique has allowed us to predict the position of a static contact line in 3-D without having to introduce slipping along the die wall. Dependency of the solutions upon the viscosity ratio, upon the Ca^{-1} number and upon inertia effects are presently investigated.

Incorporating the position variables as primitive unknowns together with the pressure and velocity components leads to a full Newton-Raphson's iterative scheme, which has been proved to be a powerful and robust numerical technique for calculating stratified flows.

5.   ACKNOWLEDGEMENTS

The results presented in this paper have been obtained within the framework of Interuniversity Attraction Poles initiated by the Belgian State, Prime Minister's Office, Science Policy Programming. V. Legat wishes to acknowledge a scholarship from the Fonds National de la Recherche Scientifique. Texas Institute for Computational Mechanics (TICOM) is also gratefully acknowledged.

REFERENCES

1.   V. Legat, J.M. Marchal, Int. J. Numerical Methods in Fluids, 14, (1992), 609-625.
2.   V. Legat, J.M. Marchal, Int. J. Numerical Methods in Fluids, (1993), in press.
3   V. Legat, J.M. Marchal, XIth Int. Congress in Rheology, (Brussel, 1992).
4.   S.F. Kistler, S.E. Scriven, Coating Flows in Computational Analysis of Polymer Processing, Pearson & Richardson, (1983), 243-299.
5.   D. Berghezan, F. Dupret, J. Comp. Physic, (1993), in press.
6   R.J. Ruschak, Computers & Fluids, Vol. 11, 4, (1983), 391-401.
7.   J. Dheur, M.J. Crochet, Rheologica Acta, 26, (1987), 401-413.

Distortion of large, isolated two and three dimensional bubbles

J.D. Bugg

Department of Mechanical Engineering, The University of Saskatchewan, Saskatoon, Saskatchewan, Canada

ABSTRACT

Small bubbles released in quiescent liquids undergo little distortion since the stabilising surface tension force dominates. For large bubbles, however, distortion is very great and the bubble transforms from an initially cylindrical or spherical shape to a radically different steadily rising shape. The numerical investigation presented here uses an explicit finite difference model employing a volume fraction interface specification. Cylindrical and spherical bubbles ranging in diameter from 20 to 80 mm are released from rest in a quiescent fluid and their distortion and rise velocity are studied. Several critical features observed experimentally are reproduced in the simulations. The initial acceleration from rest is properly predicted. The transformations of initially cylindrical bubbles into cylindrical caps and initially spherical bubbles into toroids are also reproduced.

INTRODUCTION

The dynamics of gas bubbles moving in liquids is a complex phenomena governed by liquid and gas properties and bubble size. Many experimental and several numerical studies have investigated the relationship between the shape of a steadily rising bubble and its size. These efforts have shown that increasing bubble size results in shape changes which progress from spherical for small bubbles, through oblate spheroids and finally to spherical caps for large bubbles. A good discussion of bubble dynamics in general is given by Clift, Grace and Weber[1]. The vast majority of work in this area is restricted to both the steadily rising case and rather small bubbles.

Large bubbles have important applications in fluidised beds, nuclear reactor accident scenarios and undersea oil well blowouts. Although it is recognised that the manner in which the bubbles would be formed in such applications would vary greatly, this work considers only the more amiable problem of release, from rest, of a "gas" with zero density into quiescent water. The most fundamental previous work in this area was performed by Walters and Davidson[2],[3]. Numerical efforts to model these phenomena have been reported by Baker and Moore[4] and Bugg and Rowe[5]. This work reported results only for a single cylindrical bubble size, matching the experiments of Walters and Davidson. The current research extends this effort to investigate the effect of bubble size on large bubble distortion.

NUMERICAL METHOD

The numerical procedure is discussed in Bugg and Rowe[5]. It uses an approach similar to the SOLA–VOF technique[6] and solves the transient, two-dimensional Navier–Stokes equations using a volume-tracking technique to specify the position of the gas–liquid interface. The free–surface boundary condition is prescribed at the gas–liquid interface and includes the effect of surface tension. This interface is advected using the donor–acceptor algorithm of Hirt and Nichols[7]. Because the interface advection algorithm contains an inherent restriction that the Courant number be less than unity, an explicit scheme is used to advance the underlying flow field solution in time. No provision for modelling turbulence is included.

The initial configuration for all runs in this paper can be represented by figure 1. The size of the solution domain and the initial position of the bubble are normalised by the initial bubble radius, a. For the case of cylindrical bubbles, the centreline shown on figure 1 is a *plane* of symmetry while for spherical bubbles it becomes an *axis* of symmetry. All solutions presented in this paper use a 50 by 200 uniform grid with $\delta x = \delta y = D/25$. The liquid density (1000 kg/m^3) and kinematic viscosity (10^{-6} m^2/s) are those of water. The pressure inside the bubble is initially set equal to the hydrostatic pressure at its centroid and thereafter recalculated in response to volume changes with isentropic relationships.

RESULTS

Cylindrical Bubbles
Truly two–dimensional bubbles, also called cylindrical bubbles, exist only in theory. They are approximated in the laboratory by trapping a volume of gas between two vertical plates otherwise containing liquid. The spacing of the plates has to be small enough that the flow remains approximately two–dimensional but large enough that wall effects do not dominate. A

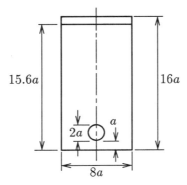

Figure 1: Schematic diagram of initial conditions.

discussion of wall effects in such experiments is given by Collins[8]. The cylindrical case is attractive for model development since it allows solution algorithms to be tested in a simpler, two–dimensional framework.

Cylindrical bubble motion from rest can be divided into three phases. First, there is an initial acceleration phase where little distortion occurs. Next the bubble undergoes very large distortions where its shape is transformed into that which persists during the final, steadily rising phase. Figure 2 illustrates the predicted shape evolution of a 50 mm bubble. Several quantitative features of these predictions will now be discussed.

The most fundamental characteristic of the initial stage of bubble motion is the upward acceleration. In the case of a cylindrical bubble this is g. Figure 3 shows the vertical position of the bubble's centre of gravity versus time for bubble sizes ranging from 20 to 80 mm and for a constant acceleration of g. This confirms that for $0 \leq T \geq 0.5$ the acceleration is g for all bubble sizes modelled. For the remainder of the time modelled, all bubble sizes show much the same behaviour. Only for $T \geq 2$ do differences begin to appear with the larger bubbles lagging slightly behind the smaller bubbles. For $T \geq 4$ this order begins to reverse. However, this is after shedding of small gas bubbles from the cusped edges of the bubble has begun. Since *all* of the gas is included in the y_{cg} calculation, this data is suspect above $T \approx 4$.

A measure of bubble distortion is given by the vertical "diameter", d, of the bubble along its centreline. This is plotted in figure 4 for various initial

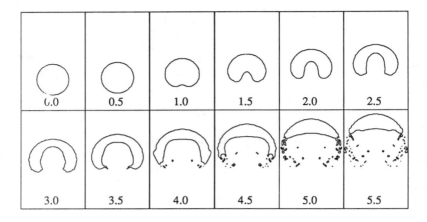

Figure 2: Cylindrical bubble shape change when released from rest in a quiescent liquid. $D = 50\ mm$. Times shown are $T = t\sqrt{g/a}$.

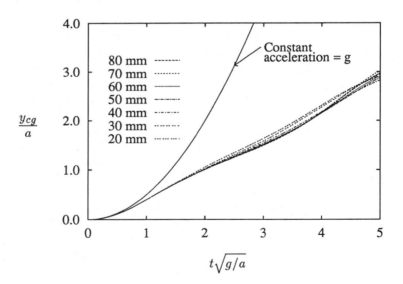

Figure 3: Vertical position of cylindrical bubble centre of gravity versus time for various initial bubble sizes.

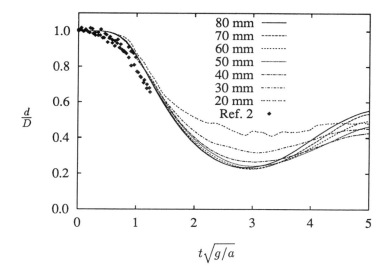

Figure 4: Distortion of cylindrical bubbles released from rest.

bubble diameters. For $D \geq 50$ mm, d/D reaches a minimum of about 0.25 at $T \approx 3$. As bubble size is decreased this minimum becomes less pronounced. Smaller bubbles have less dramatic distortion and a smoother transition to a cylindrical cap. The experimental data presented in Walters and Davidson[2] for a 50.8 mm bubble is also shown. Over the range for which experimental data was provided in that paper, there is no significant difference in behaviour for bubbles in the size range 20 $mm \leq D \geq 80$ mm.

The final, steadily rising portion of motion is not reproduced by the present simulations. However, it must be realised that bubble sizes this large are inherently unstable and a complete shattering of the large bubble is not an unrealistic final configuration. It is suspected that the final, steadily rising cylindrical cap observed by Walters and Davidson[2] is possible only with the stabilising influence of the walls. The failure of the model occurs in the form of erosion of the cusped edges of the cylindrical cap (see figure 2, $T \geq 5$) and eventual breakup of the bubble.

Spherical Bubbles
The behaviour of spherical bubbles differs from cylindrical bubbles in several important respects identified by Walters and Davidson[3]. The initial acceleration of a spherical bubble is $2g$. The nature of the distortion is

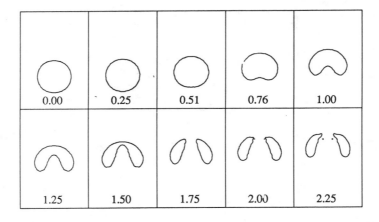

Figure 5: Spherical bubble shape change when released from rest in a quiescent liquid. $D = 50$ mm. Times shown are $T = t\sqrt{g/a}$.

much the same, the penetration of liquid through the bottom surface of the bubble, but in the spherical case this penetration typically continues until it reaches the top surface of the bubble. The result of this complete penetration is a toroidal bubble rather than a spherical cap.

These critical features of spherical bubble behaviour are reproduced quite well by the model (see figure 5). The initial acceleration matches $2g$ very well up to $T = 0.5$. Beyond that point, the acceleration reduces but all bubble sizes tested behave essentially the same. As for the two–dimensional case, the vertical diameter at the centreline of the bubble is a measure of distortion during the initial stages of growth. Figure 6 shows this deformation for various initial bubble sizes. The plots end at the point where the penetrating liquid contacts the top surface of the bubble. As bubble size increases this occurs sooner but reaches a constant of $T = 1.6$ for $D > 50$ mm. Experimental data for an 80 mm bubble from Walters and Davidson[3] is also plotted in figure 6. This experimental data compares quite well but could not be obtained to the point of toroidal bubble formation since the penetrating liquid is optically obscured. Data for a larger range of initial diameters are given in Reference 3 but are not distinguishable from those given in figure 6.

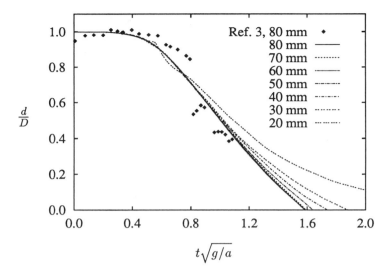

Figure 6: Distortion of spherical bubbles released from rest.

CONCLUSIONS

- The initial acceleration of g and $2g$ for cylindrical and spherical bubbles released from rest is confirmed and remains constant for $T \leq 0.5$.

- The minimum vertical diameter during distortion of two–dimensional bubbles is $d/D = 0.25$ and is essentially constant for $D > 50$ mm.

- The dimensionless time $(t\sqrt{g/a})$ after release for transition of a spherical bubble to a toroidal bubble decreases with increasing D.

- For spherical bubbles with $D > 50$ mm, the transition time to a toroid becomes constant at $T = 1.6$.

NOMENCLATURE

a	Initial bubble radius
D	Initial bubble diameter.
d	Vertical diameter of bubble on the centreline.
g	Acceleration due to gravity.

y_{cg}	Vertical displacement of bubble's centre of gravity.
t	Time.
T	Dimensionless time, $T = t\sqrt{g/a}$.

ACKNOWLEDGEMENTS

This work is supported by a Research Grant from the Canadian Natural Sciences and Engineering Research Council.

REFERENCES

[1] R. Clift, J.R. Grace, and M.E. Weber. *Bubbles, Drops and Particles*. Academic Press, New York, 1978.

[2] J.K. Walters and J.F. Davidson. The initial motion of a gas bubble formed in an inviscid liquid, pt.1: The two-dimensional bubble. *Journal of Fluid Mechanics*, 12(2):408–417, 1962.

[3] J.K. Walters and J.F. Davidson. The initial motion of a gas bubble formed in an inviscid liquid, pt.2: The three-dimensional bubble and the toroidal bubble. *Journal of Fluid Mechanics*, 17(3):321–339, 1963.

[4] G.R. Baker and D.W. Moore. The rise and distortion of a two dimensional gas bubble in an inviscid liquid. *Physics of Fluids A*, 1(9):1451–1459, 1989.

[5] J.D. Bugg and R.D. Rowe. Modelling the initial motion of large cylindrical and spherical bubbles. *International Journal for Numerical Methods in Fluids*, 13:109–129, 1991.

[6] B.D. Nichols, C.W. Hirt, and R.S. Hotchkiss. SOLA-VOF: A solution algorithm for transient fluid flow with multiple free boundaries. Technical Report LA-8355, Los Alamos National Laboratories, 1980.

[7] C.W. Hirt and B.D. Nichols. Volume of fluid (VOF) method for the dynamics of free boundaries. *Journal of Computational Physics*, 39:201–225, 1981.

[8] R. Collins. A simple model of the plane gas bubble in a finite liquid. *Journal of Fluid Mechanics*, 22:763–771, 1965.

A BEM solution for the simulation of axisymmetric viscous sintering

G.A.L van de Vorst

Department of Mathematics, University of Technology, PO Box 513, 5600 MB Eindhoven, The Netherlands

ABSTRACT

In this paper we describe a numerical method to simulate particular axisymmetric viscous sintering problems. In these problems the material transport is modelled as a viscous incompressible Newtonian volume flow driven solely by surface tension. The numerical simulation is carried out by solving the governing Stokes equations for a fixed domain through a Boundary Element Method (BEM). The resulting velocity field then determines an approximate geometry at a next time level by employing a variable step, variable order Backward Differences Formulae (BDF) method. This numerical algorithm is demonstrated for the sintering of two equal spheres.

INTRODUCTION

By sintering is meant the process of bringing a granular compact to a temperature at which the viscosity of the material becomes low enough for surface tension to cause the particles to deform and coalesce. Here the material transport is modelled as a viscous incompressible Newtonian volume: the Stokes creeping flow equations hold. The movement of the surface particles is modelled by the Lagrangian representation for the velocity of those material points. For example, the sintering of glasses can be modelled in such a way.

In the last few years a lot of work has been done in simulating the sintering of two-dimensional fluid regions. By now the evolution of some particular geometries can be solved even analytically, in particular using conformal mapping techniques, cf. Hopper [2]-[4]. The numerical simulation of viscous sintering is performed by successively solving the Stokes problem and employing a time step to predict the next level geometry.

In earlier work, cf. van de Vorst et al [10]-[12], we reported about the solution of the problem for arbitrarily shaped two-dimensional fluid regions. In that work, the Stokes problem is described by an integral formulation that is based on boundary distributions of single- and double layer hydrodynamical potentials and a BEM is employed to solve this problem.

The next step is the simulation of three-dimensional sintering geometries. The most logical fluid regions to start with are axisymmetric geometries: bodies which are formed by rotating a two-dimensional plane around a given axis. Because of this rotational symmetry, the problem can be reduced to any plane through this particular axis, i.e. actually a two-dimensional problem has to be solved.

Jagota and Dawson [6] were the first to perform the numerical simulation of some particular axisymmetric problems. They considered the sintering of both the coalescence of two equal spheres and an infinite line of equal spheres. These simulations were carried out by applying a Finite Element Method (FEM) to solve the Stokes problem. The geometry at a next time step was found by using a simple forward Euler scheme.

In this paper, we present a numerical method that is capable of simulating arbitrary simply connected axisymmetric fluid regions. The numerical algorithm is based on the two-dimensional code developed by us earlier, cf. van de Vorst et al [10]-[12]. The BEM is applied to solve the governing Stokes equations for a fixed domain. After solving the Stokes problem, the time stepping is carried out by a more sophisticated time integrator: a variable step, variable order Backward Differences Formulae (BDF) scheme.

PROBLEM DESCRIPTION

The material transport by viscous sintering is modelled as a viscous incompressible newtonian fluid driven solely by surface tension, cf. Kuiken [7]. So the Stokes creeping flow equations are valid, which read in dimensionless form

$$\triangle \mathbf{v} - \operatorname{grad} p = 0, \tag{1}$$

with the continuity equation

$$\operatorname{div} \mathbf{v} = 0. \tag{2}$$

Here $\mathbf{v}$ is the dimensionless velocity and p the dimensionless pressure. The stress tensor $\mathcal{T}$ for a Newtonian fluid is defined by

$$T_{ij} = -p\delta_{ij} + \left(\frac{\partial v_i}{\partial x_j} + \frac{\partial v_j}{\partial x_i}\right). \tag{3}$$

On the surface the tension in the normal direction is proportional to the trace of the curvature tensor $\kappa_{\alpha\beta}$,

$$\mathcal{T}\mathbf{n} = \kappa_{\alpha\alpha}\mathbf{n}, \tag{4}$$

where $\mathbf{n}$ is the outward unit normal vector and the indices α and β are varying between 1 and 2. The equations (1)-(4) can be solved uniquely for a *fixed* domain up to an arbitrary rigid body translation and rotation, cf. Ladyzhenskaya [8].

The movement of the boundary is obtained by applying the Lagrangian representation for the boundary velocity $\mathbf{v}$,

$$\frac{d\mathbf{x}}{dt} = \mathbf{v}(\mathbf{x}) \qquad (\mathbf{x} \in \Gamma), \tag{5}$$

where t is the dimensionless time. The above equation is expressing the displacement of the material boundary particles: the trajectories of those particles are followed.

INTEGRAL FORMULATION

In earlier work [10]-[12], it was shown that the BEM is ideally suited to solve two-dimensional viscous sintering problems. Therefore, it is convenient to employ the BEM for axisymmetric shapes too: thus we have to reformulate the problem in terms of an integral equation.

For a fluid blob Ω with "smooth" surface $\partial\Omega$, the derivation of the integral equation in the case of a cartesian coordinate system is described in detail by Ladyzhenskaya [8]; in this specific case we obtain,

$$c_{ij}v_j + \int_{\partial\Omega} q_{ij}v_j \, d\partial\Omega_y = \int_{\partial\Omega} u_{ij}b_j \, d\partial\Omega_y. \tag{6}$$

Here b_j, c_{ij}, q_{ij} and u_{ij} are equal to respectively:

$$b_j = \kappa_{\alpha\alpha} n_j, \qquad c_{ij} = \begin{cases} \delta_{ij} & \mathbf{x} \in \Omega \\ \frac{1}{2}\delta_{ij} & \mathbf{x} \in \partial\Omega, \end{cases}$$

$$q_{ij}(\mathbf{x},\mathbf{y}) = \frac{3(x_i - y_i)(x_j - y_j)(x_k - y_k)n_k}{4\pi|\mathbf{x} - \mathbf{y}|^5}, \tag{7}$$

$$u_{ij}(\mathbf{x},\mathbf{y}) = \frac{1}{8\pi}\left[\frac{\delta_{ij}}{|\mathbf{x} - \mathbf{y}|} + \frac{(x_i - y_i)(x_j - y_j)}{|\mathbf{x} - \mathbf{y}|^3}\right].$$

In order to obtain the integral equation for the axisymmetric case, we reformulate the above integral equation by applying cylindrical coordinates (r, θ, z), i.e.

$$(y_1, y_2, y_3) = (r\cos\theta, r\sin\theta, z). \tag{8}$$

Since the problem is rotation symmetric, we only have to determine v_r, v_z ($v_\theta = 0$) at the intersection of the surface $\partial\Omega$ and (say) the half-space $\theta = 0$. This intersection curve will be denoted by Γ; let therefore $\mathbf{x} = (R, 0, Z)$. After successive substitution of cylindrical coordinates and integration along the θ-direction of equation (6) we obtain

$$c_{ij}v_j^c + \int_\Gamma q_{ij}^c v_j^c \, d\Gamma = \int_\Gamma u_{ij}^c b_j^c \, d\Gamma. \tag{9}$$

Here the superscript c stands for cylindrical, thus $(v_1^c, v_2^c) = (v_r, v_z)$, etc. Furthermore, the coefficients q_{ij}^c and u_{ij}^c are depending on complete elliptic integrals of the first and second kind, cf. Becker [1].

Now, the above integral equation possess one degree of freedom only: a translation in the z-direction. We follow the approach of Hsiao et al [5] for making this integral equation uniquely solvable for a fixed domain: we add one additional variable α representing this particular translation freedom,

$$c_{ij}v_j^c + \int_\Gamma q_{ij}^c v_j^c \, d\Gamma + \alpha\delta_{i2} = \int_\Gamma u_{ij}^c b_j^c \, d\Gamma. \tag{10}$$

In order to prescribe the translation freedom, we require the problem to be stationary at a (reference) point in the fluid. The velocity is computed with regard to this reference point. The most natural choice for this reference point is the centre of mass: the point where the gravity forces would grip the body. Now, we obtain the needed extra relation by substituting this reference point in equation (9) and considering this equation only in the z-direction.

NUMERICAL SOLUTION

The numerical implementation of the axisymmetric integral equation is very similar to the two-dimensional case, cf. [10]; we actually have two unknowns v_r, v_z on a boundary curve. Because of this, the mesh redistribution, which is a very important item during the simulation of a particular shape, can be performed by applying the algorithms that are developed for the two-dimensional case, cf. [12]. However, the time integration has to be modified slightly, and of course the assembling of the system of equations.

A linear BEM is applied in order to discretize the integral equation (10). The typical system of equations that has to be solved can be described *formally* by

$$\mathcal{H}v = \mathcal{G}b. \tag{11}$$

Here v and b are the velocity, cq. tension, of all relevant successive nodal points.

After solving the above system of equations for a fixed region, a time step has to be carried out. From equation (5) it follows for the movement of the material points of boundary curve Γ for the axisymmetric case

$$\dot{r} = v_r$$
$$\dot{z} = v_z, \tag{12}$$

where the dot denotes the derivative with respect to the time t. Actually, we have to solve a system of nonlinear Ordinary Differential Equations (ODEs). This system can be described *formally* by

$$\dot{x} = \mathcal{H}^{-1}(x)\,\mathcal{G}(x)\,b(x), \tag{13}$$

where x is the vector of all relevant successive nodes.

In available literature about free creeping Stokes flows this system of ODEs is discretized by a simple forward Euler scheme or other explicit schemes. However, it appears that the above system of ODEs can be *stiff* for certain type of shapes (e.g. fluid regions which are having cusp's); in such a case the time step in the forward Euler scheme has to be taken very small for obtaining a stable method. Therefore, we have implemented a variable step, variable order Backward Differences Formulae (BDF) method to solve those ODEs. More details about this implementation for the two-dimensional case are available in [11].

NUMERICAL RESULTS

As an example to demonstrate our numerical code we have chosen the sintering of two equal spheres. The radius of the coalescing spheres is taken equal to 1; the initial radius of the contact circle between both spheres is set equal to 0.15. Here, this contact radius will be denoted by ρ. The development during sintering of the contact radius is of physical interest. The contact radius is a measure of how "strong" a sintering compact already is. When ρ is small, a smaller force is necessary to break the contact between both spheres than at later stages of the sintering process, when the contact radius is larger.

The collocation points of the starting shape are obtained from Hopper's analytical solution for the coalescence of two equal cylinders, cf. [3]. Thus for the initial stage we assume that the geometrical differences between two touching cylinders and two touching spheres can be ignored. Only nodal points from the first quadrant of the $\theta = 0$ plane are needed because of the double symmetry of the body. This symmetry is preserved during the calculations.

Figure 1 is showing the coalescence at a subsequent number of times t. As can be observed, the fluid is deforming to a sphere when time is increasing, i.e. a minimum surface around a certain amount of material. For the tolerance of the time integrator we took 10^{-4} and the number of

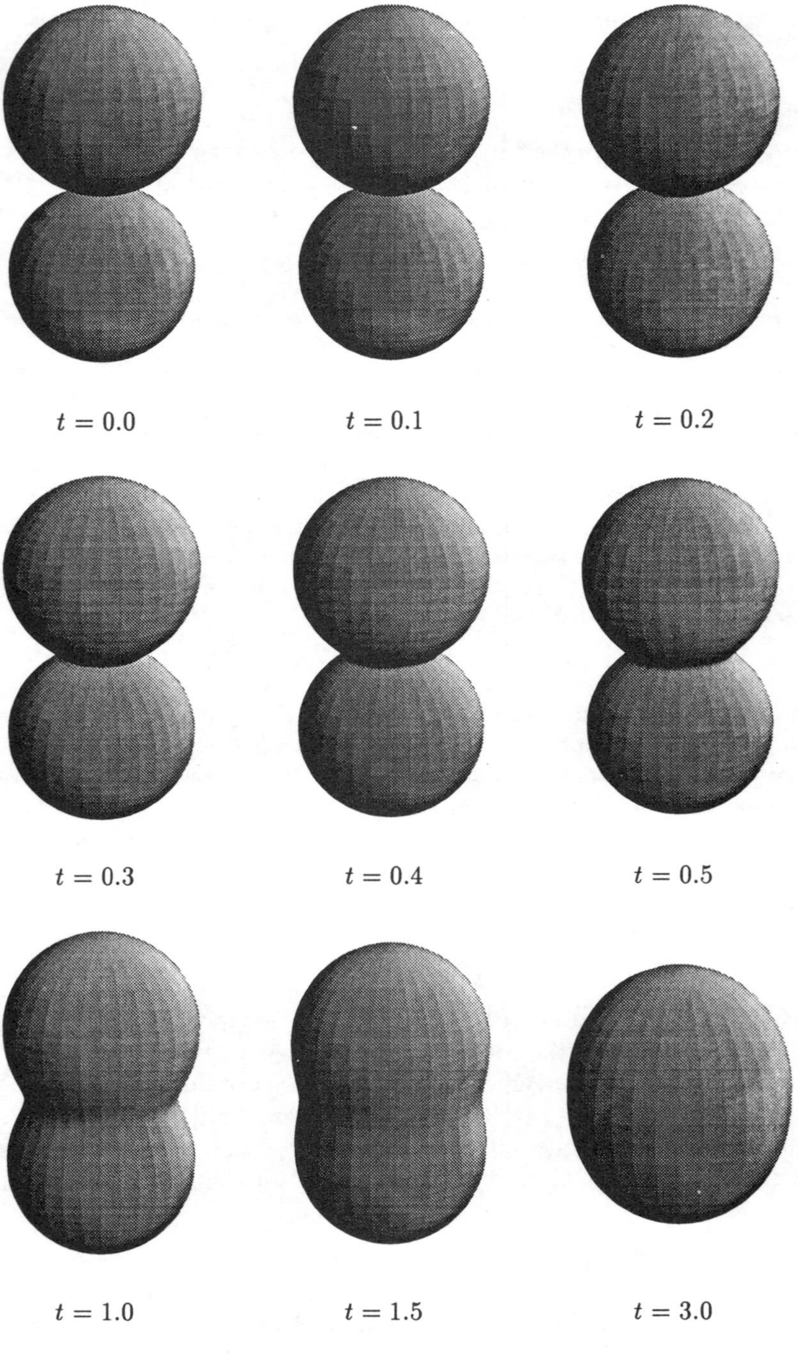

Figure 1: The coalescence of two equal spheres

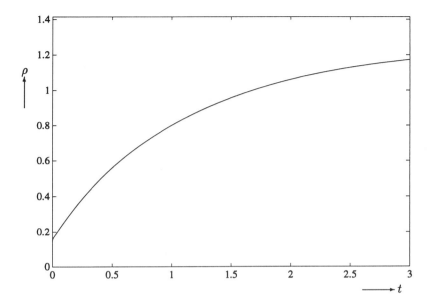

Figure 2: The contact radius ρ of the two spheres.

nodal points of the symmetry part was varying between 22-36 during the computation. The algorithm assembled and solved the system of equations (11) 124 times before $t = 3.0$ was reached. Furthermore, the BDF method took 76 time steps and required 36 Jacobian update.

Since the fluid is modelled to be incompressible, the difference in volume between the starting geometry and the finally obtained shape is giving a measure of the error that is made by this simulation. It appears that this difference was equal to 2%, which was caused by the remeshing algorithm; the difference of volume between two successive time steps without a remeshing was approximately 0.01%.

In figure 2 we have plotted the numerically obtained contact radius between both spheres. As can be seen, the contact radius ρ is going to its limiting value $\sqrt[3]{2} \approx 1.26$ as time increases, i.e. the radius of the final sphere.

ACKNOWLEDGMENT

The author thanks Prof. R.M.M. Mattheij for critically reading the paper. This research was supported by the Technology Foundation (STW).

REFERENCES

1. Becker, A.A. *The Boundary Element Method in Engineering* McGraw-Hill Book Company, London, 1992.

2. Hopper, R.W. 'Plane Stokes flow driven by capillarity on a free surface' *J. Fluid Mech.*, Vol.213, pp. 349-375, 1990.

3. Hopper, R.W. 'Plane Stokes Flow driven by capillarity on a free surface, 2: Further Developments' *J. Fluid Mech.*, Vol.230, pp. 355-364, 1991.

4. Hopper, R.W. 'Stokes Flow of a Cylinder and Half-Space Driven by Capillarity' *J. Fluid Mech.*, Vol.243, pp. 171-181, 1992.

5. Hsiao, G.C., Kopp, P., Wendland, W.L. 'Some applications of a Galerkin collocation method for boundary integral equations of the first kind' *Math. Methods in the Appl. Sciences*, Vol.6, pp. 280-325, 1984.

6. Jagota, A., Dawson, P.R. 'Simulation of the Viscous Sintering of Two Particles' *J. Am. Ceram. Soc.*, Vol.73, pp. 173-177, 1990.

7. Kuiken, H.K. 'Viscous sintering: the surface-tension-driven flow of a liquid form under the influence of curvature gradients at its surface' *J. Fluid Mech.*, Vol.214, pp. 503-515, 1990.

8. Ladyzhenskaya, O.A. *The Mathematical Theory of Viscous Incompressible Flow* Gordon and Beach, New York-London, 1963.

9. Lee, S.H., Leal, L.G. 'The Motion of a Sphere in the Presence of a Deformable Interface. Part 2: Numerical study of the translation of a sphere normal to an interface' *J. Colloid Interface Sci.*, Vol.87, pp. 81-106, 1982.

10. van de Vorst, G.A.L., Mattheij, R.M.M., Kuiken, H.K. 'A Boundary Element Solution for Two-Dimensional Viscous Sintering' *J. Comput. Phys.*, Vol.100, pp. 50-63, 1992.

11. van de Vorst, G.A.L., Mattheij, R.M.M. 'A BDF-BEM Scheme for Modelling Viscous Sintering' in BETECH/92 (Ed. Brebbia, C.A. and Ingber, M.S.), pp. 59-74, *Proc. Conf. on Boundary Element Technology VII*, Albuquerque, USA, 1992. Elsevier, Amsterdam, 1992.

12. van de Vorst, G.A.L., Mattheij, R.M.M. 'Numerical Analysis of a 2-D Viscous Sintering Problem with Non Smooth Boundaries', *Computing*, Vol.49, to appear, 1992.

Invited Paper

Boundary elements formulation for the interaction of a deformable bubble with a rigid wall at small Reynolds number

H. Power

Wessex Institute of Technology, University of Portsmouth, Southampton, England. (on leave from Universidad Central de Venezuela, Facultad de Ingeniería, Instituto de Mecánica de Fluídos, Caracas, Venezeuela

Abstract

The unsteady viscous flow induced by a deformable gas bubble approaching a rigid boundary is investigated for small Reynolds number. The Stokes equation was solved by means of a Boundary Element method that leads to a unique surface velocity regardless the shape of the bubble. The bubble motion is driven by buoyancy force. The good agreement with previous works using different numerical techniques confirms the reliability of the numerical technique developed.

Introduction:

The practical importance of studying the deformation of bubbles moving under the action of gravity in an ambient suspending fluid is due to their common occurrence in many industrial and biological systems as well as in a number of technological processes. For instance, the motion of a bubble towards a rigid wall is related with film drainage problems, being the initial state of the latter.

In this work we will consider the low Reynolds number deformation of an initially spherical gas bubble moving towards to a plane wall π, which we shall take to be

$x_3 = 0$, the geometric center of the bubble will be chosen to be at $x_1 = 0$, $x_2 = 0$ and $x_3 = h$. Under this condition, the velocity field and pressure $(\vec{u}, p)$, satisfy as a first approximation the Stokes' system of equations:

$$\mu \frac{\partial^2 u_i}{\partial x_j \partial x_j} = \frac{\partial p}{\partial x_i}, \qquad \frac{\partial u_j}{\partial x_j} = 0 \qquad \text{for } x \in \Omega \tag{1}$$

where Ω is the domain above π exterior to the bubble bounded by a Lyapunov surface S.

The flow field has to satisfy the following asymptotic and boundary conditions:

$$u_i(x) = 0 \quad \text{at} \quad x \in \pi, \qquad u_i(x) = O(|x|^{-1}), \qquad p \to p^\infty \qquad \text{as } |x| \to \infty \tag{2}$$

where p^∞ is the uniform pressure far from the bubble, and

$$\sigma_{ij}(\vec{u})\, n_j + p^*\, n_i = -n_i\, (\gamma\kappa + \Delta\rho g x_3) \qquad \text{on } S, \tag{3}$$

where the driving force is the buoyancy, here

$$\sigma_{ij}(\vec{u}) = -p\delta_{ij} + \mu \left(\frac{\partial u_i}{\partial x_j} + \frac{\partial u_j}{\partial x_i} \right), \qquad \text{and } \kappa = \left(\tfrac{1}{R_1} + \tfrac{1}{R_2} \right) \tag{4}$$

with R_1, R_2 as the principal radii of curvature, p^* the gas pressure, $\vec{n}$ the unit normal to S outward to the bubble, $\Delta\rho$ the density difference, x_3 the vertical direction, μ the ambient fluid viscosity and γ is the interfacial surface tension at the bubble interface.

The bubble will deform due to the action of shear at the bubble surface, exerted by the external fluid as the bubble rises. The rate of deformation is determined by the kinematic boundary condition at S, which states that the normal component of the fluid velocity at a point x on the surface bubble is equal to the normal component of the surface velocity at that point:

$$\frac{dx_i}{dt} n_i = u_i n_i \qquad \text{at } x \in S. \tag{5}$$

For an incompressible bubble, besides (2) and (3), the flow has to satisfy the following no flux condition across the bubble surface S:

$$\int_S u_i n_i \, dS = 0, \tag{6}$$

equation (6) gives the incompressibility constraint for the gas bubble, i.e. the requirement of constant bubble volume.

Introducing the disturbance flow, $v_i = u_i$, $q = p - p^\infty$ and non-dimensionalizing all distances by a, the radius of the initial spherical bubble in the absence of any deformation; all velocities by $g\Delta\rho a^2/\mu$ and the stress tensor in the liquid phase by $g\Delta\rho$, equations (1)-(6) become:

$$\frac{\partial^2 v_i}{\partial x_j \partial x_j} = \frac{\partial q}{\partial x_i}, \qquad \frac{\partial v_i}{\partial x_i} = 0 \qquad \text{for } x \in \Omega \tag{7-a}$$

$$v_i(x) = 0 \quad \text{at} \quad x \in \pi, \qquad v_i(x) \to 0, \qquad q \to 0 \qquad \text{as } |x| \to \infty \tag{7-b}$$

$$\sigma_{ij}(\vec{v})n_j = -n_i \left(T\kappa + (p^* - p^\infty) + x_3 \right) \qquad \text{at } x \in S \tag{7-c}$$

$$v_i n_i = \frac{dx_i}{dt} n_i \qquad \text{at } x \in S \tag{7-d}$$

$$\int_S v_i n_i \, dS = 0, \tag{7-e}$$

where the dimensionless parameter T is equal to $\gamma/a^2 \Delta \rho g$, and

$$\sigma_{ij}(\vec{v}) = -q\delta_{ij} + \left(\frac{\partial v_i}{\partial x_j} + \frac{\partial v_j}{\partial x_i} \right).$$

Taking into account the quasi-static character of the present problem, we can solve the boundary value problem (7) for a given bubble shape $S(t)$, and with the computed surface disturbance velocity $v(t)$ and a time step Δt, we can determine the shape of the deformed bubble $S(t + \Delta t)$ using the kinematic condition (7-d). The scheme starts with a given initial bubble shape $S(t = 0)$, then at each instant of time t, (7-b,c) defines a boundary-value problem for the Stokes' equation, i.e. given stresses on a known surface $S(t)$ and zero velocity at the plane π. At the initial moment the bubble is assumed to be at rest, its shape spherical and the ambient liquid quiescent.

The simplest possible configuration consists of a single bubble moving at zero Reynolds number in an infinite ambient fluid. Given that in this case the bubble is immersed in an infinite ambient quiescent fluid, and given also the surface traction boundary conditions on the surface of the bubble, the integral representation formulae applied to the disturbance velocity $\vec{v}$

$$\frac{1}{2}v_i(\xi) + \int_S K_{ij}(\xi, y)v_j(y) \, dS_y = \int_S J_{ij}(\xi, y)\sigma_{jl}(\vec{v}(y))n_l(y) \, dS_y \quad \text{for } \xi \in S, \tag{8}$$

here

$$J_{ij}(x, y) = -\frac{1}{8\pi}\left(\frac{\delta_{ij}}{r} + \frac{(x_i - y_i)(x_j - y_j)}{r^3} \right); \qquad r = |x - y| \tag{9}$$

is the fundamental singular solution of Stokes' equations, known as Stokeslet located at the point y, and

$$K_{ij}(x, y) = \sigma_{ij}(J_{lk}e_l)_y \, n_k(y) = -\frac{3}{4\pi}\frac{(x_i - y_i)(x_j - y_j)(x_k - y_k)}{r^5} \, n_k(y). \tag{10}$$

Substitution of (7-c) into (8) gives a second kind Fredholm integral equation for the unknown surface disturbance velocity, $\vec{v}(\xi)$. As shown by Ladyzhenskaya ((1963), page 7), the adjoint to the homogeneous part of (8), is

$$\frac{1}{2}\psi_i(\xi) + \int_S K_{ji}(y, \xi)\psi_j(y) \, dS_y = 0 \tag{11}$$

has a single eigensolution, equal to $n_i(\xi)$, and therefore the homogeneous part of
(8) has also a single eigensolution u_i^e. Thus, (8) has solutions if and only if its
right-hand side is orthogonal to $\vec{n}$, i.e.

$$\int_S n_i(\xi) \int_S J_{ij}(\xi, y) \sigma_{jl}(\vec{v}(y)) n_l(y) \, dS_y \, dS_\xi =$$

$$\int_S \sigma_{jl}(\vec{v}(y)) n_l(y) \int_S J_{ij}(\xi, y) \, n_i(\xi) \, dS_\xi \, dS_y = 0$$

and this will always be the case, since every single-layer potential with $\vec{n}$ as a
density is identically zero in the region exterior to the density carrying surface
(see Ladyzhenskaya (1963) page 60), that is to say

$$\int_S J_{ij}(x, y) n_j(y) \, dS_y = 0 \qquad \text{for every point exterior to the bubble.}$$

In the above orthogonality property, we use the symmetry $J_{ij}(x, y) = J_{ji}(y, x)$;
hence a particular solution $\vec{v}^{(p)}$ of (8) does indeed exist. Nevertheless, since the
complete solution of (8) will contain an unknown multiple of $\vec{u}^e$, the surface
disturbance velocity, $\vec{v}$, is not uniquely determined by this method.

It can be noted that $K_{ij}(\xi, y)$ is self-adjoint for the spherical shape, i.e. $K_{ij}(\xi, y)$
$= K_{ji}(y, \xi)$ (see Kim and Karrila (1991) chapter 17 section 17.2.1). Among other
things, this result also requires the eigenfunction $\vec{u}^e$ to be proportional to the normal vector, therefore the non uniqueness of the surface velocity coming from the
eigenfunction $\vec{u}^e$ makes no contribution upon the shape of the sphere, although it
contributes upon its final volume. Youngren and Acrivos (1976) conjectured that
the same was true for axisymmetric bubbles of not unusual geometrical shape,
so their method could be used to determine the shape evolution of a deformable
bubble which does not depart much from the spherical shape.

The extension of the above method to the case of rising bubble near a plane wall is
trivial, by using the corresponding Green's function. However as in the previous
case, this approach can only be guaranteed in the case where the deformable
bubble does not depart much from the spherical shape.

Recently, Power (1991) explained how integral equations of the second kind can
be obtained leading to a unique bubble surface velocity for the cases of general
bubble shapes. He observed that although a single layer representation, that
originates a second kind integral equation coming from the jump property of the
surface traction field of a single layer potential across the density carrying surface,
will yield an integral equation with a non unique solution, the representation may
be completed by adding a source harmonic potential located in the interior of the
bubble, with strength chosen linearly proportional to the unknown density of the
single layer potential (every flow velocity due to a harmonic potential coupled
with a constant pressure is a Stokes' flow). In this manner the resulting second
kind integral equation possesses a unique solution.

The main objective of this paper is to extend Power completed boundary integral equation method to the problem of bubble of arbitrary shape moving arbitrarily near a plane wall using the method of the image.

Proposed form of solution

Following Power (1991) completed method, we will seek the solution for the velocity field of the above boundary value problem in the following form:

$$v_i(x) = \int_S J_{ij}(x,y)\phi_j(y) \, dS_y + \int_S J_{ij}^*(x,y^*)\phi_j(y) \, dS_y +$$

$$\frac{\alpha x_i}{4\pi R_0^3} - \frac{\alpha x_i}{4\pi(R_0^*)^3} \tag{12}$$

with $R_0 = |x - y_0|$, $R_0^* = |x - y_0^*|$, y_0 is the point $(0,0,h)$ and y_0^* is the point $(0,0,-h)$.

In the above equation $J_{ij}^*(x,y^*)$ is the corresponding image of a Stokeslet located at a point y needed to satisfy the non-slip boundary condition at the plane π (see appendix 1), and $-\alpha x_i/(4\pi(R_0^*)^3)$ is the image velocity field of a source harmonic potential with velocity field $\alpha x_i/(4\pi(R_0)^3)$, located at the point y_0.

It can be observed that we have added to a single-layer potential, an image single layer, coming from the distribution of the Stokeslet $J_{ij}^*(x,y^*)$ over the surface of the bubble with the same unknown density $\vec{\phi}(y)$ of the original single layer, the flow field due to a source harmonic potential located at point y_0 in the interior of the bubble with intensity α coupled with zero pressure, and its corresponding image. It will be convenient for later use, to choose α depending linearly upon the density $\vec{\phi}$ of the single-layer potential as follows:

$$\alpha = \int_S \phi_i n_i \, dS. \tag{13}$$

Since the single-layer potential yields zero total flux across any closed surface and the image systems used are regular Stokes flow yielding zero flux, it can be concluded that in this case, the net flux on the exterior incompressible fluid due to the volume change in the bubble is equal to the intensity α of the source.

Applying the boundary condition (7-c) to the flow field (12) and using the known stress jump property of single-layers, leads to the following linear Fredholm integral equation of the second kind for the unknown density $\vec{\phi}$:

$$\lim_{x \to \xi \in S} \sigma_{ij}(\vec{v})n_j = n_i \left(T\kappa(\xi) - (p^* - p^\infty) + \xi_3\right) =$$

$$-\left(\frac{1}{2}\phi_i(\xi) + \int_S K_{ji}(y,\xi) \, \phi_j(y)dS_y + \int_S K_{ji}^*(y^*,\xi) \, \phi_j(y)dS_y\right) +$$

$$\sigma_{ij}(\vec{u}^s(\xi))n_j(\xi) \int_S \phi_j n_j \, dS + \sigma_{ij}(\vec{u}^{s*}(\xi))n_j(\xi) \int_S \phi_j n_j \, dS \tag{14}$$

for every $\xi \in S$, where

$$\sigma_{ij}(\vec{u}^s(\xi)) = \sigma_{ij}\left(\frac{\alpha\xi}{4\pi R_{0\xi}^3}\right) = \frac{\alpha}{2\pi}\left(\frac{\delta_{ij}}{R_{0\xi}^3} - 3\frac{\xi_i\xi_j}{R_0\xi^5}\right)$$

and

$$\sigma_{ij}(\vec{u}^{s*}(\xi)) = \sigma_{ij}\left(-\frac{\alpha\xi}{4\pi(R_{0\xi}^*)^3}\right) = -\frac{\alpha}{2\pi}\left(\frac{\delta_{ij}}{(R_{0\xi}^*)^3} - 3\frac{\xi_i\xi_j}{(R_0\xi^*)^5}\right)$$

with $R_{0\xi} = |\xi - y_0|$ and $R_{0\xi}^* = |\xi - y_0^*|$.

To show that (14) possesses a unique solution, it is sufficient, according to Fredholm's alternative, to show that the following homogeneous integral equation admits only the trivial solution in the space of continuous functions:

$$0 = \frac{1}{2}\phi_i^0(\xi) + \int_S K_{ji}(y,\xi)\,\phi_j^0(y)dS_y + \int_S K_{ji}^*(y^*,\xi)\,\phi_j^0(y)dS_y -$$

$$\sigma_{ij}(\vec{u}^s(\xi))n_j(\xi)\int_S \phi_j^0 n_j\,dS - \sigma_{ij}(\vec{u}^{s*}(\xi))n_j(\xi)\int_S \phi_j^0 n_j\,dS \qquad (15)$$

for every $\xi \in S$. The previous equation can be rewritten as:

$$\frac{1}{2}\phi_i^0(\xi) + \int_S K_{ji}(y,\xi)\,\phi_j^0(y)dS_y + \int_S K_{ji}^*(y^*,\xi)\,\phi_j^0(y)dS_y =$$

$$\sigma_{ij}(\vec{u}^s(\xi))n_j(\xi)\int_S \phi_j^0 n_j\,dS + \sigma_{ij}(\vec{u}^{s*}(\xi))n_j(\xi)\int_S \phi_j^0 n_j\,dS \qquad (16)$$

The homogeneous from of the above equation, i.e.

$$\frac{1}{2}\phi_i^0(\xi) + \int_S K_{ji}(y,\xi)\,\Phi_j^0(y)dS_y + \int_S K_{ji}^*(y^*,\xi)\,\Phi_j^0(y)dS_y = 0 \qquad (17)$$

has a single eigensolution equal to $\Phi_i^0(\xi) = Cn_i(\xi)$. Equation (17) shows that the single layer potential with density $\vec{\Phi}^0$ plus its image system, needed to satisfy the zero velocity condition at the plane π, which is a regular Stokes flow field in Ω, has zero surface traction value at every point ξ belonging to the surface S. Therefore, from the uniqueness of solution of the present problem, it follows that this combination of single layer and its image system, has to be zero for every point x belonging to Ω and the same has to be true for the limit value coming from Ω of the velocity vector, $\vec{v}$, at every points $\xi \in S$. Since the single layer potential has continuous velocity vector across its density carrying surface and the image system of the single layer potential used here is regular at every point above the plane π, it follows that the zero velocity vector of this combination can be extended continuously across the density carrying surface S, and therefore inside the bubble, this flow combination has zero velocity and constant pressure, i.e. $\sigma_{ij}n_j = Cn_i$. On the other hand, from the jump property of the surface traction of a single layer potential across its density carrying surface, we obtain:

$$(\sigma_{ij}(\vec{V}(\xi))n_j + \sigma_{ij}(\vec{V}^*(\xi))n_j)_{(i)} - (\sigma_{ij}(\vec{V}(\xi))n_j + \sigma_{ij}(\vec{V}^*(\xi))n_j)_{(e)} = \Phi_i^0(\xi)$$

the subscript (i) denotes the limiting value coming from the inside of the bubble and the subscript (e) the limiting value coming from the outside. Therefore, the eigenfunction $\vec{\Phi}^0$ has to be proportional to the normal vector, since from the above statement, we can conclude that $(\sigma_{ij}(\vec{V}(\xi))n_j + \sigma_{ij}(\vec{V}^*(\xi))n_j)_{(e)} = 0$ and $(\sigma_{ij}(\vec{V}(\xi))n_j + \sigma_{ij}(\vec{V}^*(\xi))n_j)_{(i)} = Cn_i$.

Therefore the adjoint to the homogeneous equation (17) has a single eigensolution equal to $\vec{v}^e$ (for the relation between the kernel of the adjoint homogeneous equation and the surface traction of the image of a Stokeslet see appendix 1), thus (16) has a non-trivial solution, if and only if, the following orthogonality condition is satisfied:

$$\int_S v_i^e(\xi)\,(\sigma_{ij}(\vec{u}^s(\xi))n_j(\xi) + \sigma_{ij}(\vec{u}^{s*}(\xi))n_j(\xi))\left(\int_S \phi_j^0 n_j\,dS\right)\,dS_\xi =$$

$$\left(\int_S \phi_j^0 n_j\,dS\right)\int_S v_i^e(\xi)\,(\sigma_{ij}(\vec{u}^s(\xi))n_j(\xi) + \sigma_{ij}(\vec{u}^{s*}(\xi))n_j(\xi))\,dS_\xi = 0$$

and this will be the case, if and only if:

$$\int_S \phi_j^0 n_j\,dS = 0 \tag{18}$$

since

$$\int_S v_i^e(\xi)\,(\sigma_{ij}(\vec{u}^s(\xi))n_j(\xi) + \sigma_{ij}(\vec{u}^{s*}(\xi))n_j(\xi))\,dS_\xi =$$

$$-\int_S (u_i^s(\xi) + u_i^{s*}(\xi))\,n_i(\xi)\,dS_\xi = -1$$

is the flux due to a unit sink, located in the interior of the bubble, here we have used the reciprocal theorem and the fact that the double layer potential $\vec{W}(x, v^e)$ plus its image system needed to satisfy the zero velocity condition at the plane π has a surface tension proportional to the normal $\vec{n}$, i.e. $\sigma_{ij}(\vec{W}(x, \vec{v}^e))\,n_j + \sigma_{ij}(\vec{W}^*(x, \vec{v}^e))\,n_j = Cn_i$, and $-\vec{v}^e$ as surface velocity (see appendix 2).

Thus (16) reduces to (17), and necessarily, $\vec{\phi}^0 = C\vec{n}$. From equation (18) we have:

$$C\int_S n_j n_j\,dS = 0$$

therefore $C = 0$, implying that $\vec{\phi}^0 = 0$ in S, q.e.d. Hence, the density $\vec{\phi}$ is uniquely determined, in contrast with the formulation based upon the integral representation formulae with the corresponding Green's function type of solution previously presented.

The disturbance velocity $\vec{v}(\xi)$ at the surface of the compressible bubble is thus found in the form equation (12), where the density $\vec{\phi}$ is given by the unique solution of integral equation (14). The bubble deformation is determined by the kinematic condition and is accompanied by a volume change, and the corresponding pressure change can be found from the ideal-gas law $p^* V = \text{constant}$.

Once the interfacial velocity is obtained, the new position of the fluid interface is found by integration of equation $(7 - d)$, which is carried out in a differential form.

In the case of a incompressible bubble $\vec{a}$ is identically zero, since the flow field exterior to a closed surface S, represented by a single layer potential, with a vector density $\vec{\phi}$, plus its image system needed to satisfy the zero velocity condition at the plane π i.e.

$$u_i(x) = \int_S J_{ij}(x, y)\phi_j(y)dS_y + \int_S J_{ij}^*(x, y^*)\phi_j(y)dS_y,$$

satisfies the no-flux condition, *i.e*

$$\int_S n_i(\xi)\left(\int_S J_{ij}(\xi, y)\ \phi_j(y)\ dS_y\ d_S\xi + \int_S J_{ij}^*(\xi, y^*)\ \phi_j(y)\ dS_y\right)\ dS_\xi =$$

$$\int_S \phi_j(y)\ \left(\int_S J_{ij}(y, \xi)\ n_i(\xi)\ dS_\xi + \int_S J_{ij}^*(y^*, \xi)\ n_i(\xi)\right)\ dS_\xi dS_y = 0$$

where we have used the continuity property across the density carrying surface of the single layer potential, the symmetry $J_{ij}(x, y) = J_{ji}(y, x)$, the fact that the image system is a regular Stokes flow in Ω and therefore yields zero flux across any closed surface there, and the zero velocity field at every $x \in \Omega$ of a single-layer potential, with $\vec{n}$ as density, plus its image system.

It can be observed, that in this case, when $\vec{a} = 0$, this type of solution also leads to a non unique density $\vec{\phi}$, since the homogeneous form of (14) is just equation (17), and then, it is necessary that $\vec{\phi} = \vec{\phi}^p + c\vec{n}$, where c is an arbitrary real constant. Nevertheless, in this case, the surface disturbance velocity is uniquely determined, since

$$v_i(x) = \int_S J_{ij}(x, y)(\phi_j^p(y) + cn_j(y))\ dS_y + \int_S J_{ij}^*(x, y^*)(\phi_j^p(y) + cn_j(y))\ dS_y =$$

$$\int_S J_{ij}(x, y)\phi_j^p(y)\ dS_y + \int_S J_{ij}^*(x, y^*)\phi_j^p(y)\ dS_y \qquad \text{for every } x \in \Omega, \qquad (19)$$

because every single-layer potential with $\vec{n}$ as density plus its image is identically zero in the region exterior to the density carrying surface.

To test the numerical method developed in this section, the problem of an initially spherical gas bubble of diameter 20 mm in glycerin, with an Eotvos number $E = g(2l)^2\rho/\gamma = 119.48$, where $l = (3V/a\pi)^{1/3}$ and V is the initial volume of the bubble, is worked out. Figure (1) illustrates, using the method developed here, the evolution of a bubble for the case of an incompressible internal inviscid gas fluid, solution that is in agreement with the one found by Shopov et. al (1990) for the case of small Reynolds number using a finite element solution of the complete Navier Stokes equations. Also in figure (1), we present the same evolution but for the case of a compressible internal fluid, the case of rising *compressible* gas bubble in an otherwise quiescent fluid, at small Reynolds number, is of less physical importance, in comparison with the case of *incompressible* bubble, however it is not physically impossible. Here, we present both cases for numerical comparison.

Appendix 1

The image system of the Stokeslet needed to satisfy the non-slip boundary condition at the wall was found by Blake (1971) and it is equal to:

$$J_i^{*j}(x, y^*) = -J_i^j(x, y^*) + 2h(\delta_{j\alpha}\delta_{\alpha k} - \delta_{j3}\delta_{3k})$$

$$(hD_i^k(x, y^*) - JD_{il}^k(x, y^*)\delta_{l3}) \tag{A1.1}$$

here the tensor $(\delta_{j\alpha}\delta_{\alpha k} - \delta_{j3}\delta_{3k})$ is not zero only when $j = k$; its value is $+1$ for $j = 1$ or 2, and -1 for $j = 3$,

$$D_i^k(x, y^*) = \frac{1}{8\pi}\frac{\partial}{\partial x_k}\left(\frac{x_i - y_i^*}{(r^*)^3}\right)$$

$$r^* = |x - y^*| \tag{A1.2}$$

is the velocity field due to a Source doublet placed at the point y^* and oriented in the k-th direction,

$$JD_{ij}^k(x, y^*) = \frac{\partial}{\partial x_k}(J_i^j) \tag{A1.3}$$

is the velocity field due to Stokes doublet oriented in the k-th direction, coming from the derivative of a Stokeslet placed at the point y^* and oriented in the j-th direction.

Pozrikidis (1990) showed that $\sigma_{ij}(\vec{J}^k(x, y) + \vec{J}^{*k}(x, y^*))_y g_{jk}$, for any constant tensor g_{jk}, is a legitimate Stokes' velocity field, with vanishing value along the wall π. Therefore, since $\sigma_{ij}(\vec{J}^k(x, y))_y n_k(y) = K_{ij}(x, y)$, it should be that $K_{ij}^*(x, y^*) = \sigma_{ij}(\vec{J}^{*k}(x, y^*))_y n_k(y)$ and then

$$W_i^*(x) = \int_S K_{ij}^*(x, y^*)\phi_j(y)\, dS_y \tag{A1.4}$$

is the image system of the double layer potential

$$W_i(x) = \int_S K_{ij}(x, y)\phi_j(y)\, dS_y \tag{A1.5}$$

Appendix 2

Let us consider a double-layer potential plus its image system needed to satisfy the zero velocity condition at the plane π:

$$H_i = W_i + W_i^* = \int_S K_{ij}(x, y)v_j^e(y)\, dS_y + \int_S K_{ij}^*(x, y^*)v_j^e(y)\, dS_y \tag{A2.1}$$

which is everywhere defined but discontinuous across S. Taking the limiting value of $\vec{H}$ as $x \in \Omega_i$ tends to a point $\xi \in S$, where Ω_i is the domain interior to the bubble, gives (see Ladyzhenskaya, (1963), page 55):

$$H_i(\xi)_i = \frac{1}{2}v_i^e(\xi) + \int_S K_{ij}(\xi,y)v_j^e(y)\, dS_y + \int_S K_{ij}^*(\xi,y^*)v_j^e(y)\, dS_y \qquad (A2.2)$$

where $H_i(\xi)_i$ denotes the limiting value of $H_i(x,\vec{v}^e)$ as x approaches a point $\xi \in S$ from inside the bubble.

From the adjoint to the homogeneous equation (17), it follows that $H_i(\xi)_i = 0$, and from the jump property of such double-layers, we conclude that $H_i(\xi)_e = -v_i^e(\xi)$; here $H_i(\xi)_e$ denotes the limiting value of $H_i(x,\vec{u}^e)$ as x approaches a point $\xi \in S$ from Ω, the domain exterior to the bubble.

Since $H_i(x,\vec{v}^e)$ is a regular Stokes' flow in Ω, Green's formula can be applied to yield:

$$H_i(x,\vec{v}^e) = -\int_S K_{ij}(x,y)H_j(y,\vec{v}^e)\, dS_y - \int_S K_{ij}^*(x,y^*)H_j(y,\vec{v}^e)\, dS_y +$$

$$\int_S J_{ij}(x,y)\sigma_{ij}(\vec{H})n_j\, dS_y + \int_S J_{ij}^*(x,y^*)\sigma_{ij}(\vec{H})n_j\, dS_y \qquad (A2.3)$$

Using $H_j(y,\vec{v}^e) = -v_j^e(y)$, it follows that:

$$\int_S J_{ij}(x,y)\sigma_{ij}(\vec{H})n_j(y)\, dS_y + \int_S J_{ij}^*(x,y^*)\sigma_{ij}(\vec{H})n_j(y)\, dS_y = 0 \qquad (A2.4)$$

Taking the surface tension of (A2.4) when $x \in \Omega$ tends to a point $\xi \in S$, gives:

$$\frac{1}{2}\sigma_{ij}(\vec{H}(\xi))n_j(\xi) + \int_S K_{ji}(y,\xi)\sigma_{jl}(\vec{H}(y))n_l(y)\, dS_y +$$

$$\int_S K_{ji}^*(y^*,\xi)\sigma_{jl}(\vec{H}(y))n_l(y)\, dS_y = 0. \qquad (A2.5)$$

From (17), it follows that $\sigma_{ij}(\vec{H})n_j = cn_i$.

References

- Blake, J.R. (1971), A Note on the Image System for a Stokeslet in a No-Slip Boundary, *Proc. Cambridge Philos. Soc.*, Vol. 70.

- Kim, S. and Karrila, S.J. (1991), *Microhydrodynamics: Principles and Selected Applications*, Butterworth-Heinemann, London.

- Ladyzhenskaya, O.A. (1963), *The mathematical theory of viscous incompressible flow*, Gordon and Breach, New York.

- Power, H. (1991), The Low Reynolds Number Deformation of a Gas Bubble in Shear Flow - A General Approach via Integral Equations, *Engineering Analysis with Boundary Elements*, Vol. 9, N1 31-38.

- Pozrikidis, C. (1990), The Deformation of a Liquid Drop Moving Normal to a Plane Wall, *J. Fluid Mech.*, Vol. 215.

- Shopov, P.J., Minev, P.D., Bazhlekov, I.B. and Zapryanov, Z.D. (1990), Interaction of a deformable bubble with a rigid wall at moderate Reynolds numbers, *J. Fluid Mech.* Vol. 219, pp 241.

- Youngren, G.K. and Acrivos, A. (1976), On the shape of a gas bubble in a viscous extensional flow, *J. Fluid Mech.* Vol. 76, pp 433.

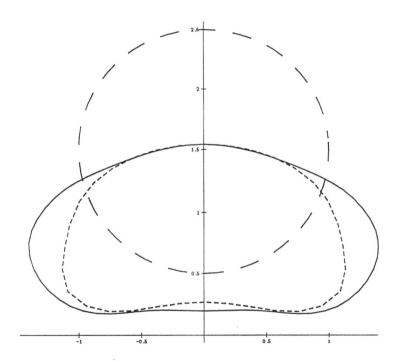

Figure 1 The evolution of a gas bubble approaching a plane wall, — — initial spherical bubble, ——— incompressible gas bubble, - - - - compressible gas bubble.

SECTION 4: CAVITATIONAL FLOW

Calculation of the plane and axisymmetric Riabouchinsky cavitational flows by the direct boundary element method

N.N. Yas'ko

Mechanical and Mathematical Faculty, Dniepropetrovsk University, 320625 Dniepropetrovsk-10, Ukraine

ABSTRACT

A numerical algorithm is proposed for the solution of the steady cavitating flows around the arbitrary plane and axisymmetrical blunt-ended bodies with the fixed separation point. The fluid is assumed as incompressible and weightless, and the flow is assumed as potential. For a description of the cavitational flow the Riabouchinsky cavitating scheme ("with the mirror") was used and the length of the free streamline was chosen as a parameter. Numerical results for the drag coefficients, the shape of cavities and cavitation numbers are presented for cavitating flows behind the cones and wedges with half-angle in range $[10^{\circ}, 120^{\circ}]$. These results are compared with the data of other authors for the disk (90°) and the cones.

INTRODUCTION

The tasks of designing the high speed submarine apparatus and predicting their performance have preoccupied engineers for many years. Although there are only a small number of numerical axisymmetric fully cavitating flows calculation methods. The numerical calculation of axisymmetrical cavitating flows is based on two techniques:
- finite difference method proposed by Brennen [1]. The solutions are obtained for cavities behind a disk and a sphere in different size of solid wall tunnel. The same problem was also treated by Garabedian [2] who approached the axisymmetric case by successive corrections to the corresponding planar flow, each correction involving the solution of a linear mixed boundary-value problem.
- boundary integral equation methods in works of Amromin and Ivanov [3], Gyzevsky [4] and Kojouro [5]. In these works the vortex surface distribution was used and resulting system of nonlinear algebraic equations solved by the different numerical methods. In present work the new numerical iterative algorithm based on direct boundary element method is proposed

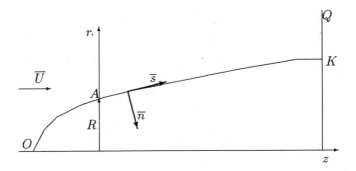

Figure 1. The sketch of the cavitational flow.

for the calculation of the cavitational flows.

PROBLEM DEFINITION

Cavitating flow around an axisymmetric body is generally a three-dimensional problem. If the case is limited to zero angle of attack, this problem may be described in the same manner as a two-dimensional problem.

The uniform stream with the velocity U_o flows round the blunt-ended body shown in figure 1. Axis Oz is a line (plane) of a symmetry. The line OA is a wetted surface of a body and AK is a free streamline. The line KQ is a plane of symmetry of Riabouchinsky flow. The positions of the boundaries AK and KQ as well as the shape of the latter are initially unknown.

The governing equation for the plane and axisymmetric potential flows in dimensionless variables is

$$\nabla^2 \phi = 0, \tag{1}$$

where ϕ is the disturbed velocity potential; the velocity in coordinate system (r, z) is $V_z = 1 + \phi_{,z}, V_r = \phi_{,r}$. The boundary conditions can be described in following way. The kinematic condition on wetted and free surfaces is

$$\phi_{,n} = -r'(s), \tag{2}$$

where $\bar{n}$ is the unit outward normal vector. Equation (2) indicates that the flow rate through the boundary is zero. Assuming uniform cavity pressure, on free streamline is valid the dynamic condition

$$\phi_{,s} = U_c - z'(s), \tag{3}$$

where U_c is a constant velocity on the free surface; s represents the curvilinear abscissae of the point on free streamline. On the line of symmetry KQ

$$\phi = 0. \tag{4}$$

The equation (3) can be integrated over the free streamline with the condition (4) and it becomes

$$\phi(s) = z_K - z(s) + U_c(s - s_*), \tag{5}$$

where s_* is length of the free streamline.

For Riabouchinsky model, one parameter defines a unique solution: cavitation number, $\sigma = \frac{p_o - p_c}{\frac{1}{2}U_o^2} = \frac{U_c^2}{U_o^2} - 1$, where p_o, p_c are the remote upstream and cavity pressures and ρ is the density of the fluid; or half-length of the cavity $z_L = z_K - z_A$; or length of the free streamline s_*. The lengths of this curve are chosen arbitrary as input data.

NUMERICAL METHOD

Let the initial location of the free surface be known. The boundary integral representation of solution of the equation (1) is [8]

$$\frac{1}{2}\phi_M = \int_S [\phi_{P,n}(F_{MP} - F_{LP}) - \phi_P(F_{MP,n} - F_{LP,n})]\rho^\epsilon dS_P \tag{6}$$

where $\epsilon = 0$ for plane case and $\epsilon = 1$ for axisymmetric case; $M(r, z)$ and $P(\rho, \zeta)$ are points on the boundary, $L(r, 2z_K - z)$ is a point symmetric relatively plane KQ; $F_{MP} = -\frac{1}{\pi}\ln r_{MP}$ is a fundamental solution for isotropic 2D medium; $F_{MP} = \frac{1}{\pi}\frac{1}{\sqrt{(\rho+r)^2+(\zeta-z)^2}}K(\gamma)$ is fundamental solution for axisymmetric case; $\gamma^2 = \frac{4\rho r}{(\rho+r)^2+(\zeta-z)^2}$; r_{MP} is the distance between points $M(r, z)$ and $P(\rho, \zeta)$. In axisymmetric case, the complete elliptic integrals of the first $K(\gamma)$ and second kinds may be approximated by polynomial approximations [7]. In this equation, the integrals are considered singularity when P tends towards M.

The discretization of (1), which leads to the classic 'boundary element method' technique (see, Brebbia and others [8]) described below. In the boundary element method, the above integral equation is solved numerically by dividing the boundary S into $N + L$ elements (N intervals on the free boundary and L intervals on the wetted surface of the body in this case), in each of which ϕ and $\phi_{,n}$ are approximated by constants. We denote these values by ϕ_i and $\phi_{i,n}, i = 1, \ldots N + L$; and apply equation (6) at one nodal point M_i in each boundary element to obtain

$$\frac{1}{2}\phi_i = \sum_{j=1}^{N+L}(\phi_{j,n}\int_{S_j} G_{iP}dS_P - \phi_j\int_{S_j} G_{iP,n}dS_P), \tag{7}$$

where S_j denotes integration over the jth boundary element. In plane case the coefficients of the linear system of equations (7) are integrated analytically over intervals. In an axisymmetric case numerical integration is used over the boundary element, parameterising this interval in an appropriate manner and taking into account the singularity in the integrals when $i = j$.

Eliminating the ϕ_i from each element on the free surface and $\phi_{i,n}$ from each element on the wetted boundary by applying the corresponding boundary condition in each nodal point, we thus obtain a system of $N + L$ simultaneous linear algebraic equations with $N + L + 1$ unknowns (N unknowns $\phi_{i,n}$ on free surface, L unknowns ϕ_i on body surface and value of the velocity on free boundary U_c). Additional equation for U_c we obtain by equating value of the potential in the separation point, calculated in (5) and value obtained by linear extrapolation by two points on the wetted surface

$$z_K - z_A - U_c s_* = \phi_{N+1} + (\phi_{N+1} - \phi_{N+2})\frac{\Delta_{N+1}}{\Delta_{N+1} + \Delta_{N+2}}, \qquad (8)$$

where Δ_j is the length of the jth boundary element. The system of $N + L + 1$ linear algebraic equations (7,8) was solved by the direct Gaussian elimination method.

In order to solve the problem of cavitating flow, the shape of the cavity must be calculated by successive iterations. The new location of the free surface has been calculated by integration

$$r_i' = -\frac{\phi_{i,n}}{\sqrt{\phi_{i,n}^2 + z_i'^2}} \qquad (9)$$

$$z_i' = sign(r_{i+1}' - r_i')\sqrt{1 - r_i'^2} \qquad (10)$$

with initial condition $r(0) = R$, $z(0) = z_A$. If the iteration process is coincided, then formula (9) translates in kinematic condition (2). The iterative procedure is continued until a converge criterion is satisfied. Usually, $6 \div 12$ iterations demanded for the coincidence. On the cavity, the velocity component normal to the cavity surface will be zero only at the convergence of the iterative process. After finishing the iterative process, the cavitation number σ must be retained as a solution parameter.

NUMERICAL RESULTS

To demonstrate the numerical scheme developed above, we consider a plane cavitational flow behind the wedges and plate. This problem has analytical solution in complex variables (see, Riabouchinsky [7]). Comparison of numerical results for plane flow (65 boundary elements) and analytical data

Table 1. Comparison of numerical and analytical results for wedges

α^o	σ	R_K/R calc.	R_K/R anal.	c_d calc.	c_d anal.	z_L/R calc.	z_L/R anal.
90	0.45	3.491	3.4847	1.2808	1.2788	15.58	15.568
90	0.30	4.727	4.7305	1.1470	1.1451	31.74	31.798
90	0.10	12.07	12.201	0.9644	0.9680	243.3	245.6
45	0.30	3.441	3.454	0.8360	0.8361	22.88	23.94

Table 2. Comparison of numerical C_d^* with data of Gyzevsky [4] ($\sigma = 0.25$)

α^o	90	60	30
Gyzevsky [4]	0.223	0.223	0.224
present work	0.2186	0.2198	0.2207

made in table 1. Here α is the half-angle of the wedge ($\alpha = 90^o$ corresponds by the plate).The differences between calculated and analytical values are very small. For anaxisymmetric case numerical values $c_d^* = F_d/\pi R_K^2$ for cones compare with the numerical data of Gyzevsky [4] in table 2. Coincidence between numerical data of Gyzevsky [4] and present work is close also.

The computed and experimentally observed (Brennen [1]) position free streamline behind the disk are presented in figure 2 for cavity number $\sigma = 0.2$. The agreement of these data is very close. The pressure distribution on the wetted surface of the disk for $\sigma = 0.24$ has been presented on the scale of the figure 3. There is close agreement with the experimental data of Rouse and McNown from [1]. The dependencies of the drag coefficient c_d and cavity radius R_K of the half-angle of the cone are presented in figure 4 for cavity number $\sigma = 0.1$. Here the value $\alpha = 90^o$ corresponds by the disk.

CONCLUSIONS

The boundary element method has been presented in this paper for the simulation of plane and axisymmetric cavitational flows in nonlinear formulations. Comparisons with analytical, numerical and experimental data suggests that the solutions obtained by the present numerical method are quite accurate. The flow is partially well modelled in the case of the blunt ended bodies with a fixed separation point, namely the disk.

REFERENCES

1. Brennen, C.A. 'Numerical Solution of Axisymmetric Cavity Flows' *J. Fluid Mech.*, v.37, p.4,pp. 671-688,1969.

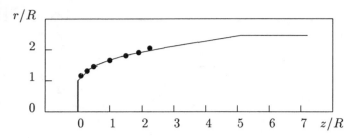

Figure 2. Comparison of theoretical and experimental cavity profiles for disk ($\sigma = 0.2$), • Brennen [1]

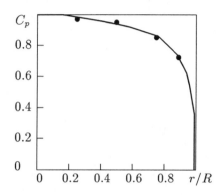

Figure 3. Pressure distribution on the surface of the disk ($\sigma = 0.24$), experimental data • for $\sigma = 0.24$ from [1].

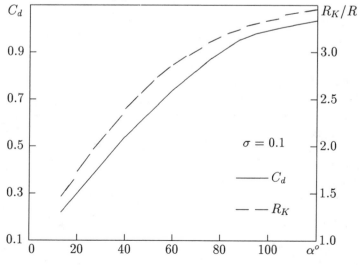

Figure 4. Variation of the drag coefficient and cavity radius with half-angle of the cone for $\sigma = 0.1$.

2. Garabedian, P.R. 'The Calculation of Axially Symmetric Cavities and Jets' *Pacif. J. Math.,* v.6, 1955.

3. Amromin, E.,L and Ivanov, A.N. 'Axisymmetric flows round bodies in regime of the developed cavitation' *Inf Sov. Acad. Sci. Mech. of Fluids and Gas* No 3, pp.37-42, 1975 (into Russian).

4. Gyzevsky, L.G. 'Numerical analysis of cavitational flows' *Sub. Div of Sov. Acad Sci. In—t Thermophysics* Preprint No 40, 1979 (into Russian).

5. Kojouro, L.A. 'Calculation of Axisymmetric Stream Flows Round of the Bodies by Ryabouchinsky scheme' *Sci. Note of CAHI* v.11,No.5, pp.109-115, 1980 (into Russian)

6. Riabouchinsky, D. 'On Steady Fluid Motion with Free Surface' *Proc. Lond. Math. Soc.,* v.19, pp. 202-212, 1920.

7. Abramovitz, M. and Stegun, I.A. (Eds) *Handbook of Mathematical Functions* New York: Dover, 1974.

8. Brebbia, C.A., Telles, J.C.F. and Wrobel, L.C. *Boundary Element Techniques Theory and Applications in Engineering* Springer-Verlag, Berlin and New York,1984.

Invited Paper

Potential flow past a bluff body with and without separation

D. Lesnic, L. Elliott, D.B. Ingham

*Department of Applied Mathematical Studies,
University of Leeds, Leeds LS2 9JT, UK*

ABSTRACT

In this study the two-dimensional steady potential flow past
various shaped bodies with separation is determined and compared
with the corresponding flow with no separation. The study has a
concrete application in the sampling of particles on different
shaped obstacles based on the principle of inertial impaction.
Whether the flow separates or not will affect the
characteristics of the flow in front of the obstacle and thus
the collection efficiency of the sampler and its predictability.
Using the method of Kirchhoff for mapping rigid boundaries, the
problem reduces to a mixed boundary-value problem on the
boundary of the obstacle and on the free surfaces for the
logarithm of the complex velocity. By referring to the general
solution of the Riemann-Hilbert problem the solution for the
fluid velocity is obtained in an integral form which is solved
using the boundary element method. An iterative procedure is
employed and the shape of the free surface determined. Once the
velocity distribution on the boundary and on the free surface is
obtained, one may use a direct form of the boundary element
method to determine the fluid velocity. Finally, differences
between the fluid flows as predicted assuming that there is, or
there is not, separation in the case of a flat plate and
cylinders of various shapes, are illustrated.

INTRODUCTION

In many practical situations when a body moves through a fluid
at high enough speed, the flow usually separates from the
obstacle along the free streamlines and gives rise to the
formation of a downstream wake or a cavity, and in general this
region is filled with fluid vapour. The problem is complicated

by the fact that the solution domain has an unknown boundary on which known conditions are to be imposed. When the phenomenon of separation is taken into account only a few simple polygonal shapes of obstacles possess an analytical solution for the fluid flow, see for example Milne-Thomson [6]. In addition, most of the previous numerical schemes determine only the shape of the free streamlines, and it is not easy to determine the fluid velocity to a high degree of accuracy. However, accurate values for the components of the fluid velocity everywhere in the fluid are required to calculate the collection efficiency by differently shaped obstacles. The method of solution presented in this paper is mainly indirect and models the separation phenomenon as potential flow around semi-infinite bodies which appear to the oncoming flow to be either flat or consist of a circular arc, which may be convex or concave. Such shapes can be taken as good approximations for the collection surfaces of various collectors used for particle sampling, such as dust and smoke gauges (see Ralph and Hall [8]) and fogwater samplers (see Krämer and Schütz [2]). In order to determine the particle trajectories, and implicitly the collection efficiency of such samplers, one must first determine the characteristics of the fluid flow. The present analysis refers to single obstacles and has been studied by two different models; firstly in terms of a potential unseparated flow and secondly in terms of a potential flow with separation.

POTENTIAL FLOW PAST A BLUFF BODY WITHOUT SEPARATION

The potential flow past the following bodies without separation are well known, see Milne-Thomson [6],
(i) The potential flow past a flat plate of length 2l which is situated perpendicular to a uniform stream U_0. The complex potential is given by

$$w = U_0 \ (z^2+l^2)^{1/2} \tag{1}$$

and the complex velocity is given by

$$u_x - iu_y = - U_0 z \ (z^2+l^2)^{-1/2} \tag{2}$$

This flow has a stagnation point at the centre of the plate and the fluid speed approaches infinity at both sharp corners of the plate.
(ii) The potential flow past an infinitely long cylinder of radius a containing a vertical slit which subtends an angle of $(2\pi-4\alpha)$ at the axis of the cylinder and which is perpendicular to the undisturbed uniform stream U_0. The complex potential is given by

$$w = - U_0 \sin \alpha \left(Z + \frac{a^2}{Z} \right) \tag{3}$$

where the Z-plane is linked to the physical z-plane through the conformal transformation

$$Z^2 \sin \alpha - Z (z-a) - az \sin \alpha = 0 , \qquad |Z| > a . \qquad (4)$$

Also the complex velocity is given by

$$u_x - iu_y = U_0 \sin \alpha \left(1 - \frac{a^2}{Z^2} \right) \left(\frac{Z + a \sin \alpha}{a - z + 2Z \sin \alpha} \right) . \qquad (5)$$

For $\alpha = \pi/2$ the motion corresponds to the potential flow past a circular cylinder and the speed is finite everywhere in the fluid domain and on the boundary of the cylinder, whilst for $\alpha \in (0,\pi/2)$ the motion corresponds to the potential flow past a cylinder with an aperture and the speed becomes infinite at the edges of the vertical slit. Hence, in this case, the solution cannot represent the complete physical situation. In order to avoid the speed becoming infinite at both edges of the vertical slit the analysis should include the phenomenon of separation, which is most likely to occur in practice. This is treated in the next section following a similar numerical method to that applied by Ingham and Wen [1] for circular cylinders.

POTENTIAL FLOW PAST A BLUFF BODY WITH SEPARATION

This study is concerned with Helmholtz motions, defined as follows:
(a) The motion takes place in free space, i.e. gravity is neglected.
(b) The motion is steady, i.e. $p + \frac{1}{2} \rho u^2 = $ constant, where p, ρ and u are the pressure, the density and the speed of the fluid, respectively.
(c) The pressure along the cavity, p_c, is equal to the pressure in the undisturbed stream, p_∞, and therefore the cavitation number, $\sigma = 2(p_\infty - p_c)/\rho U_0^2$, vanishes.

The numerical method employed in this paper is decribed for the case of the cylinder with an aperture, although the case of separating flow past a flat plate will be discussed in the last section of this paper and compared with the known analytical solution, see for example Milne-Thomson [6].

Hence, the uniform flow of velocity U_0 past an infinitely long cylinder of radius a containing a vertical slit which subtends an angle of $(2\pi-4\alpha)$, $\alpha \in (0,\pi/2)$, on the axis of the cylinder, placed at right angles to the stream is investigated, see figure 1a. The dividing streamline which strikes the obstacle at the stagnation point S divides, and follows the arc to A and A', and then forms the free streamlines AB_∞ and $A'B'_\infty$.

In order for the fluid velocity to be finite at the points A and A' we assume that the flow leaves the surface tangentially at these points. The vacuous region between these free streamlines constitutes the cavity in which the fluid is considered to be at rest. For convenience we assume the dividing streamline to be $\psi = 0$ and we shall take the velocity potential to be $\phi = 0$ at S, where ψ and ϕ are the streamfunction and the velocity potential, respectively. Then ϕ will be infinite at the points B_∞ and B'_∞. The complex potential plane $w = \phi + i\psi$ is shown in figure 1b, where for clarity the portions $B'_\infty A'S$ and $B_\infty AS$ are shown slightly separated although in fact they coincide with the positive ϕ-axis. We next consider the complex velocity $\underline{u} = (u_x, u_y)$, non-dimensionalised with respect to U_0, in the form

$$u_x - iu_y = dw/dz = u\,e^{-i\theta} \qquad (6)$$

in which u is the non-dimensionalised fluid speed and θ is the inclination of the direction of the fluid velocity to the positive x-axis. Then Kirchhoff's function is given by

$$\Omega = i\,\ln(dw/dz) = \theta + i\tau \qquad (7)$$

where $\tau = \ln u$, and τ, dw/dz and Ω are analytical functions. We now map the w-plane onto the upper half-plane of the auxiliary t-plane by the transformation

$$t = \sqrt{w} \quad \text{or} \quad w = t^2 \qquad (8)$$

see figure 1c.

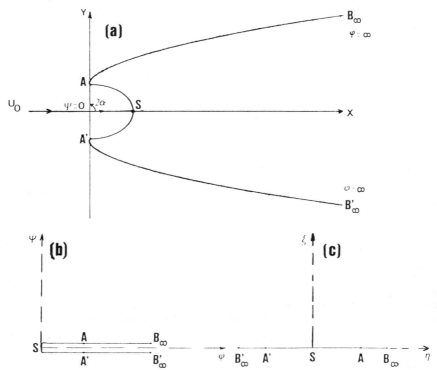

Figure 1. (a) The physical z-plane. (b) The complex potential w-plane. (c) The auxiliary t-plane.

Along the free streamlines AB_∞ and $A'B'_\infty$ the application of Bernoulli's equation results in

$$P_\infty + \frac{1}{2}\rho U_0^2 = P_c + \frac{1}{2}\rho u^2 \tag{9}$$

so, following hypothesis (c), $u = 1$ on AB_∞ and $A'B'_\infty$.

The boundary conditions on the real η-axis of the t-plane ($t = \eta + i\xi$) are

$$Im\ \Omega(\eta) = \tau(\eta) = 0 \qquad\qquad \eta < -a \tag{10a}$$

$$Re\ \Omega(\eta) = \beta(\eta) \qquad\qquad -a < \eta < a \tag{10b}$$

$$Im\ \Omega(\eta) = \tau(\eta) = 0 \qquad\qquad a < \eta \tag{10c}$$

in which $a = \sqrt{\phi_A}$, ϕ_A is the velocity potential at the point A and $\beta(\eta)$ is the local inclination of the segment AA'. At infinity the non-dimensional speed is unity and the free streamlines are horizontal, i.e.

$$\lim_{t \to \infty} \Omega(t) = 0 \text{ or } (\lim_{t \to \infty} \tau(t) = 0 \text{ and } \lim_{t \to \infty} \theta(t) = 0) . \tag{11}$$

The problem now reduces to a mixed boundary-value problem in the upper half of the t-plane. By referring to the general solution of the Riemann-Hilbert problem, see Muskhelishvilli [7], we obtain the solution for Ω in the form

$$\Omega(t) = \frac{\sqrt{t^2-a^2}}{\pi} \int_{-a}^{a} \frac{\beta(\eta)\ d\eta}{\sqrt{a^2-\eta^2}\ (\eta-t)} . \tag{12}$$

Using the condition at infinity (11), yields

$$\int_{-a}^{a} \frac{\beta(\eta)d\eta}{\sqrt{a^2-\eta^2}} = 0 \tag{13}$$

or, by symmetry,

$$\beta(\eta) = -\beta(-\eta) \quad \text{for} \quad 0 < \eta < a . \tag{14}$$

Hence, equation (12) becomes

$$\Omega(t) = \frac{\sqrt{t^2-a^2}}{\pi} \int_{0}^{a} \frac{\beta(\eta)\ 2\eta\ d\eta}{\sqrt{a^2-\eta^2}\ (\eta^2-t^2)} . \tag{15}$$

Since the flow is symmetrical about the x-axis we need only consider the upper half of the physical plane, or the first quadrant of the t-plane. In equation (15) we let t be in the upper half-plane and then let t tend to the value on the real η axis and take the Cauchy Principal Value. Separating the real and imaginary parts of Ω, then the logarithm of the speed on SA is given by

$$\tau(t) = - \frac{\sqrt{a^2-t^2}}{\pi} \int_0^a \frac{\beta(\eta)\ 2\eta\ d\eta}{\sqrt{a^2-\eta^2}\ (\eta^2-t^2)}\ , \qquad 0 < t < a \qquad (16)$$

where $\int$ is the Cauchy Principal Value and the angle $\theta(t)$ on the free streamline AB_∞ is given by

$$\theta(t) = \frac{\sqrt{t^2-a^2}}{\pi} \int_0^a \frac{\beta(\eta)\ 2\eta\ d\eta}{\sqrt{a^2-\eta^2}\ (\eta^2-t^2)}\ , \qquad a < t < \infty\ . \qquad (17)$$

Now considering the problem in the physical plane and taking the stagnation point S as the origin of the arc coordinate, along the boundary SA and along the free streamline AB_∞ the angle $\theta = \theta(s)$, the speed $u = u(s)$ and the velocity potential $\phi = \phi(s)$ are functions of s, and from equation (8) we have

$$d\eta = \frac{u(s)\ ds}{2\eta(s)} \qquad (18)$$

$$\frac{d\phi(s)}{ds} = u(s) \qquad (19)$$

$$\frac{dx(s)}{ds} = \cos\theta(s),\ \frac{dy(s)}{ds} = \sin\theta(s) \text{ on the free streamline.} \qquad (20)$$

Using expression (18) we may rewrite expressions (16) and (17) in the physical plane as follows:

$$\tau(s) = - \frac{\sqrt{a^2-t^2(s)}}{\pi} \int_{SA} \frac{\beta(1)\ u(1)\ dl}{\sqrt{a^2-\eta^2(1)}\ (\eta^2(1)-t^2(s))}\ , \qquad s \in SA \qquad (21)$$

$$\theta(s) = \frac{\sqrt{t^2(s)-a^2}}{\pi} \int_{SA} \frac{\beta(1)\ u(1)\ dl}{\sqrt{a^2-\eta^2(1)}\ (\eta^2(1)-t^2(s))}\ , \qquad s \in AB_\infty \qquad (22)$$

in which $\eta(1) = \sqrt{\phi(1)}$ and $t(s) = \sqrt{\phi(s)}$ on SAB_∞.

For given solid walls, $\beta(1)$ is a known function because the curvilinear integrals are performed along the streamlines, and this fact enables the method to be generalized to deal with arbitrary solid boundaries.   In the actual case of the cylinder with a vertical slit of angle $(2\pi-4\alpha)$,

$$\beta(1) = 1 + \pi/2\ , \qquad 0 < 1 < 2\alpha\ . \qquad (23)$$

Furthermore, on integrating expressions (19) and (20) the velocity potential is given by

$$\phi(s) = \int_0^s u(1)\ dl \qquad (24)$$

and the profile of the upper free streamline is represented by

$$x(s) = \cos(2\alpha) + \int_{2\alpha}^{s} \cos \theta(l) \, dl , \qquad s \in AB_{\infty} \qquad (25a)$$

$$y(s) = \sin(2\alpha) + \int_{2\alpha}^{s} \sin \theta(l) \, dl , \qquad s \in AB_{\infty} . \qquad (25b)$$

From expression (24) we have

$$\phi_A = a^2 = \int_{0}^{2\alpha} u(l) \, dl \qquad (26)$$

and applying $u(l) = 1$ for $2\alpha < l < \infty$ results in

$$\phi(s) = a^2 + \int_{2\alpha}^{s} u(l) \, dl = a^2 + s - 2\alpha , \qquad s \in AB_{\infty} . \qquad (27)$$

The boundary integral equations (21) and (22) can now be solved using the iterative procedure described in the next section.

THE ITERATIVE METHOD FOR THE BOUNDARY INTEGRAL EQUATIONS

The boundary SA is discretised into small arc elements $\partial\Omega_j$ such that

$$SA = \bigcup_{j=1}^{N} \partial\Omega_j \qquad (28)$$

Near the edge A on the boundary of the arc the velocity changes very rapidly and hence the elements were taken much smaller in this vicinity than elsewhere. Along each element the boundary value β is assumed constant and takes the value at the midpoint of the element. Therefore expression (23) results in

$$\beta(l) = \beta(l_j) = \beta_j = \pi/2 + (l_{aj}+l_{bj})/2 \quad \text{on } \partial\Omega_j, \text{ for } j = \overline{1,N} \qquad (29)$$

where l_j is the arc-coordinate of the midpoint of the element $\partial\Omega_j$ and l_{aj} and l_{bj} are the arc-coordinates of its end points. Then equation (21) becomes

$$\tau(s) = - \frac{\sqrt{a^2-t^2(s)}}{\pi} \sum_{j=1}^{N} \beta_j \int_{l_{aj}}^{l_{bj}} \frac{u(l) \, dl}{\sqrt{a^2-\eta^2(l)} \, (\eta^2(l)-t^2(s))} , \qquad (30)$$

and using expression (18) results in

$$\tau(s) = - \frac{\sqrt{a^2-t^2(s)}}{\pi} \sum_{j=1}^{N} \beta_j \int_{t_{aj}}^{t_{bj}} \frac{2\eta \, d\eta}{\sqrt{a^2-\eta^2} \, (\eta^2-t^2(s))} , \qquad s \in SA \qquad (31)$$

where $t_{aj} = \sqrt{\phi(1_{aj})}$, $t_{bj} = \sqrt{\phi(1_{bj})}$, $\phi(1_{aj}) = (\phi(1_j)+\phi(1_{j-1}))/2$ and $\phi(1_{bj}) = (\phi(1_{j+1})+\phi(1_j))/2$ for $j = \overline{1,N}$ with the convention $\phi(1_0) = 0$ and $\phi(1_{N+1}) = \phi_A$. The advantage of this approximation is that the integrals

$$I_j(s) = \int_{t_{aj}}^{t_{bj}} \frac{2\eta \ d\eta}{\sqrt{a^2-\eta^2} \ (\eta^2-t^2(s))} \ , \qquad j = \overline{1,N} \tag{32}$$

can now be evaluated analytically. In equation (31) we take $s = 1_i$ for $i = \overline{1,N}$ and thus obtain

$$\ln u_i = \tau_i = - \frac{\sqrt{a^2-t_i^2}}{\pi} \sum_{j=1}^{N} \beta_j \ I_{ji} \ , \qquad i = \overline{1,N} \tag{33}$$

where $u_i = u(1_i)$, $\tau_i = \tau(1_i)$, $t_i = \sqrt{\phi(1_i)}$ and $I_{ji} = I_j(1_i)$.

In order to determine the velocity and the velocity potential on the boundary the following iterative procedure is used:
(i) Assume the approximate velocities $u_j^0 = u^0(1_j)$ for $j = \overline{1,N}$, and then the values of $\phi_j^0 = \phi^0(1_j)$ for $j = \overline{1,N}$ are obtained from expression (24) in the form

$$\phi_j^0 = \sum_{k=1}^{j} u_k^0 s_k \qquad \text{for } j = \overline{1,N} \tag{34}$$

where $s_k = 1_{bk} - 1_{ak}$ is the length of the arc element $\partial\Omega_j$. In addition the values of $\phi_A^0 = a_0^2$ must be obtained from expresion (26) in the form

$$\phi_A^0 = \phi_N^0 + \int_{1_N}^{2\alpha} u(1) \ dl = \phi_N^0 + s_N (1 + u_N)/4 \ . \tag{35}$$

(ii) By putting the values of ϕ_A^0 and ϕ_j^0 for $j = \overline{1,N}$ into expression (33), the values u_i^1 at the nodes can be computed, and from expressions (24) and (26) the values of ϕ_i^1 and $\phi_A^1 = a_1^2$ are again determined and then used as the new approximations. This iterative procedure is repeated until

$$\sum_{j=1}^{N} |(u_j^n - u_j^{n-1}) / u_j^n| < \varepsilon_1 \qquad \text{and} \qquad |(\phi_A^n - \phi_A^{n-1}) / \phi_A^n| < \varepsilon_2 \tag{36}$$

where u_j^n and ϕ_A^n are the values after the n-th iteration and ε_1

and ε_2 are typically taken to be $O(10^{-4})$.   Finally, this procedure provides the values of the velocity and the velocity potential at the nodes on the boundary.

In order to determine the angle $\theta(s)$ on the free streamline AB_∞ we use equation (22) in the discretised form, namely

$$\theta(s) = \frac{\sqrt{t^2(s)-a^2}}{\pi} \sum_{j=1}^{N} \beta_j \int_{1_{aj}}^{1_{bj}} \frac{u(1)\ dl}{\sqrt{a^2-\eta^2(1)}\ (\eta^2(1)-t^2(s))}$$

$$= \frac{\sqrt{t^2(s)-a^2}}{\pi} \sum_{j=1}^{N} \beta_j\ I_j(s) \qquad (37)$$

in which $t^2(s) = \phi(s) = a^2 + s - 2\alpha$, see expression (27).   In this way, $\theta(s)$ is known everywhere on the free streamline AB_∞ and a further integration of equation (25) enables the free surface to be determined.   Finally, on using equation (6) the components of the fluid velocity are determined everywhere on the boundary $B'_\infty A' SAB_\infty$.   In order to determine the fluid velocity everywhere in the fluid domain, which is the region outside the partial open boundary $B'_\infty A' SAB_\infty$, one may use the Boundary Element Method, see for example Lesnic et al. [3].

RESULTS AND DISCUSSION

The mathematical model for the calculation of the region of separation which occurs downstream of a circular arc has been explained in the previous sections.   The shape of the free streamlines are plotted in figures 2 for the flat plate and cylinders containing a vertical slit which subtends an angle of $(2\pi-4\alpha)$, with $\alpha \in \{\pi/4,\ 5\pi/12,\ \pi/2\}$. It should be noted that when $\alpha = \pi/2$ then the problem reduces to the separating potential flow past a circular cylinder, or equivalently the flow past a convex arc of angle 54.845^d (see Ingham and Wen [1]), whilst for $\alpha \in \{\pi/4,\ 5\pi/12\}$ the separating flow is past a concave arc facing the oncoming flow.   Each of the figures 2 also presents an enlargement of the region where the free streamline detaches from the boundary showing that these streamlines detach tangentially from the boundary and in the case of the concave arcs move upstream of the obstacle for a distance of about 3% of the radius of the circular arc.   In these models the fluid speed remains finite at the sharp edges, in fact, from Bernoulli's equation it is equal to the free stream velocity, in contrast to the potential flow without separation where the flow does not separate to form a free streamline.   Figure 2a also presents a comparison with the available analytical solution for the flat plate.

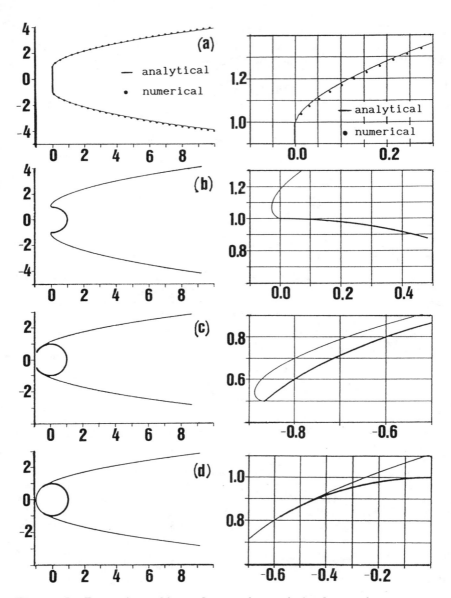

Figure 2. Free streamlines for various obstacles and
        enlargements of the regions where the free streamline
        detaches from the boundary.
        (a) flat plate. (b) cylinder with an aperture $\alpha = \pi/4$.
        (c) cylinder with an aperture $\alpha = 5\pi/12$. (d) circular
        cylinder $\alpha = \pi/2$.

        The iterative method adopted provided the values of the
velocity at the nodes on the solid boundary and on the free

streamline, then the Boundary Element Method was used in order
to determine the fluid velocity everywhere in the fluid domain.
Figures 3 present the fluid velocity upstream of the body on y =
0, i.e. the centre-line velocity, for both the separated and
unseparated flows, and, figure 3a illustrates the agreement
between the numerical and the analytical solution.   The
knowledge of the centre-line velocity enables the gradient of
velocity at the stagnation point to be evaluated using finite
differences and this quantity has a possible application for the
determination of the critical Stokes number, see Levin [4].

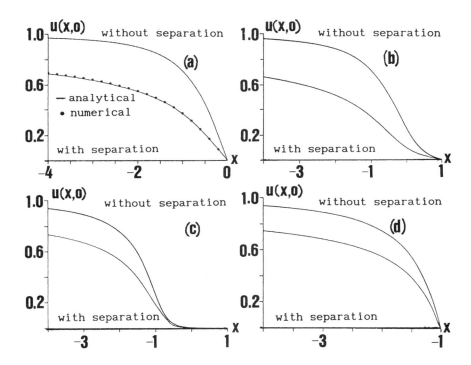

Figure 3. Centre-line velocity for various obstacles in
          separated and unseparated potential flow.
          (a) flat plate. (b) cylinder with an aperture $\alpha = \pi/4$.
          (c) cylinder with an aperture $\alpha = 5\pi/12$. (d) circular
          cylinder $\alpha = \pi/2$.

     Finally, figure 4 presents the collection efficiency of a
flat plate which is placed normal to the oncoming flow for the
separated and nonseparated model as a function of the Stokes
number.   It is observed that the results which have been
obtained for the separated flow past a flat plate are in good
agreement with the experimental results of May and Clifford [5].
Furthermore, the photographs of the streamlines presented in May

and Clifford [5] indicate that the fluid flow separates almost tangentially from the plate and, in fact, this is exactly the condition of tangential detachement that was used in the separated model presented in this paper. This research is ongoing and the particle trajectories and collection efficiency for the other circular shapes both with and without separation are being investigated.

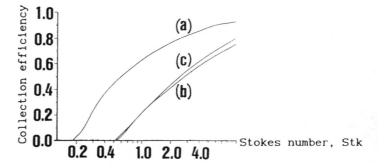

Figure 4. Collection efficiency for a flat plate.
(a) flat plate without separation. (b) flat plate with separation. (c) experimental results of May and Clifford [5].

ACKNOWLEDGEMENTS

The authors would like to thank the Health and Safety Executive for some financial support of this work. Also, Mr. D. Lesnic would like to acknowledge the support from the Tempus Project.

REFERENCES

1. Ingham, D.B. and Wen, X. 'Separating Inviscid Flows' *Acta Mechanica*, No.86, pp. 1-14, 1991.
2. Krämer, M. and Schütz, L. 'Collection Efficiency of the Mainz Rotating Arm Collector' *J. Aerosol Sci.*, Vol.21, Suppl.1, pp. S653-S656, 1990.
3. Lesnic, D., Elliott, L. and Ingham, D.B. 'Boundary Element Methods for Determining the Fluid Velocity in Potential Flow Theory' submitted to *Boundary Elements for Engineering*, 1993.
4. Levin, L.M. 'Investigations in the Physics of Coarse Dispersed Aerosols' *FTD-HT-23-1593-67*, 1961.
5. May, K.R. and Clifford, R. 'The Impaction of Aerosol Particles on Cylinders, Spheres, Ribbons and Discs' *Ann. Occup. Hyg.*, Vol.10, pp. 83-95, 1967.
6. Milne-Thomson, L.M. *Theoretical Hydrodynamics* 5th ed. Macmillan & Co Ltd., London, 1968.
7. Muskhelishvilli, N.I. *Singular Integral Equation* Noordhoff, Groningen, The Netherlands, 1953.
8. Ralph, M.D. and Hall, D.J. 'Performance of the BS Directional Dust Gauge,' pp. 115-120, *Proceedings of the 3rd Ann. Aerosol Soc. Conf.*, West Bromwich, England, 1989.

SECTION 5: FREE SURFACE FLOW

Boundary element method of analysing non-linear phenomena on gas-liquid two-phase free surface at middle and higher Reynolds numbers*

W-Q. Lu

Department of Physics, Division of Thermal Science, Graduate School, Chinese Academy of Sciences, PO Box 3908, Beijing 100039, China

ABSTRACT

A boundary element method for analysing non-linear phenomena on gas-liquid two-phase free surface at middle and higher Reynolds numbers has been developed. Employing this method we analyze two kinds of non-linear phenomena on gas-liquid two-phase free surface (1) Solitary wave on free falling thin liquid film. (2) Surface tension drives convective flows in open-boat type crystal-growth techniques in microgravity environment.

INTRODUCTION

Although some new schemes of discretizing convective terms are developed as QUICK and QUICK ER in finite difference methods[FDM] and finite element methods[FEM], but it is very difficult to avoid numerical diffusion introduced by convective discretizations, especially, at high Reynolds number.

In [1], they developed a boundary element iterative scheme(BEIS) to calculate convective terms and compared the advantages of using upwind or central difference schemes and BEIS. As shown as numerical results, BEIS of the convective terms was the most accurate of the two approaches. However, computation was complex.

The main objective of this research is to develop a boundary element method for analysing some non-linear phenomena on gas-liquid two-phase free surface at middle and higher Reynolds numbers. On the basis of the boundary element formulation with the pressure penalty function, the divergence theorem is applied to the non-linear convective volume integral of the boundary element formulation. Consequently, velocity gradients are eliminated, the complete formulation is written in terms of velocity. This avoids the difficulty of convective discretizations, and provides considerable reducing storage and computational requirement while improving accuracy. In order to calculate free surface, we construct shooting iterative method of free surface on the basis of normal stress balance condition

Project supported by the National Natural Science Foundation of China

similar to [2][3].

The method is applied to analyze two kinds of free surface problems.

(1) Solitary wave on free falling thin liquid film.

This problem was researched by Wasden and Kheshgi etc. with finite difference method [4] and finite element method [5]. However, in finite difference method[4], one applied an adjustment procedure for wave velocity in order to obtain reasonable flow fields, in finite element methods[5] numerical solution was limited to low flow rates. Moreover, the upwind schemes of discretizing convective momentum terms common to FDM and FEM introduce numerical diffusion or oscillatory behavior of the wave peak region, more importantly, the upwind scheme lacks sensitivity to cross stream diffusion and source terms which are especially important in the case of a thin film. Therefore it is valuable to research a non-traditional numerical method such as BEM.

(2) Surface tension drives convective flows in open-boat type crystal growth techniques in microgravity environment.

The analytical or numerical study of free surface problem in crystal-growth techniques is very difficult. We shall restrict ourselves to model a problem of open-boat type crystal growth technology, and we only study the melt-gas free boundary, assume the melt-crystal interface shape is flat. The free surface problem of open-boat type is simplified as the free surface problem in open rectangular cavity. The left vertical boundary of the cavity can be interpreted as the crucible wall. The right vertical boundary of the cavity can be interpreted as the melt-crystal interface. The temperatures equal θ_l and θ_r, respectively. Some important numerical results are presented in paper.

BASIC EQUATIONS

We consider a system of steady incompressible viscous liquid in a open rectangular cavity with differentially heated lateral walls (the temperature difference is $\triangle\theta^*$). There is a gradient of surface tension on the free surface since the distribution of temperature is non-homogeneous. The gradient of surface tension drives the convection of liquid.

On the basis of the basic law of fluid mechanics and Boussinesq approximation, the governing equations of these problems can be described by a tensor notation and a non-dimensional form as follow:

continuity equation

$$v_{j,j} = 0 \tag{1}$$

momentum equations

$$v_j v_{i,j} + p_{,i} - \frac{1}{R_e}(v_{i,j} + v_{j,i})_j - \delta_{im}\frac{G_r}{R_e^2}(\theta - \theta_r) = 0 \tag{2}$$

energy equation

$$v_j \theta_{,j} - \frac{1}{M_a}\theta_{,j\,j} = 0 \tag{3}$$

where, δ_{im} is the Kronecker delta symbol, $m = x$ for solitary wave, $m = y$ for thermocapillary convection. The lengths, velocities are scaled with respect to H,

U_o, respectively. The relation between pressure p^* and non-dimensional pressure p is $p = \frac{p^* + \rho g H m}{\rho U_o^2}$. $U_o = \frac{H \Delta \theta^* \sigma_T'}{L \mu}$, where H is the left initial height of free surface, L is the length in cavity, σ_T' is the temperature coefficient of the surface tension of the liquid and μ is the absolute viscosity. The parameters are: Reynolds number, $R_e = \frac{\rho U_o H}{\mu}$, Prandtl number, $P_r = \frac{\mu}{\rho \varphi}$, Marangoni number, $M_a = R_e P_r$, Grashof number, $G_r = \frac{\rho^2 g \beta \Delta \theta^* H^3}{\mu^2}$, where ρ, φ, g, β are liquid density, thermal diffusivity, gravity acceleration and coefficient of expansion, respectively. In equation (3), $\theta = \frac{\theta^*}{\Delta \theta^*}$, $\Delta \theta^* = \theta_l^* - \theta_r^*$, θ^* is the temperature, subscript l, r refer to left and right boundary, respectively.

Second problem to study is solitary wave on free falling thin liquid film, which shape remains constant with time, wave velocity is constant U_o. A Cartesian coordinate system at constant velocity U_o is chosen, so that solitary wave is fixed and wall moves upward at velocity U_o. The flow in thin film can be treated as two-dimensional steady incompressible viscous and isothermal flow. Therefore, the left last term of momentum equation is eliminated, and it is not necessary to consider energy equation in numerical solution, and the boundary conditions also become simpler. The lengths, velocities are scaled with respect to the H, U_o, respectively. However, U_o is the velocity of solitary wave, H is the inlet liquid film thickness. The $-x$ is the direction of gravity.

We use a penalty function technique[1] to calculate the pressure:

$$p = -\lambda v_{i,i} \tag{4}$$

where λ is the penalty parameter. Taking a large value of λ will make $v_{i,i}$ approach zero and satisfy mass conservation in an approximate manner. Substituting equation (4) into equations (2), we obtain:

$$\left(\lambda + \frac{1}{R_e}\right) v_{j,ji} + \frac{1}{R_e} v_{i,jj} = v_j v_{i,j} - \delta_{im} \frac{G_r(\theta - \theta_r)}{R_e^2} \tag{5}$$

The equations (5) are similar to the Navier equations of elasticity.

BOUNDARY INTEGRAL EQUATIONS

Applying the well known Kelvin's fundamental solution of the Navier equations and the weighted residual approach, the equations (5) are transformed into following integral equations:

$$\int_A \left[\left(\lambda + \frac{1}{R_e}\right) v_{j,ji} + \frac{1}{R_e} v_{i,jj} - v_j v_{i,j} + \delta_{im} \frac{G_r(\theta - \theta_r)}{R_e^2}\right] U_{ki} dA = 0 \tag{6}$$

Employing Gauss divergence theorem, one obtains the following integral equations:

$$\alpha_{ij} v_j(\xi) + \int_\Gamma T_{ij}(\xi, \eta) v_j(\eta) d\Gamma - \int_\Gamma U_{ij}(\xi, \eta) t_j(\eta) d\Gamma$$
$$= \int_A U_{ij}(\xi, \eta)(v_k(\eta) v_{j,k}(\eta) - \delta_{im} \frac{G_r(\theta - \theta_r)}{R_e^2}) dA \tag{7}$$

where, $t_j = \sigma_{ij}n_i$, $\sigma_{ij} = (\lambda + \frac{1}{R_e})v_{j,i} + \frac{1}{R_e}v_{i,j}$. The convective terms appear in the domain integral of equations (7). The values of these convective terms can be obtained either by writing integral equations directly for $[v_j v_{i,j}]$, or by employing finite difference scheme[1]. The former calculation is complex and tedious, but the latter lost the accuracy. We use the divergence theorem to the domain integrals of (7).

$$\int_A U_{ij}v_k v_{j,k}\,dA = \int_\Gamma U_{ij}v_k v_j n_k\,d\Gamma - \int_A U_{ij,k}\,v_k v_j\,dA$$

Then the equations (7) are transformed into:

$$\alpha_{ij}(\xi)v_j(\xi) + \int_\Gamma T_{ij}(\xi,\eta)v_j(\eta)d\Gamma(\eta)$$

$$- \int_\Gamma U_{ij}(\xi,\eta)[v_k(\eta)v_j(\eta)n_k(\eta) + t_j(\eta)]d\Gamma(\eta)$$

$$= -\int_A [U_{ij,k}(\xi,\eta)v_k(\eta)v_j(\eta) + U_{ij}(\xi,\eta)\delta_{im}\frac{G_r(\theta - \theta_r)}{R_e^2}]dA(\eta) \qquad (8)$$

where $\alpha_{ij}(\xi) = \delta_{ij}$, for $\xi \in A$, and $\alpha_{ij}(\xi) = \frac{1}{2}\delta_{ij}$, for $\xi \in \Gamma$. These fundamental solutions U_{ij}, T_{ij} are known as Kelvin's solutions and have the form:

$$U_{ij} = -\frac{1}{8\pi(1-\beta)\gamma}[(3-4\beta)lnr\delta_{ij} + r_{,i}\,r_{,j}] \qquad (9)$$

$$T_{ij} = -\frac{1}{4\pi(1-\beta)r}[((1-2\beta)\delta_{ij} + 2r_{,i}\,r_{,j})r_{,n}$$

$$-(1-2\beta)(r_{,i}\,n_j - r_{,j}\,n_i)] \qquad (10)$$

where $\beta = \frac{\lambda}{2(\lambda + \frac{1}{R_e})}$, $\gamma = \frac{1}{R_e}$, $r = |\xi - \eta|$, n_k is the direction cosines of the outward normal to the boundary of the domain. We can express   the differentials of Kelvin's solution as:

$$U_{ij,k} = -\frac{1}{8\pi(1-\beta)\gamma r}[(3-4\beta)\delta_{ij}r_{,k}$$

$$+2r_{,i}\,r_{,k}\,r_{,j} -\delta_{ki}r_{,j} -\delta_{kj}r_{,i}] \qquad (11)$$

Otherwise applying Green's second theorem, similarly a boundary integral equation equivalent to Poisson equation can be found for the energy equation (3).

$$\chi\theta - \int_\Gamma \Theta_m\,\theta d\Gamma + \int_\Gamma \Theta\theta_{,n}\,d\Gamma = Ma\int_A \Theta v_k\theta_{,k}\,dA \qquad (12)$$

Similarly, we use the divergence theorem to the domain integral with convective term. One obtains :

$$\int_A \Theta v_k\theta_{,k}\,dA = \int_\Gamma \Theta v_k\theta n_k d\Gamma - \int_A \Theta_{,k}\,v_k\theta dA \qquad (13)$$

The equation(12) is transformed into:

$$\chi(\xi)\theta(\xi) - \int_\Gamma \Theta_{,n}\,\theta d\Gamma + \int_\Gamma \Theta(q - M_a\theta v_k n_k)d\Gamma$$
$$= -M_a \int_A \theta\Theta_{,k}\,v_k dA \qquad (14)$$

$$q = \theta_{,n}$$

where $\chi(\xi) = 2\pi$, for $\xi \in A$, and $\chi(\xi) = \pi$, for $\xi \in \Gamma$. The fundamental solution is known as the solution of Poisson equation:

$$\Theta = lnr \qquad (15)$$

BOUNDARY CONDITIONS

On the free surface S_f

$$v_y = v_x tg\beta \qquad (16)$$

$$-q = Bi(\theta^4 - \theta_e^4) - - - - - thermocapillary \qquad (17)$$

where Bi is Biot number, $Bi = \frac{\epsilon\zeta\Delta\theta^{*3}H}{k}$, ϵ, ζ, k are the emissivity, the stefan-Boltzmann constant and the thermal conductivity, respectively. θ_e is ambient gas non-dimensional temperature

The tangential stress balance conditions are:

$$C_a^t t_i \tau_i = \frac{\partial\theta}{\partial\tau} - - - - - thermocapillary \qquad (18)$$

$$t_x = -tg\beta t_y - - - - - solitary \qquad (19)$$

where $C_a^t = \frac{\mu U_\varrho}{\sigma_T^*} = \frac{H}{L}$, τ_i are tangential vector. The surface tension σ_o, which is scaled with respect to $\sigma_T^*(= \sigma_T' \Delta \theta^*)$, is assumed to vary linearly with the temperature (thermocapillary) or to be constant (solitary). Gas viscosity is further eliminated.

The normal stress balance conditions are:

$$\kappa = \frac{C_a^t}{\theta}t_i n_i - \frac{1}{\theta}\frac{\partial\theta}{\partial n} - - - - - thermocapillary \qquad (20)$$

where κ is the curvature of free interface.

$$\kappa = \kappa(0) + C_a^s(t_i n_i - t_i(o)n_i(0)) - - - - - solitary \qquad (21)$$

where $C_a^s = \frac{\mu U_\varrho}{\sigma_o}$ is capillary number.

$$Sin(\beta^{j+1}(x)) = -\int_0^x \kappa^{j+1}dx \qquad (22)$$

$$\frac{dy}{dx} = tg(\beta) \qquad (23)$$

where the angle β is the tangent τ of free surface makes with the coordinate x, moreover, we fix the contact angle at 90°.

On the wall S_w

$$v_y = 0 \qquad (24)$$

$$v_x = 0 \;-----\; thermocapillary \qquad (25)$$

$$v_x = 1 \;-----\; solitary \qquad (26)$$

$$q = 0 \;-----\; thermocapillary \qquad (27)$$

On both lateral boundary

$$v_y = 0 \qquad (28)$$

$$v_x = 0 \;-----\; thermocapillary \qquad (29)$$

On left boundary S_l

$$\theta = 1 + \theta_r \;-----\; thermocapillary \qquad (30)$$

$$v_x = \frac{1}{2}y^2 - \frac{4}{3}y + 1 \;------\; solitary \qquad (31)$$

On right boundary S_r

$$\theta = \theta_r \;-----\; thermocapillary \qquad (32)$$

$$t_x = 0 \;-----\; solitary \qquad (33)$$

NUMERICAL METHOD OF THE PROBLEM

By the use of standard discretization methods, boundary integral equations (8)(14) can be discretized as following algebraic equations:

$$A_{ij}v_{yj} + B_{ij}v_{xj} + C_{ij}t_{yj} + D_{ij}t_{xj} = W_{yi} \qquad (34)$$

$$E_{ij}v_{yj} + F_{ij}v_{xj} + G_{ij}t_{yj} + H_{ij}t_{xj} = W_{xi} \qquad (35)$$

$$X_{ij}\theta_j + Z_{ij}q_j = W_{\theta i} \qquad (36)$$

We calculate the matrices including Green's function U_{ij}, T_{ij} and Θ by accurate Gaussian quadrature to achieve the better numerical accuracy.

We calculate thermocapillary convection in cavity by the iterative method including following steps:

(1)Given initial free surface and given initial velocities and temperatures at internal nodal points, allowing domain integrals W_{xi}, W_{yi} and $W_{\theta i}$ to be calculated.

(2) Solving the simultaneous equations (34)(35)(36), calculate boundary unknown v_i or t_i, θ or q.

(3) Employing boundary new v_i, t_i,θ and q, which are obtained in (2), recompute the velocity and temperature at the internal nodal points by using equation (34)(35)(36). Finally, applying normal stress balance condition (20), calculate the curvature of free surface and further calculate the shape of free surface by equation (22)(23).

(4) Examine the convergence of v_i and θ by comparing its values at the 1st, 2nd and 3rd steps. Examine the convergence of the shape of free surface.

(5) If results are not convergent, apply the updated values of the velocity and temperature at the internal nodal points, the updated shape of free surface, obtained in the (3) step, to calculate W_{xi}, W_{yi}, $W_{\theta i}$ and to restart (2) step.

For solitary wave problem, same iterative steps are applied, however, it is not necessary to numerically solve energy equation (36), and needs to transform boundary conditions.

Since problems are non-linear, in order to achieve convergence, it is necessary to use non-linear iterative methods as Newton-Raphson scheme. However, as shown by our numerical results, the under-relaxation iterative scheme has better convergence and it is easier to implement.

NUMERICAL RESULTS

(1) Solitary wave

We chose inlet film thickness $H = 0.236mm$, the distance between inlet and outlet is 225 mm; fluid properties are: density $1010\frac{kg}{m^3}$, absolute viscosity $8.50 \times 10^{-4}\frac{kg}{m.s}$, and surface tension $7.12 \times 10^{-2}\frac{N}{m}$, $U_o = 1.577\frac{m}{s}$, capillary number $C_a^s = 1.88 \times 10^{-2}$,Reynolds number $R_e = 442$, i.e. film Reynolds number $R_e^* = 880$, which is defined as $R_e^* = \frac{4\rho Q}{\mu}$, where Q is the mass flow rate per unit perimeter. An typical solitary wave shape (wave amplitude=3.01) and streamline map are presented in fig.1. A clear recirculatory region appears in flow fields. It is important that the presence of large normal velocities near the front and rear of the recirculating region can be a mechanism to enhance heat and mass transport. In fig.2, comparison of our results to experimental results and FDM results of [4] is made. Note that there is good agreement between our results and experimental results, but the discrepancies between measured and computed results of [4] in wave peak region are clear.

(2) Surface tension drives convective flows in open-boat type crystal-growth techniques in microgravity environment.

We calculate the influence of different physical parameter on free surface problem. The physical parameters are chosen : $G_r = 0$, the prandtl number $P_r = 1.0$,

$C_a^t = 1.0$, $B_i = 0$, $M_a = 50,150$. The influence of the Marangoni number on the free surface shape, temperature distribution and flow fields are drawn in figure 3, 4. As shown as figures the free surface is higher at the cold wall and lower at the hot wall. The deviation between both lateral free surface height increases with increasing M_a numbers.

CONCLUSIONS

Since the divergence theorem is applied to the non-linear convective volume integral of the boundary element formulation. Consequently, velocity gradients are eliminated, the complete formulation is written in terms of velocity. This avoids the difficulty of convective discretization, and provides considerable reducing storage and computational requirement while improving accuracy. This method is successfully applied to analyze solitary wave of free falling thin liquid film and to model surface tension driven convection in open-boat type crystal growth techniques.

REFERENCES

1. Kitagawa, K., Brebbia, C.A., Wrobel, L.C., Tanaka, M., "Boundary Element Analysis of Viscous Flow by Penalty Function Formulation", Engineering analysis, v.3, n.4, pp194-200, 1986.

2. Lu, W.-Q., Chang, H.-C., "An Extension of the Biharmonic Boundary Integral Method to Free Surface Flow in Channels", J. Comp. Physics, v.77, n.2, pp340-360, 1988.

3. Lu, W.-Q., "Boundary Element Analysis of Free Surface Problems of Axisymmetric Taylor Bubbles", Boundary Elements XII, v.2, pp131-143, edited by Brebbia, C.A., Springer-verlag, 1990.

4. Wasden, F.K., Dukler, A.E., "Insights into the Hydrodynamics of Free Falling Wavy Films AIChE J. v.35, n.2, pp187-195, 1989.

5. Kheshgi, H.S., Scriven, L.E.,"Disturbed Film Flow on a Vertical Plate", Phy. Fluids, v.30, pp990-, 1987.

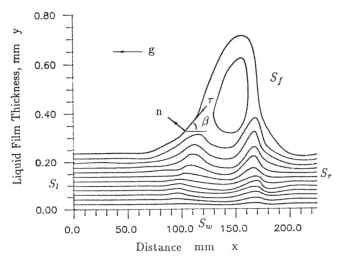

Fig.1 Streamline map of solitary wave (wave amplitude=3.01)

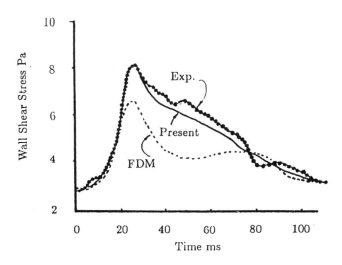

Fig.2 Wall shear stress comparison for solitary wave

(wave amplitude=3.01)

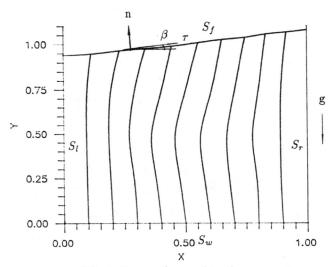

Fig.3 Free surface and isotherm map in
thermocapillary convection for $M_a = 50$

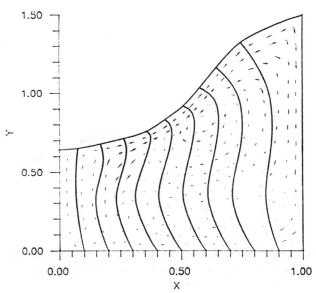

Fig.4 Free surface, velocity vector and isotherm map
in thermocapillary convection for $M_a = 150$

A porosity method to compute 3d turbulent free surface flows

S. Ouillon, D. Dartus

Institute de Mécanique des Fluides de Toulouse, 2, Allée du Professeur C. Soula, 31400 Toulouse, France

ABSTRACT

A method used to track a moving surface boundary and to follow its evolution, using a one–phase three–dimensional (3D) Reynolds solver, with rigid grids, by means of a transient porosity field is exposed. The porosities are geometric factors which multiply, before being used in the transient, convective, diffusive and source terms, the areas and volume of cells in the computational domain. The free surface is located in cells with a porosity varying between zero and one. A description of the algorithm used to compute the free surface evolution is given. The computation of the free surface evolution is associated with the choice for appropriate boundary conditions and with the flow field calculation. Results of a test case on the flow around a groyne are given. The isolines of water depths are presented. A comparison of the reattachment length prediction using the free–surface model and the rigid–lid assumption is given.

INTRODUCTION

Different types of 3D Computational Fluid Dynamics softwares for transient free surface flows can be distinguished by their ways of determining the pressure field or their techniques to track the free surface. Indeed the pressure field has the main effect on the velocity field for incompressible fluid rather than the fluid density. When the correct pressure field is substituted into the momentum equation, the continuity equation can be satisfied by the resulting velocity field. Two methods are mainly employed to determine the pressure field : (1) pressure correction methods, and (2) methods solving Poisson's equation for pressure. The Computational Fluid Dynamics softwares for 3D transient free surface flows using either the first or the second method differ by their technique to determine the free surface shape. The authors have developed a method to track the free surface and to follow its evolution based on a transient porosity field which specifies the flow domain. Such a method is to be connected with a 3D Reynolds solver to compute free–surface flows. It has been applied in this paper with a Reynolds solver using the SIMPLE algorithm, which is one of the most relevant pressure correction methods (Patankar and Spalding, [1]).

Two kind of problems arise in the simulation of transient free surface flows : the evolution of the moving boundary and the determination of the variable fields. The authors have focussed on modelling the free surface evolution. The method used to track the free surface is first dressed. The algorithm to compute its evolution in connection with the SIMPLE algorithm is presented. Test case results follow.

USING THE POROSITY TO TRACK THE FREE SURFACE

Several methods are suitable to track the free surface and to compute its time–dependent evolution :

The MAC (Marker And Cell) method developed   in the Los Alamos Scientific Laboratory (Harlow and Welch, [2]) follows the evolution of particles moving with the fluid. The free surface is defined as lying at the boundary between regions with and without marker particles. The volume of fluid (VOF) method proposed by Hirt and Nichols [3] is used more. It considers a step function value F which is one in fluid and zero elsewhere. Cells with F values varying between zero and one contain a free surface. The time dependence of F is governed by equation :

$$\frac{\partial F}{\partial t} + U \frac{\partial F}{\partial x} + V \frac{\partial F}{\partial y} + W \frac{\partial F}{\partial z} = 0 \qquad (1)$$

These methods are efficient and flexible for treating complicated free surface configurations. Other methods have been proposed, which also entail the resolution of a direct partial equation for an auxiliary variable, over each cell of the domain. However, the numerical diffusivity, which depends on the numerical scheme, may produce an unreasonably smeared scalar field. As an alternative to this problem, the authors have adopted another approach : the direct calculation of the water depth on every water column, by means of the depth–integrated continuity equation. The unsteady fluid domain is specified in a fixed mesh grid by means of a transient porosity field.

The porosities are geometric factors which multiply before they are used for convection and diffusion fluxes or for source terms the areas and volume of cells in the computational domain. A zero porosity of a cell makes it empty of fluid whereas a one porosity makes it full of fluid. The free surface may be determined in a cell with a porosity varying between zero and one. The surface porosities are defined by multiplying the geometric areas by the smaller of the two adjacent volumetric porosities (see fig.1).

The purpose of the Porosity Method is to implicitly compute the surface position of the moving domain and to solve the pressure and velocity fields through it. Several iterations are necessary on the surface evolution calculation, and several iterations on pressure and velocity between two of those iterations, before obtaining converged variable fields inside a well–definite domain.

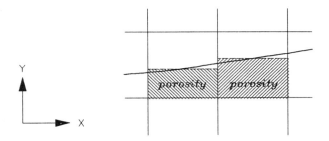

Figure 1   2-dimensional representation of the surface tracking

ENHANCEMENT OF THE HH–SIMPLE ALGORITHM

General equations

A turbulent and 3-dimensional incompressible flow may be described by the Reynolds equations. When coupled with the Boussinesq approximation and with a first order turbulence closure, the equations read :

$$\frac{\partial U_i}{\partial x_i} = 0 \qquad\qquad i = x, y, z \qquad (2)$$

$$\frac{\partial U_i}{\partial t} + U_j \frac{\partial U_i}{\partial x_j} = g_i - \frac{1}{\rho}\frac{\partial P}{\partial x_i} + \frac{\partial}{\partial x_j}\left(\nu_t \frac{\partial U_i}{\partial x_j} \right) + S_i \qquad i, j = x, y, z \qquad (3)$$

These equations are coupled in this study with a $k - \epsilon$ turbulence model. A description of the model with standard wall boundary conditions is to be found in Rodi [4]. At the free surface, the boundary conditions proposed by Celik and Rodi [5] for the k and ϵ equations were employed.

In order to test the Porosity Method, it was applied with a Reynolds solver using the SIMPLE algorithm. A general method to adapt this algorithm to some free surface problems has been exposed by Zhou and Zhang [6] : the HH–SIMPLE algorithm. It does not need the use of the hydrostatic pressure assumption. From the Reynolds equations, the splitting of pressure and some additional equations are required.

The splitting of pressure

Pressure terms are to be separated into both the hydrodynamical pressure (P_d) and the hydrostatic pressure (P_s), as :

$$P = P_d + P_s \qquad (4)$$

where $$P_s = \rho\, g\, (H(x, z, t) - y) + P_{atm} \qquad (5)$$

if the spatial description of the domain remains as indicated in figure 1.
The pressure gradient can be expressed as :

$$-\frac{\partial P}{\partial x} = -\frac{\partial P_d}{\partial x} - \rho\, g\, \frac{\partial H}{\partial x} \qquad (6)$$

$$-\frac{\partial P}{\partial y} = -\frac{\partial P_d}{\partial y} + \rho \, g \qquad (7)$$

$$-\frac{\partial P}{\partial z} = -\frac{\partial P_d}{\partial z} - \rho \, g \, \frac{\partial H}{\partial z} \qquad (8)$$

Determination of the water level and boundary conditions

Substituting equation (6) to (8) into equation (3) and adding equations (9) and (10) – which determine the free surface position and its kinematic boundary condition – to the sub-stituted equation and to equation (2), we obtain the entire system to be computed.

$$\frac{\partial H}{\partial t} + \frac{\partial(H - y_0)\overline{U}}{\partial x} + \frac{\partial(H - y_0)\overline{W}}{\partial z} = V(y_0) \qquad (9)$$

$$\frac{\partial H}{\partial t} + U_s \frac{\partial H}{\partial x} + W_s \frac{\partial H}{\partial z} = V_s \qquad (10)$$

The depth–averaged continuity equation (9) is used to cal-culate the surface elevation $H(x,z,t)$ (see fig.2), whereas the atmospheric pressure P_{atm} is imposed to determine the P_d boundary condition.

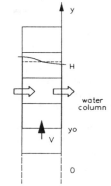

Fig. 2 Calculation on the surface elevation

At each iteration on the surface water level calculation, the new H values are used to impose adapted surface and volumetric porosities in each cell. Iterations on pressure and velocities are then necessary before applying convergence tests and eventually re–calculating the water surface elevation, using a user–chosen relaxation coefficient.

SAMPLE PROBLEM : FLOW AROUND A GROYNE

The recirculating flow around a groyne gives a relevant test case for the 3D numerical free surface flow models. Two main interests arise in the prediction of both free surface and reattachment point locations. Because of their interests, experiments have been built up and numerical simulations have been conducted in cooperation between Delft Hydraulics Laboratory, the Franzius Institut and the Institute for Fluid Mechanics and Computer Application in Civil Engineering at the University of Hannover (Holtz, [7]).

The present model was tested on one of the experimental configurations and the results are compared versus experimental data. The experiment was performed in a 30 meters length and 2.50 meters width channel with smooth vertical walls. It was run for stationary and turbulent flow conditions. Metal grid elements covered the bottom, corresponding to a 50 $m^{1/3}/s$ Manning–Strickler coefficient. The mean water depth was 0.23 m, and the mean flow velocity in the undisturbed zone was 0.345 m/s. Two types of groynes were tested, one with a sharp edge on its tip and the other rectangular in shape. They were 25 cm long and 2.5 cm wide (see fig. 3). During the experiment, spatially distributed samples on the water levels (accuracy : 0.1 mm) and flow velocities (accuracy : 1 cm/s) were taken.

From the experiment, the location of the reattachment point was measured by visual inspection of the flow. The reattachment length is the dimensionless number calculated from the quotient of distance between groyne and reattachment point versus length of the groyne. For the described configuration, no difference was noticed in the reattachment length with the sharp edge groyne or with the rectangular groyne. The digital simulation was run for a rectangular groyne. The horizontal discretization is presented on figure 4. The vertical was resolved by 7 layers.

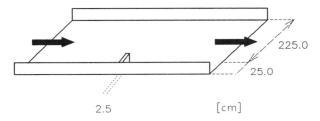

Figure 3   Flow configuration around the groyne

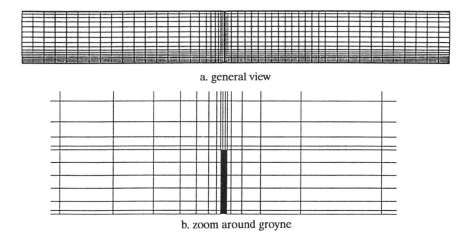

a. general view

b. zoom around groyne

Figure 4   Computational grid

A first simulation was performed using the rigid-lid assumption, for which the mean water depth was imposed all over the channel, so as to obtain initial fields for the free surface calculation. Then the simulation was carried out for a transient flow, until obtaining a steady flow.

The isolines of water depths around groyne are compared with the data in figure 5. The results agree well with the experimental data. The relative difference between both results is smaller than 0.5% on the area for which measures are available.

A zoom from the computed results is presented in figure 6. No experimental data are available for comparison in this zone. However, the results seem qualitatively good as compared with what can be seen around piers of bridge : hollow at the upstream edge of the groyne head, where the velocities increase; hollow in the recirculation zone; slight rise just behind the groyne.

A general remark is to be done, because the area of the decreasing zone as can be seen with the 22.9 cm isoline is lightly underestimated. It seems to be due to the light underestimation of the reattachment zone, rather than to the surface location calculation. This may also explain the rise of water lines on cross–lines behind groyne, more pronounced on numerical results than on measurements.

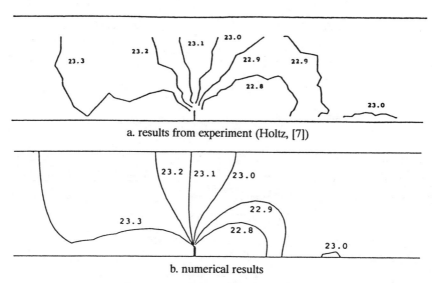

a. results from experiment (Holtz, [7])

b. numerical results

Figure 5   Isolines of water depths (in cm)

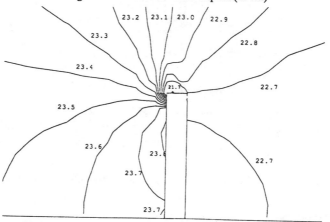

Figure 6   Computed isolines of water depths (in cm) around groyne

The reattachment point is the location where the separated flow reattaches the wall downstream of the groyne. It is to be seen on the surface velocity field, which is reproduced in figure 7.a. The reattachment length is estimated to be 10.7 from the numerical results, whereas it was estimated to be 11.5 on experiment. The calculation shows a 7% relative error. It is interesting to compare this result with the reattachment length which is got when using the rigid–lid assumption. Figure 7.b reproduces the surface velocity field in that case. The reattachment length is then underestimated from about 30% versus the experimental data. The underestimation of reattachment length is often explained by the well–known defi- ciencies of the $k - \epsilon$ model in reattachment zones. However, the present results indicate that, for a free surface flow, the turbulence model deficiency is not the major cause of the underestimation, when using the rigid–lid assumption. More results may be found in Ouillon [8].

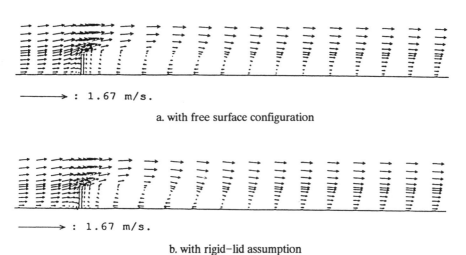

————→ : 1.67 m/s.

a. with free surface configuration

————→ : 1.67 m/s.

b. with rigid–lid assumption

Figure 7   Computed surface velocity field (zoom behind groyne)

CONCLUSION

The Porosity Method to track the free surface for transient flow computations has been expounded. Its application with a 3D Reynolds solver using the SIMPLE algorithm has been presented. The performed test case concerns the flow around a groyne in a wide rectangular channel. The computed isolines of water depths agree well with the experimental data. The major errors (smaller than 0.5%) are due to the light underestimation of the reattachment length, which is 7%. This underestimation shows a substantial improvement in the reat- tachment length prediction as compared with that obtained using the rigid–lid assumption (error about 30%) and the $k - \epsilon$ model.

KEY WORDS

Free surface flows, Hydrodynamics, Numerical modelling

NOMENCLATURE

g_i	component of gravitational acceleration
H	water surface elevation
P	pressure
P_{atm}	atmospheric pressure
P_d	hydrodynamic pressure
P_s	hydrostatic pressure
S_i	source term
U_i	velocity component
x_i	directional axe
V_s	surface y–directional velocity component
ν_t	turbulent viscosity
ρ	fluid density

REFERENCES

1. Patankar, S.V. and Spalding, D.B. 'A Calculation Procedure for Heat, Mass and Momentum Transfer in Three–dimensional Parabolic Flows' *International Journal of Heat and Mass Transfer*, Vol. 15, p.1787, 1972.

2. Harlow, F.M. and Welch, J.E. 'Numerical Calculation of Time–Dependent Viscous Incompressible Flow of Fluid with Free Surfaces' *Phys. Fluids*, Vol. 8, p.2182, 1965.

3. Hirt, C.W. and Nichols, B.D. 'Volume of Fluid (VOF) Method for the Dynamics of Free Boundaries' *Journal of Computational Physics*, Vol. 39, pp. 201–225, 1981.

4. Rodi, W. *Turbulence models and their applications in hydraulics* A.I.R.H., Delft, 1980.

5. Celik, I. and Rodi, W. 'Simulation of free–surface effects on turbulent channel flows' *Physico–Chem. Hydrodyn.*, Vol. 5, n° 3/4, pp. 217–227, 1984.

6. Zhou, S.V. and Zhang, S.N. 'Application of the HH–SIMPLE algorithm for the numerical simulation of some free surface flow problems for 3–dimensional situations' in Hydraulic and Environmental Modelling of Coastal, Estuarine and River Waters (Ed. Falconer R.A., Goodwin P. and Matthew R.G.S.), pp. 526–535, *Proceedings of the Int. Conf.*, Bradford, England, 1989. Gower Technical, Aldershot and Brookfield, 1989.

7. Holtz, K.P. 'Numerical Simulation of Recirculating Flow at Groynes' in Computer Methods in Water Resources 2 (Ed. Brebbia, C.A., Ouazar, D. and Ben Sari, D.), Vol. 2, pp. 463–477, *Proceedings of the 2nd Int. Conf.*, Marrakesh, Morocco, 1991. Springer Verlag, Berlin and New York, 1991.

8. Ouillon, S. *Modélisation mathématique de l'hydrodynamique à surface libre et du transport de Matières En Suspension non cohésives, aide à l'interprétation d'images spatiales*, Thèse de Doctorat, I.M.F.T., Institut National Polytechnique de Toulouse, Toulouse, 1993.

Nonlinear dynamics of capillary fountains

R.M.S.M. Schulkes

Department of Applied Mathematics and Theoretical Physics, University of Cambridge, Silver Street, Cambridge CB3 9EW, England

ABSTRACT

In this paper we present a numerical study of the evolution of a capillary fountain. Under the usual assumptions leading to potential theory and the additional assumption of rotational symmetry we consider the behaviour of a capillary free surface when fluid is ejected from a circular nozzle at a constant rate. The equations governing the motion of the fluid are written in terms of an integral equation which is discretised using the boundary element method. Crucial in the numerical implementation is a regridding procedure by which new Lagrangian nodes are added to the free surface during the time integration in order to control the discretisation error and to prevent numerical instabilities.

1. INTRODUCTION

Fountains occur in a wide variety of circumstances ranging from ornamental configurations in many gardens to engineering applications such as the filling of moulds. Most commonly a fountain is encountered in the form of a liquid jet emerging from a nozzle pointing (vertically) upwards. The liquid jet reaches a certain height and exhibits highly irregular and nonlinear behaviour near its apex as the descending fluid interacts with the fluid moving upwards. Notwithstanding the irregular behaviour of a 'fully developed' fountain, the evolution of a fountain shortly after it emerges from a nozzle may be very regular and highly symmetric. The regularity is lost only when the fountain reaches its maximum height and descending fluid starts to interact with the upward moving fluid.

It will be evident that the evolution of the water surface is a highly nonlinear dynamical process involving the rapid expansion of a capillary free boundary. Under the assumptions that the fountain is axisymmetric and that the fluid velocity can be written as the gradient of a velocity potential satisfying Laplace's equation, a great simplification is achieved. Namely, the velocity potential approach leads naturally to an integral formulation which, together with the symmetry assumption, leads to a one-dimensional problem defined only on the boundary of the fluid domain. The large amount of literature involving the application of an integral formulation in the treatment of (capillary) free-boundary problems is indicative of the benefits of this approach. For recent overviews of literature concerning integral formulations of potential flow problems involving free boundaries, the reader is referred to Dold [2] and Pelekasis et al. [5].

The main difficulties encountered in the work presented in this paper are related to the rapid expansion of the capillary surface. In order to control the discretisation error it is necessary to add new Lagrangian nodes to the growing capillary surface in a controlled manner. It is not a priori clear what the optimal strategy is which controls the discretisation error, prevents numerical instabilities and minimises the mass loss resulting from the relocation of nodes. These points will be dealt with in this paper.

2. PROBLEM FORMULATION

We assume that an inviscid, incompressible fluid is ejected from a cylindrical nozzle positioned vertically upwards. The fluid domain remains symmetric after ejection and $\Omega(t)$ denotes the fluid domain in the r, z-plane. The boundary Ω of $\Omega(t)$ consists of three parts: a capillary free boundary denoted by $S(t)$, the rigid side of the nozzle denoted by B and a boundary Γ on which the normal velocity is prescribed.

The governing equations will be written in dimensionless form with the radius of the nozzle R as the characteristic length scale, the characteristic time scale is given by $T = \sqrt{\rho R^3 / \sigma}$ (ρ is the fluid density and σ is the coefficient of surface tension) and a pressure scale is given by $P = \sigma/R$.

Assuming irrotational flow, the velocity field in $\Omega(t)$ can be described by a velocity potential ϕ which satisfies Laplace's equation. The corresponding integral equation in a cylindrical coordinate system with rotational symmetry is given by

$$\alpha\phi(\mathbf{x}) + \int_{\partial\Omega} \phi(\mathbf{x}')\frac{\partial G}{\partial n'}(\mathbf{x}, \mathbf{x}')r'ds(\mathbf{x}') = \int_{\partial\Omega} \psi(\mathbf{x}')G(\mathbf{x}, \mathbf{x}')r'ds(\mathbf{x}'). \qquad (1)$$

We have used the notation $\psi = \frac{\partial\phi}{\partial n}$ and $G(\mathbf{x}, \mathbf{x}')$ denotes the Greens function for the Laplace equation in cylindrical coordinates. The first integral in (1) is understood in the sense of the Cauchy principal value and the parameter α in equation (1) is the solid angle at the point $\mathbf{x}$ on the boundary subtended by the fluid domain.

On the rigid side B of the nozzle, situated at $r = 1$, the usual impermeability condition is prescribed, viz.

$$\left.\frac{\partial\phi}{\partial r}\right|_{r=1} = 0, \qquad (2)$$

while the nozzle inlet Γ, positioned at $z = 0$, the normal velocity is prescribed, giving

$$\left.\frac{\partial\phi}{\partial z}\right|_{z=0} = \sqrt{We}\Psi(r), \qquad (3)$$

in which $\Psi(r)$ denotes the dimensionless flux and $We = \rho R V^2/\sigma$ is the Weber number with V a measure of the normal velocity. Numerical experiments show that for a given volume flux, the evolution of the capillary surface is remarkably independent of the precise form of the flux $\Psi(r)$. It seems reasonable, therefore, to define the discharge rate Q via

$$Q = -2\pi\sqrt{We} \int_0^1 \Psi(r)r\,dr,$$

and regard the Bond number and the discharge rate as the relevant governing parameters. Note that when $\Psi(r) < 0$ fluid enters the nozzle at $z = 0$ so that a positive discharge rate indicates that fluid is ejected from the nozzle ate $z = 1$.

We assume that initially the free surface is situated at the nozzle outlet which we choose to be at $z = 1$. When fluid enters the nozzle at $z = 0$, incompressibility of the fluid implies that an equal amount of fluid must be ejected from the nozzle. The result is an expanding free surface above the nozzle. The three conditions required to describe the moving capillary free surface $S(t)$ are two kinematic conditions and a dynamic condition, viz.

$$\frac{Dr}{Dt} = n_r \frac{\partial\phi}{\partial n} - n_z \frac{\partial\phi}{\partial s},$$
$$\frac{Dz}{Dt} = n_z \frac{\partial\phi}{\partial n} + n_r \frac{\partial\phi}{\partial s}, \tag{4}$$
$$\frac{D\phi}{Dt} = \frac{1}{2}|\nabla\phi|^2 + \frac{1}{R_1} + \frac{1}{R_2} + p_0 - Boz.$$

In the above equations $D/Dt = \partial/\partial t + (\nabla\phi\cdot\nabla)$ denotes a Lagrangian time derivative, $\mathbf{n} = (n_r, n_z)$ is a unit vector normal to the capillary surface and s denotes the arclength along the capillary surface (in counter-clockwise direction). R_1 and R_2 are the principal radii of curvature of the free surface, p_0 is a pressure constant which is defined by the equations governing the static surface and the dimensionless Bond number $Bo = \rho g R^2/\sigma$ is a measure of the ratio of gravitational and surface tension forces.

The boundary conditions (2) and (3) on B and Γ respectively can be inserted in the integral equation (1). It follows that equations (4) describe the evolution in time of the capillary free surface with the relation between the fluxes and the velocity potential provided by the integal equation. Thus, given suitable initial conditions the problem under consideration constitutes an initial-value problem.

3. NUMERICAL IMPLEMENTATION

3.1 Discretisation

To obtain a discrete set of equations we take the usual approach by dividing the boundary of $\Omega(t)$ up into a finite number of elements. On each element the velocity potentials and the fluxes are approximated by linear interpolating functions. The Green's function for the Laplacian in cylindrical coordinates is expressed in terms of elliptic functions. These elliptic functions are approximated using polynomial expansions given by Abramowitz and Stegun [1]. The integrals defining the matrix elements are evaluated using standard 4-point Gauss interpolation formula whenever the integrals are regular. Integrals containing a logarithmic singularity are evaluated using special Gauss formula (cf. Stroud and Secrest [6]). The singular matrix elements can be calculated indirectly by summing the off-diagonal elements (cf. Van de Vorst et al. [7]).

In order to discretise the kinematic and dynamic boundary conditions we have to calculate for each element the unit normals to the free surface and the radius of curvature of the surface. We found that the most robust approximation was achieved by fitting a locally quadratic spline through three neighbouring nodes and approximating the unit normals and the curvatures using these splines.

After having applied the discretisation procedure as outlined above, the conditions on the capillary surface can be written like

$$
\begin{aligned}
\frac{D\mathbf{r}}{Dt} &= \mathbf{f}_1(\phi, \psi, \mathbf{r}, \mathbf{z}), \\
\frac{D\mathbf{z}}{Dt} &= \mathbf{f}_2(\phi, \psi, \mathbf{r}, \mathbf{z}), \\
\frac{D\phi}{Dt} &= \mathbf{f}_3(\phi, \psi, \mathbf{r}, \mathbf{z}),
\end{aligned}
\tag{5}
$$

in which $\mathbf{f}_1$ $\mathbf{f}_2$ and $\mathbf{f}_3$ are in general nonlinear functions of their arguments. Together with suitable initial conditions equations (5) constitute an initial value problem where the relation between ϕ and ψ is provided by the discretised integral equation which has the form

$$
\mathbf{H}\phi = \mathbf{G}\psi.
\tag{6}
$$

3.2 Time-stepping and regridding

To advance the solution in time of the initial-value problem defined by (5) and (6) we employed a slightly modified fourth-order Runge-Kutta scheme. The modification consists of the assumption that the matrices $\mathbf{G}$ and $\mathbf{H}$ in (6) are constant during one complete time step. At the cost of some loss of accuracy during the time integration (cf. Dommermuth and Yue [3]), this assumption leads to significant savings in computer time which is dominated by the calculation of the matrix coefficients.

We have choosen for a single-step scheme rather than a multi-step scheme (which is faster for the same accuracy), because of the frequent relocations of the nodes on the free surface. With a multi-step scheme we would have to make extensive use of interpolations in order to determine the true position of the nodal points. Frequent regridding is necessary for a number of reasons. Recall that the flux of fluid through the nozzle is constant which means that the area of the free surface increases steadily with time. In order to control the discretisation error it is, therefore, necessary to add new Lagrangian nodes to the free surface. In addition we find that the evolution of the capillary surface is by no means uniform. There are regions on the capillary surface in which the flow is largely divergent while other regions exist in which the flow is predominantly convergent. This leads to large variations in the movement of Lagrangian nodes resulting in a very uneven distribution of nodes on the surface.

The regridding procedure we have applied in our calculations is as follows. After a given number of time steps the nodes are redistributed over the surface so as to maintain an even distribution of nodes. A node is added to the surface whenever the surface area has increased sufficiently to add an extra node without violating a prescribed lower bound of the element size. This lower bound is necessary in view of the conditional stability of the Rung-Kutta scheme which related the time step to the minimum distance between any two adjacent Lagrangian nodes.

Calculations show that restricting the positioning of new nodes to the lines connecting the old nodes has a strong stiffening effect and leads to mass loss during the regridding operation. This is due to the fact that for a convex surface the lines joining the new nodes always lie entirely within the fluid domain when the new nodes are restricted to the lines connecting the old nodes.. The new nodes are therefore not positioned on the vertices connecting old nodes. Instead we calculate a locally cubic spline (based on the four old nodes surrounding the new node) and we position the new node on the spline.

In the present study, as in many other papers in which an integral formulation has been applied to study the dynamics of a potential flow involving a free boundary, short-wavelength instabilities are observed (see for example Longuet-Higgins and Cokelet [4]). However, with the regridding strategy outlined above, by which the minimum element size was bounded below, the instabilities were eliminated.

4. DISCUSSION AND RESULTS

As an example of the evolution of a capillary fountain we consider the case in which the Bond number is kept fixed at $Bo = 0.5$ while the discharge rate is varied. The flat, initial surface is discretised using 16 elements. Regridding is applied after each time step. As the area of the free surface grows, new nodes are added until the total number of nodes is equal to 120. After that regridding is only used to maintain a uniform distribution of nodes.

In figures 1a-c we show plots of the evolving free surface for the discharge rates $Q = 4, 6$ and 8 respectively. We observe that for small discharge rates ($Q = 4$, figure 1a) the fountain has the form of a sessile drop which slowly develops at the end of the nozzle. Additional calculations show that the shape of the growing drop is not modified significantly by dynamic effects whenever $Q \leq 4$. The shape of the drop is mainly determined by its volume and the balance between surface tension and gravitational forces, i.e. the Bond number. When the discharge rate is increased to $Q = 6$ (figure 1b) it is clear that dynamic effects become important. During the initial stages of the evolution, the height of the fountain increases rapidly and the fountain is columnar. Subsequently the rate at which the height increases slows down and the head of the fountain expands. We observe that the head of the fountain continues to expand until the free surface folds back onto itself at which point the calculation is terminated. A further increase of the discharge rate to $Q = 8$ (figure 1b) shows a similar development as for the case $Q = 6$ although is this case the height of the fountain has increased significantly before the lobes at the head of the fountain fold onto the fluid column supporting the head.

We find that an increase of the discharge rate beyond $Q = 10$ leads to a physical instability. The origin of this instability is related to the formation of a region with high curvature near the symmetry axis. In figure 2 we show the evolution of the fountain shortly after the exit of the nozzle for the cases $Q = 4$ and $Q = 8$. We observe the formation of a trough which is centered around

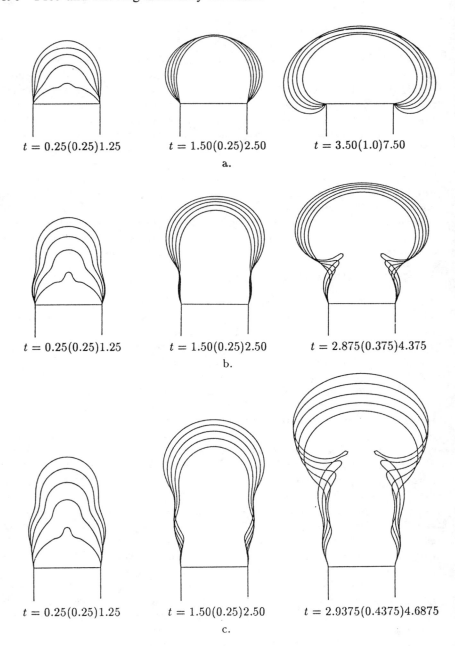

Figure 1: Figures of the evolution of the free surface for the case $Bo = 0.5$ and $Q = 4$ (a), $Q = 6$ (b) and $Q = 8$ (c). The times at which the surfaces are shown are indicated in the plots.

the symmetry axis. As time progresses the trough becomes more localised until, at some point, the large positive curvature forces the surface out of the trough resulting in a nipple-like structure near the symmetry axis. We observe that the for increasing discharge rates the trough and the protuberance become more increasingly pronounced. As the discharge rate increases beyond a critical level (approximately at $Q = 10$), the acceleration at the symmetry axis becomes so large that a bifurcation occurs. Physically this corresponds to a drop being ejected from the free surface. This phenomenon is indeed observed in laboratory experiments.

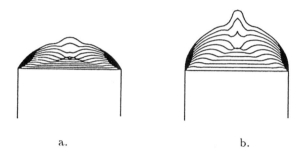

a.   b.

Figure 2: The evolution of the capillary surface shortly after fluid emerges from the nozzle for the discharge rates $Q = 4$ (a) and $Q = 8$ (b). The plots are shown at dimensionless times $t = 0.025(0.025)0.25$.

5. CONCLUSIONS

In this paper we have studied the evolution of capillary fountains by employing an integral formulation of the governing equations. Owing to the fact the area of the capillary surface increases with time, a regridding strategy is applied in which (i) nodal positions are updated so as to maintain a uniform distribution of nodes, and (ii) nodes are added to the free surface to prevent a continuous increase in the average length of elements.

It is found that for small values of the discharge rate ($Q \leq 4$) the fountain has the form of a growing sessile drop, the shape of which is not effected significantly by dynamic effects. As the discharge rate increase dynamic effects become increasingly important. For discharge rates above a critial level ($Q \approx 10$) a physical instability occurs. This instability can be identified with the ejection of a drop from the free surface.

ACKNOWLEDGEMENT This research was financed by the Commision of European Communities under contract number B/SC1-900617.

REFERENCES

1. Abramowitz, M. & Stegun, I.A. 1972 *Handbook of Mathematical Functions* Dover.

2. Dold, J.W. 1992 An efficient integral algorithm applied to unsteady gravity waves. *J. Comp. Phys.* **103**, 90-115.

3. Dommermuth, D.G. & Yue, D.K.P. 1987 Numerical simulation of nonlinear axisymmetric flows with free surface. *J. Fluid Mech.* **178**, 195-219.

4. Longuet-Higgins, M.S. & Cokelet, E.D. 1976 The deformation of steep surface waves on water I. A numerical method of computation. *Proc. R. Soc. London Ser. A* **350**, 1-26.

5. Pelekasis, N.A., Tsamopoulos, J.A. & Manolis, G.D. 1992 A hybrid finite-boundary element method for inviscid flows with free surface. *J. Comp. Phys.* **101**(2), 231-251.

6. Stroud, A.H. and Secrest, D. *Quadrature Formulas* Prentice-Hall, Englewood Cliffs, NJ., 1966

7. Van de Vorst, G.A.L., Mattheij, R.M.M. & Kuiken, H.K. 1992 A boundary element solution for two-dimensional viscous sintering. *J. Comp. Phys.* **100**(1), 50-63.

Invited Paper

Boundary element analyses of moving boundary problems in Laplacian growth

N. Tosaka[a], R. Sugino[b]

[a]Department of Mathematical Engineering, College of Industrial Technology, Nihon University, Narashino, Chiba, 275, Japan
[b]Department of Mechanical Engineering, Kisarazu National College of Technology, Kisarazu, Chiba, 292, Japan

ABSTRACT

In this paper applicability of BEM to various kinds of moving boundary problems in natural science and engineering is discussed. Especially, Laplacian growth phenomena are considered in detail. The problems to be discussed are crystal growth and Hele-Shaw flow in Laplacian growth phenomena. Pattern formations in ice crystal growing and viscous fingering from small initial disturbance in a rectangular region are analyzed by the solution procedure. Splitting, shielding and spreading phenomena in pattern formation are shown numerically.

INTRODUCTION

There exists a large class of problems with movement of interface between two phases in natural science and engineering. Such problems are mathematically referred to as moving boundary problems [1] . The Stefan problem of the melting of ice or freezing of water is a typical example. Even within the inviscid flow of fluid mechanics, there are many moving boundary problems such as sloshing of a fluid in container, multiphase fluid flow through porous media, nonlinear water wave propagation, ship slamming and so forth.

Until now we have developed the boundary element method as an effective tool for numerical simulation of moving boundary problems such as sloshing problems [2]-[4] and nonlinear water wave problems [5]-[7]. Applicability of the method has been demonstrated through notable numerical results of the above problems.

In propotion as a new scientific activity concerning the mathematical study of pattern formation increases, we are required to solve numerically moving boundary problems and to determine the pattern formed by the interface between two phases. Recently there has emerged a new theoretical viewpoint of way called fractal pattern formation in dendritic crystal growth, viscous fingering in fluids and diffusion limited aggregation [8].

In this paper the more applicability of the boundary element method developed in the previous papers [2]-[7] to moving boundary problems concerning with pattern formation phenomena is discussed. Especially, pattern formation in the field which is governed by Laplace's equation is considered. This kind of pattern formation is called the Laplacian growth phenomena [9]. We consider ice crystal growing in water vapour [10]-[16] and viscous fingering [17]-[20] which emerges when a viscous fluid is displaced by a less viscous one as typical examples of the Laplacian growth.

MATHEMATICAL FORMULATION

We consider the moving boundary problems defined in a two-dimensional domain. A region Ω is bounded by the boundary Γ which is composed of a moving boundary part Γ_m and the fixed boundary Γ_w of the domain shown in Fig.1.

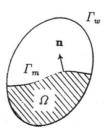

Fig.1   Configuration of mathematical model

Let us consider mathematical model of Laplacian growth phenomena. The field equation to be solved in the growth phenomena is assumed as the Laplace equation given by

$$\nabla^2\psi = \frac{\partial^2\psi}{\partial x^2} + \frac{\partial^2\psi}{\partial y^2} = 0 \quad in \quad \Omega \tag{1}$$

where ψ is the field unknown function, $\nabla = (\partial/\partial x, \partial/\partial y)$ and ∇^2 denotes the two-dimensional Laplacian.

There are two kinds of the boundary conditions to be prescribed. The first one is the fixed boundary condition (i.e., the wall boundary condition) given by

$$\frac{\partial\psi}{\partial n} = \mathbf{n}\cdot\nabla\psi \equiv \hat{q} = 0 \quad on \quad \Gamma_w \tag{2}$$

where n denotes the outward unit normal vector on the boundary. The other is the so-called moving boundary conditions to determine time-dependent shape of moving surface Γ_m. They are the kinematic and dynamic conditions.

First, the kinematic conditions that express for the interface to move with its own normal velocity are given by

$$\boldsymbol{v}\cdot\boldsymbol{n} \equiv v_n = \alpha\cdot\frac{\partial\psi}{\partial n} = \alpha\cdot(\nabla\psi)_n \quad on \quad \Gamma_m \tag{3}$$

in which α denotes some physical coefficient in relation to the growing field. Next, we can express also the dynamic condition derived from the physical requirement which corresponds to conservation law to be satisfied on the moving boundary. It is given by the following equation :

$$\psi = \psi_0 + \beta\cdot H \qquad on \quad \Gamma_m \tag{4}$$

where β denotes some constant which means a capillary number of the surface tension and H denotes the mean curvature of the interface boundary. And, ψ_0 has to be selected to a standard-value over flat interface at infinite extent.

The parameters in the above-mentioned mathematical model have to be selected by considering with situation of each physical phenomenon. For example, they are determined from Gibbs-Thomson condition in crystal growth or Darcy's law in Hele-Shaw flow, and so on. The parameters of each problem, such as ice crystal growth and Hele-Shaw flow, are shown in Table 1.

Table.1. Parameters of Laplacian growth

Case	ψ	α	ψ_0	β	H
I	C	D/ρ	C_0	Γ_D	K
II	P	$-b^2/12\mu$	P_a	$1/12Ca'$	$\frac{2}{b}+\kappa$

Here, case (I) and case (II) denote ice crystal growth and Hele-Shaw flow, respectively. Each parameter in Table 1 is explained at each section on numerical result.

In this study, we consider the mathematical model given by equations (1)-(4) as the coupled problem of the boundary-value problem of Laplace equation (1) with the initial-value problem of the system of evolutional equations(3).

SOLUTION PROCEDURE

Boundary Element Method for Boundary Value Problem

By taking into consideration the linearity of Laplace equation (1), we can easily transform the field equation (1) into the following boundary integral equation :

$$
\frac{1}{2}\psi(y) = \int_{\Gamma_m} \frac{\partial\psi}{\partial n}(x)\omega^*(x,y)d\Gamma(x) + \int_{\Gamma_w} \hat{q}\omega^*(x,y)d\Gamma(x) \tag{5}
$$
$$
- \int_{\Gamma_{m+w}} \psi(x)\frac{\partial\omega^*}{\partial n}(x,y)d\Gamma(x)
$$

in which ω^* is the well-known fundamental solution given by

$$
\omega^*(x,y) = \frac{1}{2\pi}\ln\frac{1}{r} \quad , \quad r =\| x - y \| \tag{6}
$$

If the velocity potential on the moving boundary Γ_m is known, then we can determine the value of ψ on Γ_w and its derivative on Γ_m with solution of the above boundary integral equation. In order to solve approximately equation (5), we use the boundary element method. In this study we use discretization with use of constant elements.

Time Integration Method for Initial Value Problem

The kinematic conditions (3) to be considered as the system of first-order ordinary differential equations with respect to the position vector r

of Lagrangian particle on moving boundary can be solved approximately by using the time integration scheme. Applying the Euler scheme to the above system, we can determine the new position r^{k+1} of moving boundary Γ_m at the $(k+1)$th time step as follows:

$$r^{k+1} = r^k + V^k \cdot \Delta t \qquad (7)$$

where Δt denotes the short time interval, V denotes the normal component of moving velocity (i.e., $V = \vec{v_n}$) and the superscript "k" indicates the k−th time step. By using the above numerical integration scheme in time, we can determine time-dependent configuration of the moving boundary.

NUMERICAL RESULTS OF ICE CRYSTAL GROWTH

First of all, let us consider two-dimensional growing of ice crystal in a rectangular region. A water vapour field Ω is bounded by the boundary Γ which is composed of a moving boundary part (i.e., ice crystal surface) Γ_m, a water wall part Γ_{w1} and both imaginary water vapour boundaries Γ_{w2} shown in Fig.2.

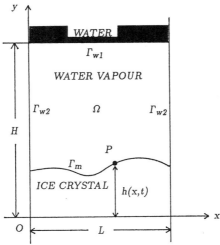

Fig.2. Configuration of mathematical model

We consider the ice crystal growth in a rectangular region which has width L and height H shown in Fig.2. In numerical performance, we adopt $L = 26.0(\mu m)$ and $H = 41.0(\mu m)$ as the dimensions of a region and time increment $\Delta t = 1.0(sec)$. And, the sinusoidal small disturbance of wave length λ and wave amplitude $A = 2.0(\mu m)$ is given as the initial profile of an ice crystal surface. Three cases of wave length are adopted at this numeraical computations. They are $\lambda = 24.0(\mu m)$, $12.0(\mu m)$ and $8.0(\mu m)$, respectively. Next, we adopt the following parameters of the water vapour diffusion field: $C_0 = 1.03 \times 10^{-6}(g/cm^3)$ as the saturation vapour density over flat ice surface and $C_L = 1.14 \times 10^{-6}(g/cm^3)$ as the saturation water vapour density at water wall. Here, the temperature of the whole system is set uniformly at $-15°C$. The capillary constant of surface tension, $\Gamma_D = 1.0 \times 10^{-7}(cm)$, the diffusion coefficient of water vapour in air, $D = 0.2(cm^2/sec)$ and the density of ice, $\rho = 0.9(g/cm^3)$ are adopted to our numerical simulations. Further, we assume that the saturation vapour density values on water vapour boundaries Γ_{w2} at both sides of the region are equal to linear interpolation from C_0 to C_L. The boundary of diffusion domain is divided into 128 boundary segments. And, both the moving boundary Γ_m and the water boundary Γ_{w1} are divided into 26 segments.

Figures 3-5 show time dependent configurations of moving boundary at each time instant through comparisons with FDM solution [13]. In these computation, we can recoginize that ice crystals grow into the water vapour diffusion field. From Figs.3-5, it is clear that the present solution agrees with the other FDM [13] solution very well except the case with $\lambda = 24.0(\mu m)$ as shown in Fig.3 (a). In this case, it is notable that emergence of splitting phenomenon can be appeared in our numerical simulation.

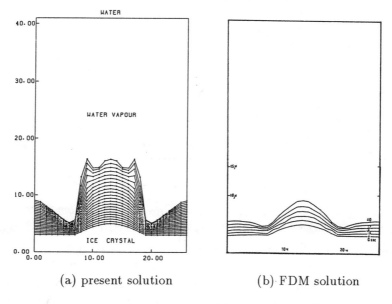

(a) present solution   (b) FDM solution

Fig.3.   Comparison of numerical results ($\lambda = 24.0(\mu m)$)

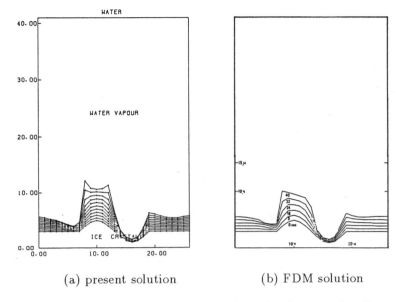

(a) present solution   (b) FDM solution

Fig.4.   Comparison of numerical results $(\lambda = 12.0(\mu m))$

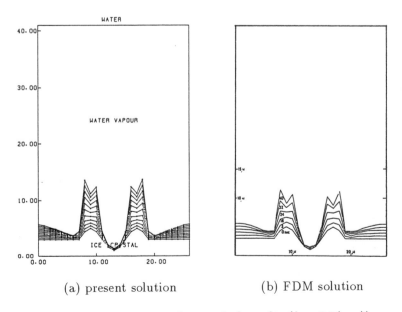

(a) present solution   (b) FDM solution

Fig.5.   Comparison of numerical results $(\lambda = 8.0(\mu m))$

NUMERICAL RESULTS OF HELE-SHAW FLOW

Next, let us consider viscous fingering of Hele-Shaw flow in a rectangular region. A high viscous fluid field Ω is bounded by the boundary Γ which is composed of a moving boundary part (i.e., interface between high viscous fluid and low one) Γ_m, an outflow part Γ_{w1} and both wall boundaries Γ_{w2} shown in Fig.6.

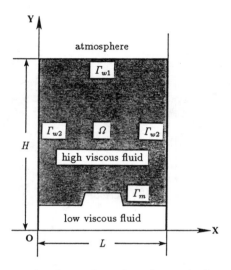

Fig.6.   Configuration of mathematical model

We simulate the Hele-Shaw flow in a rectangular region which has a width L and height H shown in Fig.6. In numerical performance, we adopt $L = 100.0(cm)$ and $H = 200.0(cm)$ on the dimensions of a region and time increment $\Delta t = 0.5(sec)$. And, the small disturbance of length l and height d is given as the initial profile of interface. Three cases of disturbance length are adopted in our numerical computations. They are $l = 8.0(cm)$, $l = 20.0(cm)$ and $l = 28.0(cm)$, respectively. Next, we adopt the following parameters of the viscous fingering in the field of Hele-Shaw cell: $P_L = 101325.0(Pa)$ as the atmospheric pressure at boundary Γ_{w1}, $P_a = 3.0 \times P_L$ asthe pressure of low viscosity fluid at Γ_m and $b = 0.1(cm)$ as the gap width of the cell. The capillary number, $C'_a = 1.0 \times 10^{-6}(cm)$ and $1000(cm)$, the viscosity coefficient of high viscous fluid, $\mu = 14.95(dyn \cdot s/cm)$ and the surface tension coefficient, $\sigma = 63.4(dyn/cm)$ are adopted in our numerical simulations. The moving boundary part Γ_m is divided into 50 boundary segments. And, the other boundaries Γ_{w1} and Γ_{w2} are divided into 20 segments.

Figures 7-10 show time dependent configurations of the moving boundary at each time instant. Figure 7 shows the difference of single fingering on capillary number adopted in numerical simulation. In Fig.8, two and three fingerings caused by the length of initial disturbance are shown. These results show the 'splitting' phenomenon. The 'shielding' phenomenon are also indicated through numerical results in Fig.9. Figure 10 shows the 'spreading' phenomenon at single and two fingerings.

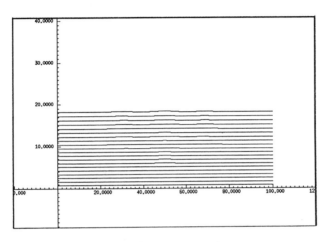

(a) $(C'_a = 1.0 \times 10^{-6})$

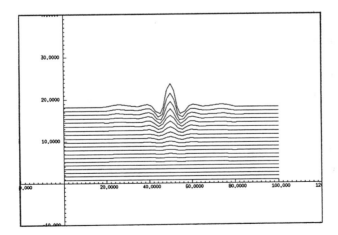

(b) $(C'_a = 1000)$

Fig.7.   Difference of single fingering on capillary number
$(l = 8.0(cm),\ d = 0.01(cm))$

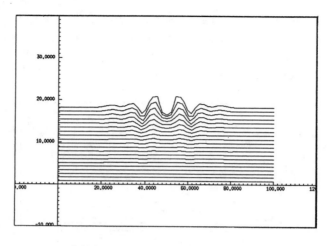

(a) $(l = 20.0(cm),\ d = 0.01(cm))$

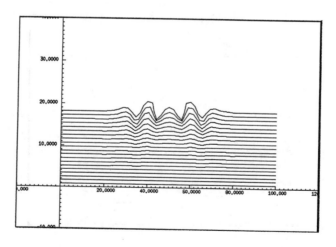

(b) $(l = 28.0(cm),\ d = 0.01(cm))$

Fig.8.　Splitting phenomena $(C'_a = 1000)$

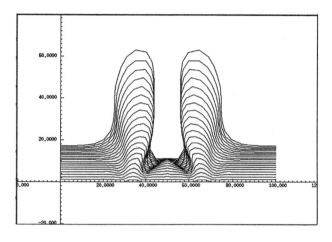

(a) $(d = 1.0, 0.1, 1.0(cm))$

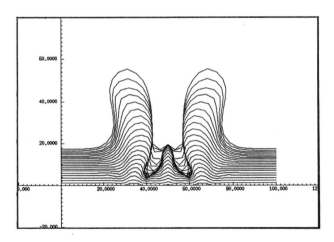

(b) $(d = 1.0, 0.3, 1.0(cm))$

Fig.9.   Shielding phenomena $(C'_a = 1000, \; l = 8.0, 4.0, 8.0(cm))$

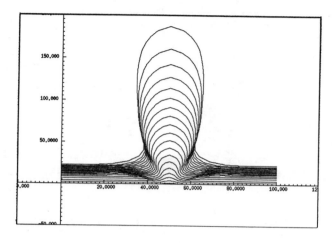

(a) $(l = 8.0(cm),\ d = 1.0(cm))$

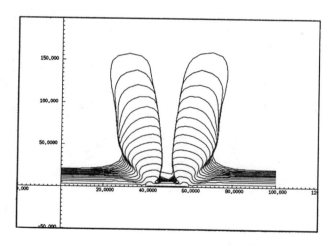

(b) $(l = 20.0(cm),\ d = 1.0(cm))$

Fig.10. Spreading phenomena $(C'_a = 1000)$

CONCLUSION

In this study, we investigate applicability of the boundary element method based on the mixed Lagrangian-Eulerian approach to numerical simulation for a moving boundary problem which is a mathematical model of the Laplacian growth phenomena. Pattern formations in ice crystal growing in the saturation water vapour field and viscous fingering in the Hele-Shaw cell are simulated. The obtained results show the crystal growth from the small initial disturbance and show a good agreement with the other numerical solution by FDM. And, the typical viscous fingering instability (i.e., 'splitting', 'shielding' and 'spreading' phenomena) could be simulated. Consequently, the present method may be one of the most efficient numerical solution procedures in simulating moving boundary problems of Laplacian growth phenomena.

REFERENCES

[1] Elliott,C.M. and J.R.Ockendon, *Weak and Variational Methods for Moving Boundary Problems* , Research Notes in Mathematics, Pitman Advanced Publishing Program, 1982

[2] Sugino,R. and Tosaka,N., Solution procedure for nonlinear free surface problems by boundary element approach, *Theoretical and Applied Mechanics*, Vol.38,University of Tokyo Press,pp.53-59,1989

[3] Sugino,R. & Tosaka,N., Sloshing analysis by boundary element method with direct differentiation procedure, *Theoretical and Applied Mechanics*,Vol.41, University of Tokyo Press,pp.191-198,1992

[4] Tosaka,N. and Sugino,R, Boundary element analysis of nonlinear free surface flow in containers, In:*Advances in Boundary Element Techniques* , Springer-Verlag,pp.428-446,1993

[5] Sugino,R. and Tosaka,N., Boundary element analysis of nonlinear water wave problems, In:*Proceedings of the Fourth Pacific Congress on Marine Science and Technology*, Vol.II,pp.309-316,1990

[6] Sugino,R. and Tosaka,N., Boundary element analysis of unsteady nonlinear surface waves on water, In:*Boundary Elements XII*, Vol.2,Compu tational Mechanics Publications, Springer-Verlag,pp.107-117,1990

[7] Sugino,R. and Tosaka,N., Direct differentiation approach to boundary element method for nonlinear water wave problems, In:*Boundary Element Methods* , Springer-Verlag,pp.314-323,1992

[8] Langer,J.S., Instabilities and pattern formation in crystal growth, *Rev.Mod.Phys*,Vol. 52,No.1, pp.1-28,1980

[9] Vicsek,T., *Fractal Growth Phenomena*, World Scientific,Singapore,1989

[10] Tosaka,N. and R.Sugino, Numerical simulation of ice crystal growing by boundary element method, In:*Applied Electromagnetices in Materials and Computational Technology*, Hokkaido University Press,pp.115-120,1992

[11] Higuchi,K., Growth of ice crystals under radiative cooling, *J. Meteo. Soc. Japan*, Vol.47, No.6, pp.446-450,1969

[12] Komabayashi,M., Shape instability of crystal of ice, carbon dixoide and ammonia grown in a cold chamber, *J.Meteo.Soc.Japan*,Vol.48,No.4, pp.270-286,1970

[13] Saito,M., Numerical experiment of growth of ice crystals by two dimensional model, *Tenki*, Vol.19,pp.293-297,1972(in Japanese)

[14] Komabayasi,M., Two dimensional computation of anisotropic ice crystal growing in air, *J.de Recherches Atmosphériques*, Vol.6,pp.307-328, 1972

[15] Saito,Y.,G.Goldbeck-Wood and H.Müller-Krumbhaar, Numerical simulation of dendritic growth, *Physical Review A*, Vol.38,No.4,pp.2148-2157,1988

[16] Yokoyama,E. and T.Kuroda, Pattern formation in growth of snow crystals occuring in the surface kinetic process and the diffusion process, *Physical Review A*, Vol.41,No.4,pp.2038-2049,1990

[17] Howison,S.D., Fingering in Hele-Shaw cells, *J.Fluid.Mech.*,Vol.167, pp.439-453,1986

[18] Chen,J.D., Growth of radial viscous fingering in a Hele-Shaw cell, *J.Fluid.Mech.*,Vol.201, pp.223-242,1989

[19] Tryggvason,G. and H.Aref, Numerical experiments on Hele Shaw flow with sharp interface, *J.Fluid.Mech.*,Vol.136, pp.1-30,1983

[20] DeGregoria,A.J. and L.W.Schwartz, A boundary-integral method for two-phase displacement in Hele-Shaw cells, *J.Fluid.Mech.*,Vol.164, pp. 383-400,1986

Finite element simulation of free surface flows using arbitrary Lagrangian-Eulerian method

A. Soulaïmani

Département de Génie Mécanique, École de Technologie Supérieure 4750 Avenue Henri-Julien, Montréal, Canada

ABSTRACT

In this paper the concept of Arbitrary Lagrangian-Eulerian kinematic description is reviewed and applied to free surface flows. The use of appropriate equilibrium equations is discussed. The corresponding variational formulations are then established. Since the variational problems are nonlinear with respect to the moving coordinates, second order approximate variational problems are derived after a linearization of the referential motion. Numerical results of of a large sloshing problem are presented at the conference.

1. INTRODUCTION

Free and moving boundary problems are very common not only in nature but also in industrial processes. The difficulties inherent to these problems are very challenging. From the computational point of view, one has to indentify the unknown part of the boundary and its motion and to solve the coupling between the boundary motion and the dynamics of the continua. The coupling may be very strong and a source of difficulties in case of flows which exhibit large boundary deformations. In this work, the Arbitrary Lagrangian-Eulerian (or referential) kinematic description is used in order to express the conservation laws in a moving domain. Two dimensional vertical and three dimensional natural free surface flows are very often simulated using a depth averaged procedure of the Navier-Stokes equations. In case of large free surface motion and strong vertical circulation such procedure is invalid.

An outline of the paper follows: the concept of ALE description is first presented along with momentum and continuity equations which are written in a moving domain. Next, the domain motion is defined for the case of a free surface with the height function as a parameter. A discussion of simplified models is then followed. The corresponding variational formulations are briefly discussed. The geometrical nonlinearities which are caused by the free or moving boundary are expressed analytically into the conservation equations and into the variational models. The principle of a linearization method is then presented. Some numerical simulations of flows with large free surface motions will be shown at the conference.

2. GOVERNING EQUATIONS

Mathematical formulation of conservation laws depends, among other considerations, upon the type of kinematic description of the material particles. Spatial or Eulerian decsription is very often used in fluid dynamics while the material or Lagrangian one is common in solid mechanics. When the material body contains free boundaries or is subjected to large deformation, a mixed description partially Lagrangian and partially Eulerian (also called Arbirary Lagrangian-Eulerian description) may be more appropriate for numerical computations. Indeed, Arbitrary Lagrangian-Eulerian kinematic description (or Referential) has proved to be very appropriate in the simulation of some free boundary problems encountered in both fluid (free surface flows and fluid-structure interaction prolblems) and solid (large deformation problems) mechanics. Unlike the Lagrangian and the Eulerian description, the computational domain may be animated with its proper motion in order to track the free/moving boundary positions and to maintain a reasonably regular mesh.

2.1 Arbitrary Lagrangian-Eulerian description

In the Eulerian description the classical conservation equations ca be expressed for incompressible fluids as:

$$(1) \qquad \frac{\partial \mathbf{u}}{\partial t}(\mathbf{x}, t) + (\mathbf{u}(\mathbf{x}, t) \cdot \nabla)\mathbf{u}(\mathbf{x}, t) = \mathbf{f}(\mathbf{x}, t) + \frac{1}{\hat{\rho}(\hat{\mathbf{x}}, t)} \; \text{div}_{\mathbf{x}} \underset{\approx}{\sigma}(\mathbf{x}, t)$$

and

$$(2) \qquad \nabla \cdot \mathbf{u}(\mathbf{x}, t) = 0$$

where $\hat{\rho}(\hat{\mathbf{x}}, t)$ is the density, $\mathbf{f}$ the body force and $\underset{\approx}{\sigma}$ the Cauchy stress tensor. For a Newtonian fluid, the state law relates the Cauchy stress tensor to the velocity gradient tensor by:

$$(3) \qquad \underset{\approx}{\sigma}(\mathbf{x}, t) = -p\underset{\approx}{I} + \mu(\nabla\mathbf{u} + (\nabla\mathbf{u})^t)$$

where p represents pressure and μ is the viscosity.

It is worthwhile to emphasize that equations (1-3) are written in the space domain V, i.e. $\mathbf{x}$ is the real position of a fluid particule. For free surface/moving boundary flows the space domain is unknown apriori or is continuously changing with time. From a computational point of view, if a spatial description is used one has to identify the part of the whole space which is actually occupied by the fluid (wet region) and for which equations (1-3) apply. To overcome such difficulties, we use another domain (the referential domain) Ω which is known at a specified time (say $t = 0$) and its image at time $t > 0$ under a prescribed mapping (λ) is the space domain. The referential domain represents physically the mesh over which equilibrium equations are being solved. Any point $\hat{\mathbf{x}}$ of Ω will occupy a position $\mathbf{x} = \lambda(\hat{\mathbf{x}}, t)$ at time t following the referential motion λ, with velocity:

$$\mathbf{w}(\mathbf{x}, t) = \frac{\partial\lambda}{\partial t}(\hat{\mathbf{x}}, t).$$

We will use the following convention notation: every function defined over Ω will be noted by a superscript ; for instance,
$$\mathbf{w}(\mathbf{x}, t) = \mathbf{w}(\lambda(\hat{\mathbf{x}}, t), t) = \hat{\mathbf{w}}(\hat{\mathbf{x}}, t).$$

An updated referential configuration $\lambda_t(\Omega)$ is then completely determined by the velocity field $\hat{\mathbf{w}}(\hat{\mathbf{x}}, t)$ or by the gradient deformation tensor $\underset{\approx}{\hat{F}}(\hat{\mathbf{x}}, t)$, whose components are given by:

$$\hat{F}_{ij} = \frac{\partial x_i}{\partial \hat{x}_j}.$$

In the referential kinematic description the momentum conservation equations become:

$$\hat{J}\left[\frac{\partial\hat{u}}{\partial t}(\hat{\mathbf{x}}, t) + [(\underset{\approx}{\hat{F}}^{-1}(\hat{\mathbf{u}} - \hat{\mathbf{w}})) \cdot \hat{\nabla}]\hat{u}(\hat{\mathbf{x}}, t)\right]$$

$$(4) \qquad\qquad = \hat{J}\hat{\mathbf{f}}(\mathbf{x}, t) + \frac{1}{\hat{\rho}(\hat{\mathbf{x}}, t)} \operatorname{div}_{\hat{x}} \underset{\approx}{\hat{P}}(\hat{\mathbf{x}}, t).$$

where $\text{div}_{\hat{x}}$ denotes the divergence operator with respect to $\hat{\mathbf{x}}$, $\hat{J} = \det \hat{F}$ and $\hat{P} = \hat{J}\sigma(\hat{F}^{-1})^t$ is the Piola-Kirchhoff stress tensor of the first kind. This, however, has not the same meaning as in the material description. One is also able to obtain the expression of the mass conservation equation in a referential kinematic description, which reads:

$$(5) \qquad \qquad \hat{J}\hat{\nabla}\hat{\mathbf{u}}(\hat{\mathbf{x}}, t) : \hat{F}^{-1}(\hat{\mathbf{x}}, t) = 0$$

where the left hand side stands for the double contraction of tensors $\hat{\nabla}\hat{\mathbf{u}}$ and $\hat{F}^{-1}$.

2.2 Referential motion

We consider in this section the precise definition of the mapping λ or equivalently the velocity field $\mathbf{w}(\mathbf{x}, t)$. In an Arbitrary Lagrangian-Eulerian description, the referential motion is defined in such a way as to satisfy the kinematic boundary condition at the free surface:

$$(6) \qquad \qquad (\mathbf{u} - \mathbf{w}) \cdot \mathbf{n} = 0.$$

Where $\mathbf{n}$ is the unit outward normal vector at the free surface. Equation (6) states that the free boundary moves with the normal component of the fluid velocity. Inside the domain the referential velocity is defined such that the regularity of the mesh is respected. If we consider that the free surface is completly defined by a height function $h(\mathbf{x}, t)$, the kinematic boundary conditions can then be rewritten as:

$$(7) \qquad (u_1 - w_1)\frac{\partial h}{\partial x_1} + (u_2 - w_2)\frac{\partial h}{\partial x_2} = (u_3 - w_3).$$

Since the referential motion may be arbitrarly chosen inside the computational domain, we design the referential velocity as: $\mathbf{w} = (0, 0, w_3)$ and the vertical component w_3 verifies the conditions:

$$(8) \qquad \qquad w_3(\mathbf{x}, t) = \frac{\partial h}{\partial t}$$

at the free surface and

$$(9) \qquad \qquad \Delta w_3(\mathbf{x}, t) = 0$$

inside Ω; where Δ stands for the Laplace operator. Equations (8 and 9) state the fact that the free surface is a material boundary.

2.3 Approximate models

The model presented in the last section, intends to solve the full Navier-Stokes equations, thus no apriori assumption has been used concerning the type of the flow to be simulated. In fact, it can be employed for a large variety of natural or industrial flows involving particularly large free surface deformations or complex motions. There computational solution requires however the use of efficient space and time discretization methods. Before we consider those aspects, let us discuss two approximate models which can be derived by assuming a flow where the pressure is nearly hydrostatic. Indeed, for long waves flows the vertical acceleration component may be considered as negligible compared to the gravity g, so the pressure is related to the free surface by :

$$(10) \qquad \nabla p = g \nabla h.$$

approximate model 1:

In this model only momentum equations for the horizontal components velocity are solved where relation (10) is being substituted in equation (1). The vertical component is defined from contiuity equation (3). Integrating continuity equation from the bottom, defined by a depth function H, to the free surface one obtains an other equation for h. The complete set of equations reads:

$$(11) \qquad \rho(\frac{\partial u_i}{\partial t} + u_j \frac{\partial u_i}{\partial x_j}) + g \frac{\partial h}{\partial x_i} + -\mu \Delta u_i = \rho f_i$$

for i=1 and 2;

$$(12) \qquad \frac{\partial u_1}{\partial x_1} + \frac{\partial u_2}{\partial x_2} + \frac{\partial u_3}{\partial x_3} = 0$$

and

$$(13) \qquad \frac{\partial(H+h)}{\partial t} + \frac{\partial(H+h)u_1}{\partial x_1} + \frac{\partial(H+h)u_2}{\partial x_2} = 0$$

Our original contribution in this model is to propose the use of the Arbitrary Langrangian-Eulerian concept. Thus, the computational domain follows the vertical motion of the free surface. This may be mandatory to avoid excessive mesh distortions in case of large free surface motion.

approximate model 2:

The momentum and continuity equations to be solveed are identical to those in the above approximate model but the free surface h is defined by equation (7). The new set of equations reads :

(14)
$$\rho(\frac{\partial u_i}{\partial t} + u_j\frac{\partial u_i}{\partial x_j}) + g\frac{\partial h}{\partial x_i} + -\mu\Delta u_i = \rho f_i$$

for i=1 and 2;

(15)
$$\frac{\partial u_1}{\partial x_1} + \frac{\partial u_2}{\partial x_2} + \frac{\partial u_3}{\partial x_3} = 0$$

and

(16)
$$\frac{\partial h}{\partial t} + u_1\frac{\partial h}{\partial x_1} + u_2\frac{\partial h}{\partial x_2} - u_3 = 0.$$

It turns out that the difference between the two approximate models lies in the equation which define the free surface height h. In the first model, equation (13) states that the free surface moves to allow the domain to accumulate or to release some mass balance between the outlet and the inlet boundaries. The fact that the free surface is a material boundary is implicit in the first model. In the second model however equation (16) states explicitly that the free surface is a material boundary. Furthermore, equation (13) may be retrieved by combining equations (15) and (16) . Thus, from a physical point of view the two models are equivalent. From a computational point of view however, one may appreciate many advatages in using the second model. It is indeed easier to implement and allows the use of unstructered meshs. For both models, the mesh motion is defined by equations (8) and (9)

2 Variational formulation

We look for weak solutions to the equilibrium equations formulated previously in a referential kinematic description. Let us consider a variational formulation of the full Navier-Stokes equations. A standard Galerkin formulation is obtained by multiplying equations (4,5,7 and 9) by test functions $\hat{v}(\hat{x},t)$, $\hat{q}(\hat{x},t)$, $\hat{\theta}$ and $\hat{\omega}$ respectively and by integrating by parts second order derivative terms. The weak Galerkin integral form reads:

$$(17) \qquad \mathbf{W_{GL}} = \int_\Omega \hat{\rho}\hat{J}\hat{\mathbf{v}}\frac{\partial \hat{\mathbf{u}}}{\partial t}d\hat{x} + \int_\Omega \hat{\nabla}\hat{\mathbf{v}} : \underset{\approx}{\hat{P}}^t d\hat{x}$$

$$+ \int_\Omega \hat{\rho}\hat{J}\hat{\mathbf{v}} \cdot \left[[\underset{\approx}{\hat{F}}^{-1} \cdot (\hat{\mathbf{u}} - \hat{\mathbf{w}}) \cdot \hat{\nabla}]\hat{\mathbf{u}}\right] d\hat{x}$$

$$- \int_\Gamma \hat{\mathbf{v}} \cdot (\underset{\approx}{\hat{P}} \cdot \hat{\mathbf{n}})d\gamma - \int_\Omega \hat{\rho}\hat{J}\hat{\mathbf{v}} \cdot \hat{\mathbf{f}}d\hat{x}$$

$$+ \int_\Omega \hat{q}\hat{J}(\hat{\nabla}\hat{\mathbf{u}} : \underset{\approx}{\hat{F}}^{-1})d\hat{x}$$

$$+ \int_\Omega \hat{\theta}\left(\frac{\partial h}{\partial t} + u_1\frac{\partial h}{\partial x_1} + u_2\frac{\partial h}{\partial x_2} - u_3\right)d\hat{x}$$

$$+ \int_\Omega \hat{\nabla}\hat{\omega} \cdot \nabla w_3 d\hat{x} = 0.$$

where $\underset{\approx}{\hat{P}} \cdot \hat{\mathbf{n}} = \hat{\tau}(\hat{\mathbf{x}})$ is the traction vector, and $\hat{\mathbf{n}}$ is the outward normal vector along the boundary Γ of Ω. The finite element solution verifies $\mathbf{W(t)_{GL}} = 0$ for all admissible test functions. This variational problem involves two kind of nonlinearities: convective nonliearities as in the classical Navier-Stokes problem and geometrical nonliearities due to the indetermination of the free boundary. The last geometrical nonliearities are found to be expressed in the conservation equations and in the variational problem through the deformation tensor, its inverse and its jacobien. Newton method is known to be prefered to solve such nonliearities since it converges quadratically. Thus, one has to evaluate, in particular, the first variation $\delta\mathbf{W_{GL}}$ of $\mathbf{W_{GL}}$ due to coordinates motion. Indeed, the position $\mathbf{x}$ in the space domain is related to $\hat{\mathbf{x}}$ by $\mathbf{x} = \hat{\mathbf{x}} + \delta\hat{\mathbf{x}}$, where $\delta\hat{\mathbf{x}}$ represents the coordinates displacement during period t. Hence, a first order approximation of the gradient deformation tensor in the neighborhood of identity tensor $\underset{\approx}{\hat{I}}$ becomes simply:

$$(18) \qquad \underset{\approx}{\hat{F}}(\hat{\mathbf{x}},t) = \underset{\approx}{\hat{I}}(\hat{\mathbf{x}}) + \hat{\nabla}\delta\hat{\mathbf{x}} = \underset{\approx}{\hat{I}}(\hat{\mathbf{x}}) + \underset{\approx}{\hat{\delta}\hat{F}}(\hat{\mathbf{x}},0)$$

and the first order approximations of its determinant and its inverse are expressed by:

$$(19) \qquad \hat{J}(\hat{\mathbf{x}},t) \equiv 1 + \text{div}_{\hat{x}}\ \delta\hat{\mathbf{x}} = 1 + \hat{\delta}\ \hat{J}(\hat{\mathbf{x}},0)$$

and by

$$(20) \qquad \underset{\approx}{\hat{F}}^{-1}(\hat{\mathbf{x}},s) \equiv \underset{\approx}{\hat{I}}(\hat{\mathbf{x}}) - \hat{\nabla}\delta\hat{\mathbf{x}} = \underset{\approx}{\hat{I}}(\hat{\mathbf{x}}) + \underset{\approx}{\hat{\delta}\hat{F}}^{-1}(\hat{\mathbf{x}},0).$$

Inserting approximations (18-20) into (17), we obtain the first order approximation of $\mathbf{W(t)_{GL}}$ as :

$$\mathbf{W(t)_{GL}} = \mathbf{W(0)_{GL}} + \delta\mathbf{W_{GL}}$$

where $\mathbf{W(0)_{GL}}$ is obtained from $\mathbf{W_{GL}}$ by taking $\hat{\underset{\approx}{F}} = \underset{\approx}{\hat{I}}$ and $\hat{J} = 1$. Similarly, $\delta\mathbf{W_{GL}}$ is derived from $\delta\mathbf{W_{GL}}$ by replacing $\hat{\underset{\approx}{F}}$ by $\hat{\nabla}\hat{\delta}\hat{\mathbf{x}}$ and $\hat{J}$ by $\mathrm{div}_{\hat{x}}\hat{\delta}\hat{\mathbf{x}}$.

Conclusion

A finite element formulation is presented to solve the full Navier-Stokes equations in presence of a free surface. Arbitray Langrangian-Eulerian method is very appropriate to handle moving domains. We have presented also a method to solve geometrical nonlinearities. Some examples will be shown that demonstrate the effectiveness of the model.

References

[1] J. Donéa: "Arbitrary Lagrangian-Eulerian Finite Element Methods". Computational Methods for Transient Analysis, Vol. 1, 473-516 (1983).

[2] A. Soulaïmani: " Contribution à la résolution numérique des problémes hydrodynamiques à surface libre". Thése de doctorat, Génie civil, Sciences et Génie, Université Laval, Août 1987.

[3] A. Soulaïmani, M. Fortin, G. Dhatt and Y. Ouellet: " Finite element simulation of twa- and three-dimensional free surface flows". Computer Methods in Applied Mechanics and Engineering, Vol. 86, n0.3 , 1991.

[4] T.J.R. Hughes, W.K. Liu and T.K. Zimmermann: "Lagrangian-Eulerian finite element formulation for incompressible viscous flows". U.S. Japan Seminar on Interdisciplinary Finite Element Analysis, Cornell University, Ithaca, NY, 1978.

h-adaptive boundary element schemes for free surface flow problems

A. Naji[a], D. Ouazar[a], L.C. Wrobel[b]

[a] *Université Mohammed V, Ecole Mohammadia d'Ingénieurs, LASH, Laboratoire Associé au CNCPRST, Rabat, Morroco*

[b] *Wessex Institute of Technology, University of Portsmouth, Southampton, England*

ABSTRACT

An analysis of free boundary value problems for the steady, irrotational, plane flow of an inviscid, incompressible fluid was performed using an h-adaptive boundary element method. The error estimator and indicator used in the adaptive scheme are based on computation of the residual function. Two approaches for computing predicted errors were used: Gauss quadrature [1] and Rank's scheme [2], with errors defined either in the L^2 or H^1 norms. Adjustment of the free surface has been made using iterative numerical procedures [3, 4]. Numerical results for two different cases: a sluice gate flow and a torrential flow, are presented at the end of the paper.

INTRODUCTION

The difficulty of modelling free surface problems is associated to the nonlinearity of the free surface boundary conditions, the unknown location of the free surface which has to be determined as part of the solution, and to possible singularities or discontinuities at the intersection between free surfaces and fixed ones. Boundary element methods are very well suited to the modelling of this class of problems due to their ability to confine all approximations to the boundary of the region under consideration, and the ease of mesh updating. However, as with any numerical method, the quality of the solution largely depends on the mesh used to model the free boundary, so the discretization must be refined during the iteration process to properly represent the variation of geometry and functions. Discretization of the boundary can be made either based on knowledge of the engineer or automatically, based on results from an initial mesh, with the program adjusting it until a desirable accuracy for the problem is obtained. In this paper, an h-adaptive scheme based on calculation of a residual function to define the predicted error, is applied to refine the mesh locally by subdividing existing elements. The iteration scheme is guided by an error estimator which provides information about the global accuracy of the solution, and by error indicators which verify if the solution is locally compatible, *i.e.* if the discretization is sufficient to model the variation of the solution and geometry.

ADAPTIVE PROCESS

Error analysis

Since problems considered in this paper are governed by Laplace's equation subject to appropriate boundary conditions, the application of Green's theorem gives the boundary integral equation [5]:

$$c(p)u(p) + \int_\Gamma u(s)q^*(p,s)d\Gamma(s) = \int_\Gamma u^*(p,s)q(s)d\Gamma(s) \tag{1}$$

where u^* is the fundamental solution of Laplace's equation, q^* is its normal derivative, p and s are the source and field points, and c is the curvature coefficient. Equation (1) is satisfied at all nodal (collocation) points but its application to other boundary points will produce some error or residual. This residual function can be defined by the difference between both sides of equation (1).

Theoretical studies have shown that the residual function can be taken as an approximation or estimation of the exact error. Integrating the square of the residual over the boundary defines the error estimator, and over each element defines the error indicators. These two errors provide an accurate and reliable mechanism for automatic redesign of a mesh, and have been developed by various authors [1, 2, 6] in the context of the boundary element method. They are given by the following two equations:

$$\nu^2 = \| r \|_{L^2}^2 = \int_\Gamma r^2 d\Gamma = \sum_{e=1}^{n_e} \lambda_e^2 \tag{2}$$

$$\lambda_e^2 = \int_{\Gamma_e} r^2 d\Gamma_e \tag{3}$$

where ν is the error estimator and λ_e is the error indicator in element e.

The error estimator is computed at each iteration to provide information on overall accuracy, and to stop the mesh refinement procedure if a specified tolerance is achieved. If the solution is not considered acceptable, refinement on each element will be controlled by error indicators which will decide where additional local refinement is required. The computation of the posterior error (local or global) requires evaluation of the residual along the boundary, so attention must be paid to this process since inaccuracy may lead to unnecessary refinement. An alternative form of calculating error estimators and indicators was proposed by Rank [2] using the H^1 norm:

$$\nu^2 = \| r \|_{H^1}^2 = \int_\Gamma \left[r^2 + \left(\frac{\partial r}{\partial t} \right)^2 \right] dt = \sum_{e=1}^{n_e} \lambda_e^2 \tag{4}$$

where t is the tangential direction.

Rank [2] used piecewise linear interpolation to approximate the residual within each element. Test points $\tau_i, i = 1, ..., n$ were defined as mid-points between the collocation points σ_i and σ_{i+1}. After some algebraic operations, the error indicator is given by the expression [2]:

$$\lambda_e^2 = \sum_{j=1}^{n_k} \left([r(\tau_j)]^2 \frac{l_j}{3} + [r(\tau_j)]^2 \frac{4}{l_j} \right) \tag{5}$$

where

$$l_j = | x(\sigma_{j+1}) - x(\sigma_j) |$$

with n_k the number of test points interior to element e.

Adaptive algorithm

The philosophy behind adaptive refinement is to determine an optimal mesh, based on minimization of the error for a given number of degrees of freedom. The objective is to decide where the mesh should be refined and when this refinement should be stopped based on some error criteria. The prediction of more accurate solutions, starting from any initial mesh, can thus be achieved without any effort from the design engineer.

In the h-adaptive strategy, refinement is performed by increasing the number of elements through subdivision of those displaying large local errors. Although some specified tolerance is used to verify convergence, other restrictions should be used to control the maximum number of nodes and the ratio between the size of neighbouring elements. The basic algorithm of h-adaptive schemes consists of the following steps [2]:

- Step 1 : Choose a basic mesh, sufficient to describe the geometry, boundary conditions and loads of the problem;

- Step 2 : Solve equation (1) subject to boundary conditions;

- Step 3 : Compute the error estimator and indicators;

- If sufficient global accuracy has been obtained, stop;

- Step 4 : Decide which elements need to be subdivided based on the local error indicators;

- Step 5 : Return to Step 2.

For free boundary problems, the adaptivity scheme is introduced at every iteration of the free surface adjustment procedure. So, starting with an initial mesh, the process is applied until an optimal mesh for the corresponding iteration is obtained. Once the free surface position is adjusted, the adaptivity scheme is applied again if the mesh for the previous iteration is not optimal for the new domain.

PROBLEM STATEMENT

Formulation

The two problems considered in this paper are governed by a Laplace equation for the stream function u. The corresponding boundary conditions are discussed next for each case.

Sluice gate flow

The vertical sluice gate considered in this work is depicted in figure 1. The associated boundary conditions are: $u = 0$ on the impermeable bottom; $u = Q$ on the free surfaces and the sluice gate, where Q is the flow rate per unit width. Assuming that there is no velocity normal to the main flow, the condition $\partial u/\partial n = 0$ holds on the inflow and outflow boundaries.

Bernoulli's equation is applied to determine the location of the free surfaces. Its form, however, is simplified by considering the pressure to be atmospheric:

$$\beta = \frac{q^2}{2g} + y \tag{6}$$

where $q = \partial u/\partial n$ and the constant ρg (ρ is the fluid density, g is the gravity acceleration) has been incorporated into the Bernoulli constant β.

Cheng et al. [4] have shown that the stream function and free surface velocity are sensitive to the free surface location in the subcritical and supercritical flow regions, respectively. Thus, a more efficient numerical scheme is obtained by applying different boundary conditions on the upstream and downstream free surfaces. The problem to be solved is then formulated as follows:

$$\begin{cases} \nabla^2 u = 0 & \text{in } \Omega \\ u = 0 & \text{on } EF \\ \frac{\partial u}{\partial n} = 0 & \text{on } DE, AF \\ u = Q & \text{on } AB, BC \\ \frac{\partial u}{\partial n} = \sqrt{2g(\beta - y)} & \text{on } CD \end{cases}$$

Torrential flow

A sketch of the torrential flow is presented in figure 2. The associated boundary conditions are: $u = 0$ on the impermeable bottom; $\partial u/\partial n = 0$ at the inflow and outflow boundaries, where the flow is uniform and horizontal; and $u = 1$ along the free surface, this being a nondimensional kinematic condition. The dynamic boundary condition at the free surface is again derived from Bernoulli's equation:

$$\frac{q^2}{2g} + y = \frac{q_0^2}{2g} + h \tag{7}$$

with q_0 the onset velocity magnitude and h the constant height away from the obstacle. The corresponding nondimensional expression, taking q_0 and h as reference values, is

$$q^{*2} \frac{Fr^2}{2} + y^* = \frac{Fr^2}{2} + 1 \tag{8}$$

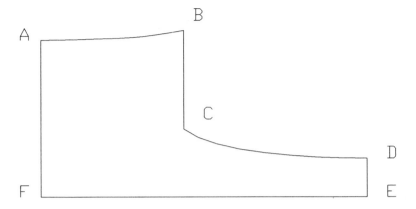

Figure 1: Definition of sluice gate flow

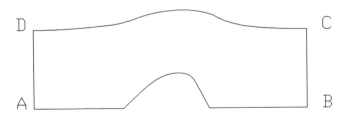

Figure 2: Definition of torrential flow

where $Fr^2 = q_0^2/gh$ is a Froude number.

The resulting problem in nondimensional form is given by (dropping the asterisks for simplicity):

$$\begin{cases} \nabla^2 u = 0 & \text{in } \Omega \\ u = 0 & \text{on } AB \\ \frac{\partial u}{\partial n} = 0 & \text{on } BC \text{ and } DA \\ u = 1 & \text{on } CD \\ \frac{\partial u}{\partial n} = \sqrt{1 + \frac{2(1-y)}{Fr^2}} & \text{on } CD \end{cases}$$

Solution Schemes

Torrential flow

The dynamic approach used by Bouhafed [3] is considered in the solution of the torrential problem. Using this approach, the problem is solved without the kinematic condition which is verified after the solution. If the kinematic condition is not satisfied the free surface is moved to a new position $y + \Delta y$ given by the equation:

$$\Delta y = \frac{1 - u}{\frac{\partial u}{\partial n}} \tag{9}$$

assuming that the stream function is extrapolated linearly along the vertical axis. The algorithm can be summarized as follows:

- Step 1: An initial free surface position is assumed;

- Step 2: The boundary is discretized and the stream function obtained through solution of the boundary value problem with the dynamic condition imposed on the free surface;

- Step 3: If the kinematic boundary condition is not satisfied the free surface nodes are moved in accordance with equation (9) and the process returns to Step 2.

Sluice gate flow

The iterative process to solve this problem is the same used by Cheng *et al.* [4]. Assume that the flux on the free surfaces is approximated by the equation

$$\frac{\partial u}{\partial n} = \frac{Q}{y}$$

Substituting into Bernoulli's equation we have :

$$\beta = \frac{Q^2}{2gy^2} + y$$

Differentiating this equation :

$$\frac{d\beta}{dy} = -\frac{Q^2}{gy^3} + 1$$

Approximating the derivative in the above equation by $\Delta\beta/\Delta y$ and rewriting:

$$\Delta y = \frac{\Delta\beta}{1 - \frac{Q^2}{gy^3}} \tag{10}$$

This equation is used if the flow rate Q is given. The term Q^2/gy^3 is a Froude number which is less than unity upstream of the gate and greater than unity on the downstream side. In case the Bernoulli constant is given, the free surface is adjusted using the equation :

$$\Delta y = -\frac{u\Delta Q}{gy^2} \frac{1}{\left(1 - \frac{u^2}{gy^3}\right)} \tag{11}$$

Alternatively, a more conservative and stable scheme can be used [4]:

$$\Delta y = \Delta Q \frac{y}{u} \tag{12}$$

The numerical procedure adopted can be summarized by the following steps:

- Step 1 : Assume the location of the two free surfaces;

- Step 2 : Solve the problem applying the kinematic condition upstream of the gate and the dynamic condition downstream;

- Step 3 : If the convergence criterium is not satisfied compute the increment Δy by equation (10) for upstream of the gate and (11) or (12) for the downstream surface, and return to Step 2.

NUMERICAL RESULTS

Torrential flow

Figure 3 shows the initial, coarse discretization for the flow with $Fr = 4$ over a symmetric obstacle defined by the equation

$$y = 0.2\left[1 - \cos\frac{2\pi(x - 4)}{3}\right]$$

together with the optimal discretizations at the end of the first iteration, before the free surface is relocated, obtained with the Gauss' and Rank's error indicators. The h-adaptive scheme has refined the free surface discretization over the obstacle where sharper variations are expected, in the region of strong curvature in the obstacle itself, and around the intersection points between the obstacle and the impermeable bottom where the flow changes direction. It can be observed that no refinement was necessary at the inflow and outflow boundaries where the velocity is constant and both the stream function and geometry are linear; thus, one element is sufficient to describe this behaviour.

Once the free surface position is moved, the adaptivity scheme is again applied in the new iteration. However, in the present and following cases, the free surface

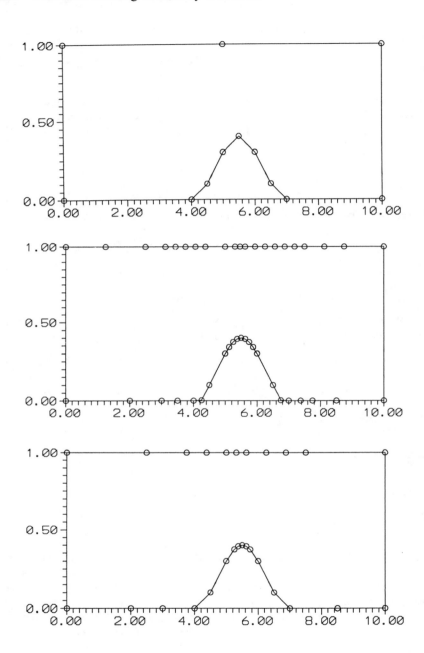

Figure 3: Initial and final discretizations for flow over symmetric obstacle: a)Initial; b)Final with Gauss' scheme; c)Final with Rank's scheme

moves in a smooth way, and the discretization of figure 3b or 3c are still optimal throughout the whole iteration process.

A similar behaviour has been observed for the flow with $Fr = 2$ over a non-symmetric obstacle defined by the equation

$$y = \frac{27}{160}(x - 4)(x - 6)^2$$

as shown in figures 4a-c. As in the previous case, Rank's indicator gave rise to a coarser discretization than the Gauss' one.

The converged free surface location is shown in figures 5 and 6 for both cases above. It can be seen that the results obtained with the different error indicators are very similar. They also agree very well with the results presented in reference [3].

Sluice gate

A vertical sluice gate previously studied by Cheng *et al.* [4] is presented herein. The initial geometry of the problem is defined by its six corners points (see figure 1), the total head β is equal to one and the gate opening is $b = 0.3$. The initial position of the upstream free surface is taken to be flat at $y = 1$, and for the downstream one a straight line is defined by the two points $(0, 0.3)$ and $(2, 0.15)$. Although only six elements have been used in the initial mesh, a greater refinement near the singular point C (figure 1) has been achieved during the adaptive process. The location of the two free surfaces is presented in figures 7 and 8. These results agree very well with those of Cheng *et al.* [4].

CONCLUDING REMARKS

The results of test problems show that the h-adaptive scheme achieves accurate solutions for free surface problems, both for the stream function variation and the free surface position. Refinement is concentrated near corner points to account for singularities, and also on some parts of the free surface where its geometry is expected to change rapidly.

The test problems also demonstrated that, in case of smoothly-varying free surfaces, the h-adaptive scheme needs only be used in the first iteration of the surface adjustment process since no refinement was necessary in other iterations.

Comparing the performance of the two methods implemented, the Gauss' scheme requires numerical integration leading therefore to higher computation costs. Rank's scheme, on the other hand, is very sensitive to the choice of the error estimator and indicator tolerance.

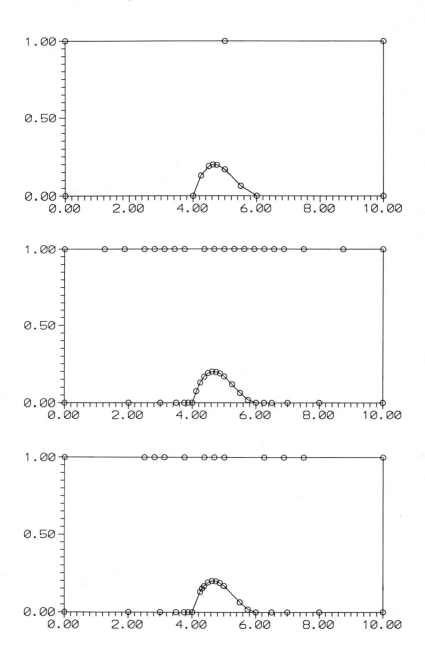

Figure 4: Initial and final discretizations for flow over non-symmetric obstacle: a)Initial; b)Final with Gauss' scheme; c)Final with Rank's scheme

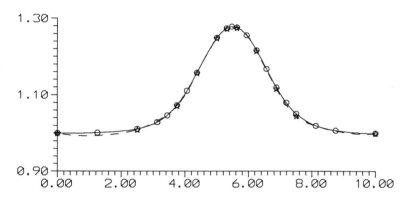

Figure 5: Converged free surface location for flow over symmetric obstacle

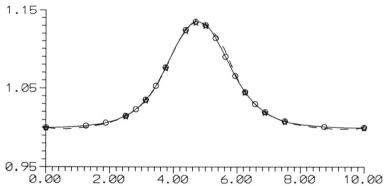

Figure 6: Converged free surface location for flow over non-symmetric obstacle

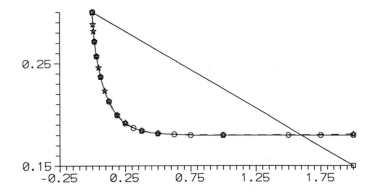

Figure 7: Downstream free surface location for sluice gate flow

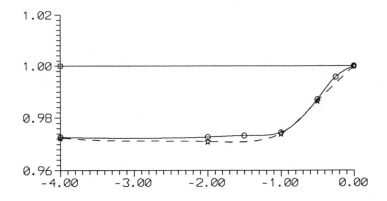

Figure 8: Upstream free surface location for sluice gate flow

References

[1] Parreira, P., Further development on error indicators and estimators for adaptive hierarchical boundary elements, in *Advances in Boundary Elements, Vol. 1: Computations and Fundamentals*, Computational Mechanics Publications, Southampton and Springer-Verlag, Berlin, 1989.

[2] Rank, E., Adaptive $h-,p-$ and $hp-$versions for boundary integral element methods, *International Journal for Numerical Methods in Engineering*, Vol. 28, pp 1335-1349, 1989.

[3] Bouhafed, M., Contribution a L'etude des Ondes de Surface dans un Canal. Application a L'ecoulement au dessus d'un Obstacle Immerge. PhD Thesis, Universite de Poitiers, 1988.

[4] Cheng, A.H-D., Liggett, J.A. and Liu, P.L-F., Boundary calculation of sluice gates and spillway flows, *J. Hydraulics Division, ASCE*, Vol. 107, pp. 1163-1178, 1981.

[5] Brebbia, C.A., Telles, J.C.F. and Wrobel, L.C., *Boundary Element Techniques*, Springer-Verlag, Berlin, 1984.

[6] Rencis, J. and Mullen, R.L., A self-adaptive mesh refinement technique for the boundary element solution of the Laplace equation, *Computational Mechanics*, Vol. 3, pp 309-319, 1988.

SECTION 6: SEDIMENT TRANSPORT

Invited Paper
Numerical simulation of coastal changes

K. Mizumura[a], T. Nishimoto[b], H. Tsutsui[b]

[a] *Dept. of Civil Engineering, Kanazawa Institute of Technology, 7-1, Ogigaoka, Nonoichimachi, Ishikawa Pref 921, Japan*
[b] *Magara Kensetsu Co., Ltd., 1-13-43, Hikoso, Kanazawa, Ishikawa Pref. 920, Japan*

Abstract

Two-dimensional changes of beach profile are computed by the continuity equation of sediment. Wave transformation used in the continuity equation is obtained by solving the shallow water equations numerically. The application of this method for different wave height, period, and sand particle diameters shows that this approach is reasonable.

Introduction

In Japan, most of the beautiful sand beaches which represent typical Japanese scenary were lost because of the failure of river sediment control. Therefore, keeping remaining sand beaches is the most important work for coastal engineers. Coastal changes are usually predicted by hydraulic model tests or numerical computation. Recently the principle tool for the prediction of coastal changes becomes the numerical computation because of its cost and easiness. As the first step of this research, the coastal changes are computed when on-offshore sand transport is dominated. In this case longshore movement of sand transport is neglected. This computation consists of two parts. One is the computation of wave transformation by using shallow wave equations. This computation gives the correct wave run up and back wash process. The other is the computation of water depth change due to sand movement. This study investigates the method of computation of the beach profile change due to on-offshore drift of sand.

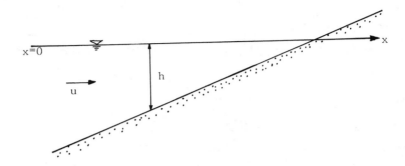

Figure 1: Coordinate System

Governing Equations

To compute beach profile change, wave transformation must be known. This is described by the following shallow water equations:

$$\frac{\partial u}{\partial t} + u\frac{\partial u}{\partial x} + g\frac{\partial h}{\partial x} = g(S_o - S_f) \tag{1}$$

$$\frac{\partial h}{\partial t} + \frac{\partial hu}{\partial x} = 0 \tag{2}$$

in which $u=$ depth averaged velocity; $h=$ water depth; $g=$ the gravitational acceleration; $t=$ time; $x=$ coordinate system(see Fig.1); $S_o =$ sea bottom slope; and $S_f =$ friction slope. To solve Eqs.(1) and (2) numerically, Lax and Wendroff numerical scheme[2] is used. Eqs.(1) and (2) are transformed into the following equation[1]:

$$U_{j,n+1} - \lambda\{\frac{1}{2}[F_{j+1,n} - F_{j-1,n}] + \Delta x G_{j,n}\} + \frac{\lambda^2}{2}\{g_{j,n} - g_{j-1,n} - \Delta x S_{j,n}\} \tag{3}$$

in which

$$U = \begin{bmatrix} m \\ h \end{bmatrix}, \quad m = uh, \quad \lambda = \frac{\Delta t}{\Delta x},$$

$$g_{j,n} = \frac{1}{2}[A(U_{j+1,n}) + A(U_{j,n})][F_{j+1,n} - F_{j,n} + \frac{\Delta x}{2}(G_{j+1,n} + G_{j,n})],$$

$$A = \frac{\partial F}{\partial U} = \begin{bmatrix} 2m/h & gh - m^2/h^2 \\ 1 & 0 \end{bmatrix},$$

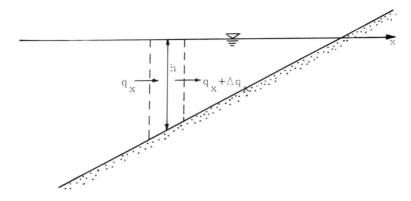

Figure 2: Derivation of Sand Continuity Equation

$$F = \begin{bmatrix} m^2/h + gh^2/2 \\ m \end{bmatrix}, G = \begin{bmatrix} -gh(S_o - S_f) \\ 0 \end{bmatrix},$$

$$S_{j,n} = \Delta x \frac{\partial G_{j,n}}{\partial t} = \Delta x \begin{bmatrix} -g(S_o - S_f)\frac{\partial h}{\partial t} + gh\{\frac{\partial S_f}{\partial h}\frac{\partial h}{\partial t} + \frac{\partial S_f}{\partial u}\frac{\partial u}{\partial t}\} \\ 0 \end{bmatrix}_{j,n}$$

The computation of the run-up and back-wash are done according to Hibberd and Peregrine[1]. The continuity equation of sediment(see Fig.2) is given by

$$\frac{\partial h}{\partial t} = \frac{\partial q_x}{\partial x} + \epsilon \frac{\partial}{\partial x}\{|q_x|\frac{\partial h}{\partial x}\} \tag{4}$$

The empirical expression of sediment transport is given by[3]

$$q_x = \frac{B_w w_o \sqrt{f}}{(1-\lambda)s\sqrt{sgd}}\frac{U_*^2 - U_{*c}^2}{g}u \tag{5}$$

in which λ = void ratio; q_x= rate of sediment transport; ϵ= constant parameter to include the effect of beach profile change; $s=\rho_s/\rho - 1$; ρ= water density; ρ_s= sand density; d= mean diameter of sand particle; $f= g\bar{n}^2/h^{1/3}$; $\bar{n}$= Manning's roughness coefficient; $B_w = 7.0$ (constant); $U_* = \sqrt{f}u$; $U_{*c}= \sqrt{\psi_c(\rho_s - \rho)gd}$; ψ_c= the critical Shields number; and w_o = the falling velocity of sand particle. The value of q_x is zero if U_* is less than U_{*c}. When the incident waves come from the offshore, sand particles in the deeper region than h_i do not move. But if the water depth becomes shallower than h_i, sand particles move as the wave passes. The limiting water depth h_i is expressed by[4]

$$\frac{H}{L} = 2.4(\frac{d}{L})^{1/3}\sinh\frac{2\pi h_i}{L}$$

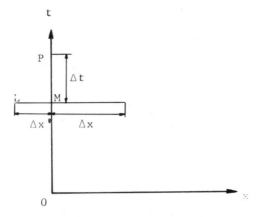

Figure 3: Coordinate System at Offshore Boundary

in which L= wave length. The continuity equation of sand is applied in the shallower water-depth region than h_i.

Boundary and Initial Conditions

The boundary conditions with respect to wave motion are located at the up-wave side (offshore boundary) and the down-wave side (onshore boundary). At the up-wave side the incident wave is given by

$$\zeta = \frac{H}{2} \sin \omega t \tag{6}$$

in which H= wave height and ω=wave frequency. The reflected wave from beach is transmitted through this offshore boundary. Due to Hino's open boundary condition assuming the velocity is zero,

$$\frac{h'_p - h_M}{\Delta t} + \frac{u_M h_M}{\Delta x'} = 0 \tag{7}$$

The value of $\Delta x'$ is almost equal to $\sqrt{gh_o}$(see Fig.3). The water depth on the offshore boundary is given by

$$h_p = \frac{h'_p - h_o}{2} + \zeta \tag{8}$$

in which h_o= the stationary water depth on the offshore boundary and $\Delta x'$ = $\Delta t \sqrt{gh_o}$. The value of 2 of the denominator on the right hand side of Eq.(8) means that the reflected wave height by a vertical wall is twice that on the open boundary. The water depth is stationary and velocity is zero at the initial time. The initial condition for sediment transport is given by the initial water depth. The boundary conditions for sediment transport at the up-wave and down-wave sides are given by

$$q_x = 0 \tag{9}$$

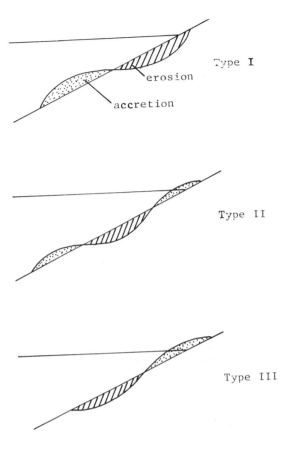

Figure 4: Classification of Beach Profile Changes

Beach Profile Changes

The two-dimensional changes of beach profile which start from the uniform slope and are caused by on-offshore sediment transport are classified into the following three types[4]: Type I is characterized by sediment transport from onshore to offshore. The direction of the sediment transport of Type III is opposite to Type I. For Type II sediment moves to the onshore and offshore. Their sketches are give in Fig.4. Considering the direction of sediment transport, Type I and III correspond to the bar and step type of beach profile. The empirical equation to classify these three types are given by

$$\frac{H/L}{(d/L)^{0.67}/(\tan \beta)^{0.27}} = C \tag{10}$$

in which $H=$ wave height; $L=$ wave length; $d=$ sand particle diameter; and $\tan \beta =$ initial slope of sea bottom. The constant value C is a parameter to discriminate these types of beach profile. For hydraulic model beach, the value is suggested as follows:

$$\begin{array}{lll} C \geq 8 & \text{Type I} & \\ 8 \geq C \geq 4 & \text{Type II} & (11) \\ C \leq 4 & \text{Type III} & \end{array}$$

For the prototype beach, the value is recommended by

$$\begin{array}{lll} C \geq 18 & \text{Type I} & \\ 18 \geq C \geq 9 & \text{Type II} & (12) \\ C \leq 9 & \text{Type III} & \end{array}$$

Considering momentum equation on a sand particle, the theoretical derivation of this kind of the equation is given by Hayasaka and Mizumura[5]. Herein, we apply the numerical result to Eq.(10) and check whether the numerical result is appropriate or not.

Numerical Result

By solving Eqs.(3) and (4) numerically, time-varying beach profiles are computed. The result is plotted in Fig.5. The pattern of this beach profile change corresponds to Type I. That is, sand in the onshore moves to the offshore. Fig.6 compares the numerical result with Eqs.(11) and (12). This result shows that this numerical computation estimates the experimental result very well.

Concluding Remarks

The wave transformation is expressed by the shallow water equations and wave run-up and back-wash are also strictly investigated. Beach profile change is computed by using the continuity equation of sediment. Sediment transport formula is described by the experimental equation. As a result, two-dimensional coastal change is numerically modelled. The determination of several parameters is not fixed, but this model predicts beach profile changes very well.

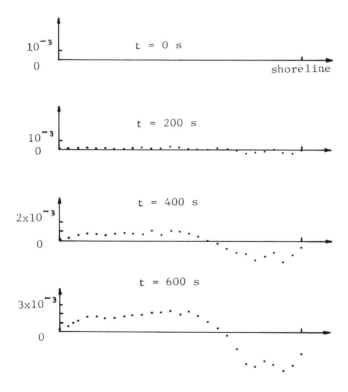

Figure 5: Numerical Beach Profile Changes

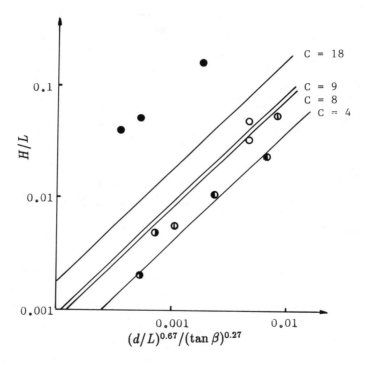

Figure 6: Classification of Beach profile Changes

References

[1] Hibberd, S. and Peregrine, D. H. Surf and run-up on a beach: a uniform bore. *Journal of Fluid Mechanics*, Vol.95, part 2, 1979, pp.323-345.

[2] Lax, P. and Wendroff, B. Systems of conservation laws. *Comm. Pure Appl. Math.*, 13, 1960, pp.217-237.

[3] Ifuku, M., Kanazawa, T., and Yumiyama, Y. Computation of Two-dimensional Wave Transformation and Coastal Changes by Method of Characteristics. *Japanese Conf. on Coastal Eng.*, Vol.38, 1991, pp.376-380 (in Japanese).

[4] Mizumura, K. *Coastal and Ocean Engineering*, Kyouritsu Shuppan Co., Ltd., Tokyo, 1992 (in Japanese).

[5] Hayasaka, M. and Mizumura, K. Theoretical Considerations on Two-dimensional Coastal Changes. *Proc. 34th Annual Conf. of JSCE*, Vol.2, 1979, pp.669-670 (in Japanese).

Numerical simulation of sand terrace formation in front of a river mouth

H. Tanaka, Q. Huimin

Water Resources Engineering Division, Asian Institute of Technology, G.P.O. Box 2754, Bangkok 10501, Thailand

ABSTRACT

The process of the formation of a sand terrace in front of a river mouth is simulated numerically by means of a finite difference method. A leap-frog explicit scheme is applied to predict two moving boundaries: a free surface and a bed surface. Comparisons of the sand terrace profile are made between experimental measurements and calculated results. It is concluded that the present numerical model is remarkably successful in predicting sand terrace formation.

INTRODUCTION

At a river mouth, sand spit is often formed and sometimes intrudes into the mouth due to predominant wave action. During a large flood, the sand spit will be flushed to form a sand terrace in front of the river mouth.

Some research work has been done on the formation of a sand terrace and this includes field measurements, laboratory experiments and numerical simulations. Sawamoto and Shuto [1] and Sasaki, Uda and Tone [2] made field observations immediately after a big flood at the Abukuma River mouth in Japan. However, with regard to the process of a sand terrace formation during a flood, the field observation is almost impossible due to the large flood discharge. Therefore, in order to understand this phenomenon, experimental or numerical investigations have been carried out so far. Butakov [3] carried out experiments to study not only the formation of a sand terrace but also the subsequent deformation due to wave motion. Deguchi and Sawaragi [4] performed laboratory experiments to investigate the effects of structure on deposition of discharged sediment around a river mouth. Deguchi and Sawaragi [4] made a numerical study to reproduce flow field and morphological change by using a finite difference method, while Hatanaka and Kawahara [5] adopted a finite element method. Tanaka and Suga [6] performed a series of experiments, and proposed a simple method for predicting a sand terrace profile.

In the present paper, a numerical method is proposed for computing time-variation of topography at a river mouth during a flood. In particular, the effects of the bottom slope and that of the lateral mixing on the sand deposition pattern are examined.

MATHEMATICAL MODEL

The present model consists of two parts: the hydrodynamic model and the morphological model. The hydrodynamic equations for this model are the equation of continuity and the equation of motion, both of which are integrated over the flow depth expressed as follows:

$$\frac{\partial \eta}{\partial t}+\frac{\partial M}{\partial x}+\frac{\partial N}{\partial y}=0 \tag{1}$$

$$\frac{\partial M}{\partial t}+\frac{\partial}{\partial x}(\frac{M^2}{D})+\frac{\partial}{\partial y}(\frac{MN}{D})+gD\frac{\partial \eta}{\partial x}+\frac{gn^2}{D^{7/3}}M\sqrt{M^2+N^2}+A_h[\frac{\partial^2 M}{\partial x^2}+\frac{\partial^2 M}{\partial y^2}]=0 \tag{2}$$

$$\frac{\partial N}{\partial t}+\frac{\partial}{\partial x}(\frac{MN}{D})+\frac{\partial}{\partial y}(\frac{N^2}{D})+gD\frac{\partial \eta}{\partial y}+\frac{gn^2}{D^{7/3}}N\sqrt{M^2+N^2}+A_h[\frac{\partial^2 N}{\partial x^2}+\frac{\partial^2 N}{\partial y^2}]=0 \tag{3}$$

where η is the water level about the still water, t the time, x and y the horizontal coordinates, M and N the flow flux per unit width in x- and y-direction, respectively, g the gravitational acceleration, D the total water depth ($D=h+\eta$, h: still water depth), n the Manning's friction coefficient, and A_h the lateral mixing coefficient.

The governing equation for the morphological model is the conservation equation of sediment mass which can be written as:

$$\frac{\partial z}{\partial t}+\frac{1}{(1-\lambda)}(\frac{\partial q_x}{\partial x}+\frac{\partial q_y}{\partial y})=0 \tag{4}$$

where z is the elevation of the bottom surface from the reference level, λ the porosity of sediment, and q_x and q_y the sediment transport rate per unit width per unit time in x- and y-direction, respectively. The bedload formula proposed by Meyer-Peter and Muller [7] is extended to the two-dimensional motion to evaluate the components of sediment transport rate on a horizontal bottom, (q_x', q_y').

$$q_x'=8\sqrt{sgd^3}\,(\tau^*-\tau^*_{cr})\frac{M}{\sqrt{M^2+N^2}}, \quad q_y'=8\sqrt{sgd^3}\,(\tau^*-\tau^*_{cr})\frac{N}{\sqrt{M^2+N^2}} \tag{5}$$

where τ^* is the Shields parameter defined in terms of the bottom shear stress, τ_0, as:

$$\tau^*=\frac{\tau_0/\rho}{sgd}=\frac{n^2(M^2+N^2)}{sdD^{7/3}} \tag{6}$$

τ^*_{cr} the critical Shields parameter for an initial motion of sand grain, s the immersed specific weight, and d the mean diameter of sediment. In Equation (5), the effect of bottom slope is not taken into account. In reality, if the local slope becomes steep, sediment grains tend to move downward owing to the gravity. This effect may vary depending not only on the local slope but also on the degree of sediment transport calculated by neglecting the slope. In order to incorporate this effect, Equation (7) is used instead of Equation (5) to calculate the change of bottom elevation (Watanabe [8]).

$$q_x=q_x'-\varepsilon_s\,|q_x'|\frac{\partial z}{\partial x}, \quad q_y=q_y'-\varepsilon_s\,|q_y'|\frac{\partial z}{\partial y} \tag{7}$$

where ε_s is a positive constant, which will be empirically determined later.

NUMERICAL COMPUTATION

The computation method in the hydrodynamic model is based on that of Goto and Ogawa [9] proposed for the numerical simulation of tsunami, although the lateral friction terms were eliminated in their calculation. A leap-frog finite difference scheme with a uniform grid spacing was used to formulate the differential equations as seen in Figure 1. To improve the numerical stability, the non-linear convection terms were expressed in terms of the upwind difference method. In the morphological model, a staggered mesh scheme was employed as shown in Figure 2. The hydrodynamic model and the morphological model were coupled to compute the water level, the velocity field, and subsequent bottom deformation, consecutively. The grid spacing and the time increment employed in the present computation were $\Delta x=\Delta y=10$cm and $\Delta t=0.05$sec, respectively.

EXPERIMENTAL DATA

Laboratory data of Tanaka and Suga [6] are compared with the simulated results. They used a laboratory basin as shown in Figure 3. The sea bed consisted of two parts: the wooden beach with a slope of 1/10 and the offshore part with a horizontal bottom made of concrete. The river channel of 30cm wide was made at the middle of the model beach. In the course of the

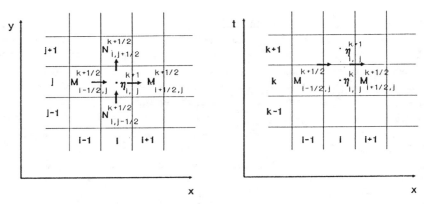

Fig.1 Leap-frog scheme in hydrodynamic model

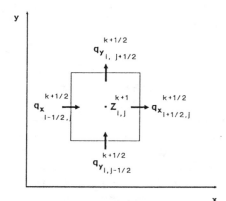

Fig.2 Staggered scheme in morphological model

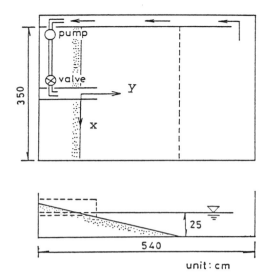

Fig.3 Laboratory basin used by Tanaka and Suga [6]

experiments, the discharge rate of the flow as well as the
sediment supply rate from the river mouth was kept constant, and
the topography change at the river mouth was measured several
times by means of a bed surface profiler. Sand with a uniform
diameter of 0.2mm was used in the laboratory experiment. Eleven
series of experiments were carried out, and Case H is selected
for the use of the comparison. The experimental conditions are
as follows: the jetty length of 15cm, the flow discharge of
2.3l/sec, and the sediment discharge 3.3l/min.

RESULTS AND DISCUSSIONS

At first, two unknown parameters, ε_s and A_h in Eqs.(2), (3) and
(7), are calibrated. It is found that the effect of ε_s is
predominant on the steep slope of the sand terrace edge; the
predicted slope becomes milder with the increase of ε_s. The
computation based on $\varepsilon_s=10$ is the most appropriate to reproduce
the measured sand slope, as recommended by Watanabe [8]. Figure
4 shows the calculated result, in which lateral friction
coefficient is assumed as $A_h=0.6Du_*$ following Fischer [10]. A
distinctly smaller value, $\varepsilon_s=2$ reported by Watanabe and Dibajnia
[11], is also applied, though the propagation of the sand
terrace stopped at t≃8min.

9

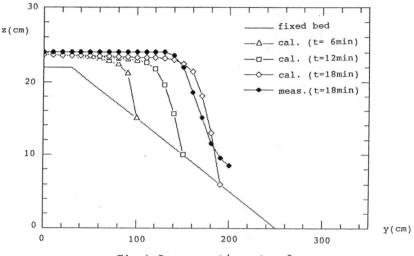

Fig.4 Cross-section at x=0m.

Regarding the coefficient of the lateral mixing, the expression derived by Fischer [10], $A_h=0.6Du_*$, as well as more simplified values, $A_h=0.001m^2/sec$ and $0.002m^2/sec$, are employed. Among these three, the first expression is found to give good results. Using other values, the width of the sand terrace is overestimated due to too large diffusivity of momentum in the lateral direction.

Figure 5 describes the sand terrace propagation in the downstream direction. The computed sand terrace profile along the centerline of the river channel is quite similar to the result obtained from the experiment except for the tail part. This must be due to the fact that, in the experiment, some part of the sediment were brought into suspension by the flow, flushed downwards and depositted on the tail part. Such a process cannot be simulated since only the bedload sediment transport is considered in the present numerical model.

CONCLUSIONS

A mathematical model is proposed for simulating a sand terrace formation in front of a river mouth during a flood. The effect of bed slope on the sediment transport capacity can be corrected by adjusting the sediment transport rate associated with the local bed slope. The horizontal mixing term is also an important

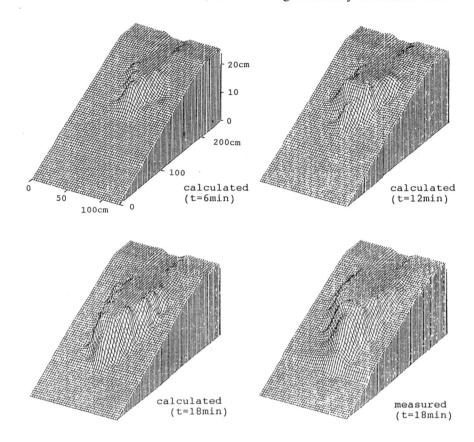

20cm

10

0

200cm

100

0

50

100cm   0

calculated
(t=6min)

calculated
(t=12min)

calculated
(t=18min)

measured
(t=18min)

Fig.5 Sand terrace profile.

factor affecting the flow field and the resulting sediment deposition pattern. Adopting a functional form developed by Fischer in the hydrodynamic model, the process of sand deposition at a river mouth can be well simulated.

REFERENCES

1. Sawamoto, M. and Shuto, N. 'Topography Change Due to Floods and Recovery Process at the Abukuma River Mouth' *Coastal Engineering in Japan*, Vol.30, No.2, pp.99-117, 1988.
2. Sasaki, T., Uda, T. and Tone, K. 'Field Investigation of Disintegration Process of A River Mouth Bar due to Flood Flow at Abukuma River' *Coastal Engineering in Japan*, Vol.32, No.2, pp.135-137, 1989.

3. Butakov, A.N. 'Study of Development and Deformation of Mouth Bar', *Proceedings of 14th Congress on IAHR*, pp.95-102, Paris, 1971. IAHR, Delft, 1971.

4. Deguchi, I. and Sawaragi, T. 'Effects of Structure of Discharged Sediment Around River Mouth', pp. 1573-1587, *Proceedings of the 21st Int. Conf. on Coastal Engg.*, Taiwan, Taipei, 1988. ASCE, New York, 1988.

5. Hatanaka, H. and Kawahara, M. 'A Finite Element Application of Sand Terrace Formation Process, *Proceedings of Int. Symp. on Sediment Transport Modeling*, pp.326-331, New Orleans, USA, 1989. ASCE, New York, 1989.

6. Tanaka, H. and Suga, K. 'Sand Terrace Formation in Front of a Small River Mouth due to Flush Flood', *Proceedings of International Conference on Hydroscience and Engineering*, Washington, U.S.A., 1993. The University of Mississippi, Jackson, 1993. (in press)

7. Meyer-Peter, E. and Muller, R. 'Formulas for Bed-Load Transport', *Proc. 2nd IAHR Meeting*, pp.39-64, Stockholm, Sweden, 1948. IAHR, Delft, 1948.

8. Watanabe, A., Maruyama, K., Shimizu, T. and Sakakiyama, T. 'Numerical Prediction Model of Three-Dimensional Beach Deformation Around A Structure', *Coastal Engineering in Japan*, Vol.29, pp.179-194, 1986.

9. Goto, C. and Ogawa, Y. 'Numerical Method of Tsunami Simulation with the Leap-Frog Scheme', *Technical Report, Department of Civil Engneering, Tohoku University*, 28pp., 1982.

10. Fischer, H. B. 'Longitudinal Dispersion and Turbulent Mixing in Open Channel Flow', pp.59-78, *Annual Review of Fluid Mechanics*, Vol. 5, 1973.

11. Watanabe, A. and Dibajnia, 'Numerical Modelling of Nearshore Waves, Cross-Shore Sediment Trnasport and Beach Profile Change', *Proceedings of Symposium on Mathematical Modelling of Sediment Transport in The Coastal Zone*, Copenhagen, Denmark, 1988. IAHR, Delft, 1988.

SECTION 7: COMPUTATIONAL HYDRAULICS

Computational hydraulics in the analysis and design of supercritical flow in curved canals connected with stilling basins, in order to make the hydraulic jump stable

J.F. Fernández-Bono, J.O. Zenteno

Department of Hydraulic and Environmental Engineering, Polytechnical University of Valencia, Spain

ABSTRACT

The aim of this research is to provide the hydraulic engineer with a dual-purpose tool capable of analysing the hydraulic behaviour of supercritical flows in curved canals and, where necessary, determining the operating instabilities of downstream stilling basins and, establishing appropiate design modifications interactively with the modelling system developer, to stabilise the hydraulic jump in the stilling basins over the whole range of operating discharges.

INTRODUCTION

In many hydraulic projects is necessary to make the canal route suitable to geological and topographical factors, which involves the building of steep-sloped and plan-curved canal reaches, bringing about supercritical flows.

The dissipation of excess energy developed by these supercritical flows is achieved by the use of stilling basins, whose design is normally dictated by the USBR design rules which arose from scale-modelling (Peterka[1]). However, these rules relate only to flows where depth and Froude number are constant across the entry cross-section and therefore are inappropiate where surface water gradient exists.

In this case, local but increasingly unstable oblique hydraulic jumps can occur, which generally result in a whole sweep of the hydraulic jump, supercritical flow extension downstream and serious hydraulic and structural problems.

This report sets out a new mathematical model, designed to overcome the above-mentioned problem of flow behaviour and hydraulic design of curved canals.

A fundamentally practicable model has been achieved using numericals tools and design standards familiar to experts in this field which, nonetheless, is a very adecuate solution from the technical point of view.

The novel aspect of this study lies in the flow analysis and in the interactive design routine of the curved canal and it is for this reason that the routines relating to hydraulic behaviour in the stilling basin and downstream channel are only mentioned, these routines being ruled by an hydraulic behaviour and design model.

ANALYSIS OF SUPERCRITICAL FLOW IN CURVED CANALS

An permanent two–dimensional supercritical flow was simulated using Navier–Stokes equations with cylindrical curvilinear coordinates, discretized by an explicit finite differences scheme, whilst the outline conditions stem from classical theoretical expressions whose coefficients were checked (and calibrated where required) using measurements made on scale–models.

Equations governing supercritical flow
Starting from the Navier–Stokes differential equations, in their non–conservative form, which for a circular, curvilinear canal with steep bed slopes both in longitudinal and transversal directions and permanent turbulent two–dimensional flow of incompressible fluid, we arrive, in accord with fig. 1,

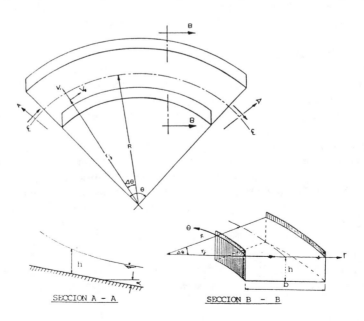

Figure 1. Cylindrical curvilinear coordinates. A general view.

Continuity equation:

$$\frac{\partial h}{\partial \theta} = -\frac{1}{v_\theta}[h\frac{\partial v_\theta}{\partial \theta} + hr\frac{\partial v_r}{\partial r} + rv_r\frac{\partial h}{\partial r} + hv_r] \qquad (1)$$

Momentum equations:

$$\frac{\partial v_r}{\partial \theta} = v_\theta - \frac{1}{v_\theta}[r\ v_r\frac{\partial v_r}{\partial r} + r\ g\ \cos\alpha\ \cos\beta\ \frac{\partial h}{\partial r} +$$

$$+ r\ v_r\ \frac{g\ v\ n^2}{h4/3}\ \sin\alpha\ \cos\beta + g\ r\ \sin\beta] \qquad (2)$$

$$\frac{\partial v_\theta}{\partial \theta} = \frac{1}{v_\theta^2\ g\ h\ \cos\alpha\ \cos\beta}[\ g\ \cos\alpha\ \cos\beta\left(r\ h\ \frac{\partial v_r}{\partial r} + r\ v_r\ \frac{\partial h}{\partial r} +\right.$$

$$+ h\ v_r - \frac{v\ v_\theta\ n^2}{h4/3} + r\ v_\theta\left(g\ \sin\alpha - v_r\ \frac{\partial v\theta}{\partial r}\right) - v_r\ v_\theta^2] \qquad (3)$$

where θ is the circular angle, r is the radius of the curve, v_θ is the tangential flow velocity, v_r is the radial flow velocity, V is the resultant velocity, p is the hydrostatic pressure, ρ is the water density, g is the gravity acceleration, α is the longitudinal slope angle, β is the transverse slope angle, n is the Manning coefficient.

The above equations may be numerically discretizated using various numerical methods. In this case Lax's explicit finite difference scheme has been chosen; a one–step first order scheme accurate in treatement and solution of partially hyperbolic differential equations which is easy to apply. Lax's discretization is applied to equations (1)–(3) and leads us to

$$h_i^j = \frac{h_{i-1}^{j+1} + h_{i-1}^{j-1}}{2} - \frac{\Delta\theta}{v_{i-1}^j}[\ r_j\ h_{i-1}^j\left(\frac{v_{r_{i-1}}^{j+1} - v_{r_{i-1}}^{j-1}}{2\ \Delta r}\right) + r_j\ v_{r_{i-1}}^j\left(\frac{h_{i-1}^{j+1} - h_{i-1}^{j-1}}{2\ \Delta r}\right) +$$

$$+ h_{i-1}^j\ v_{r_{i-1}}^j\ ] - \frac{h_{i-1}^j}{v_{\theta_{i-1}}^j}\left(v_{\theta_i}^j - \frac{v_{\theta_{i-1}}^{j+1} - v_{\theta_{i-1}}^{j-1}}{2}\right) \qquad (4)$$

$$v_{r_i}^j = \frac{1}{2}(v_{r_{i-1}}^{j+1} + v_{r_{i-1}}^{j-1}) + \Delta\theta \; v_{\theta_{i-1}}^j - \frac{\Delta\theta}{v_{\theta_{i-1}}^j}[\; r_j \; v_{r_{i-1}} \; (\frac{v_{r_{i-1}}^{j+1} - v_{r_{i-1}}^{j-1}}{2 \; \Delta r}) +$$

$$+ \; r_j \; g \; \cos\alpha\cos\beta(\frac{h_{i-1}^{j+1} - h_{i-1}^{j-1}}{2 \; \Delta r}) + g \; r_j \; \sin\alpha\cos\beta(\frac{v \; v_r}{h^{4/3}})_{i-1}^j + g \; r_j \; \sin\beta] \quad (5)$$

$$v_{\theta_i}^j = \frac{1}{2} (v_{\theta_{i-1}}^{j-1} - v_{\theta_{i-1}}^{j-1}) + \frac{\Delta\theta}{(v_\theta^2)_{i-1}^j - g \; h_{i-1}^j \; \cos\alpha \; \cos\beta}$$

$$\left\{ g \; \cos\alpha \; \cos\beta \; [\; r_j \; h_{i-1}^j \; (\frac{v_{r_{i-1}}^{j+1} - v_{r_{i-1}}^{j-1}}{2 \; \Delta r}) + r_j \; v_{r_{i-1}}^j \; (\frac{h_{i-1}^{j+1} - h_{i-1}^{j-1}}{2 \; \Delta r}) + \right.$$

$$+ \; h_{i-1}^j \; v_{r_{i-1}}^j - n^2 \; (\frac{v \; v_\theta}{h^{4/3}})_{i-1}^j \;] - v_{r_{i-1}}^j \; (v_\theta^2)_{i-1}^j +$$

$$\left. + \; r_j \; v_{\theta_{i-1}}^j \; [\; g \; \sin\alpha - v_{r_{i-1}}^j \; (\frac{v_{\theta_{i-1}}^{j+1} - v_{\theta_{i-1}}^{j-1}}{2 \; \Delta r}) \;] \; \right\} \qquad (6)$$

BOUNDARY CONDITIONS

A meticulous analysis of the boundary conditions is an important precondition for the validity and general applicability of this numerical method and is fundamental to the treatment of the hyperbolic equations because in the event of errors occurring at the limits or boundaries, these errors multiply downstream in all directions by way of the computational grid.

The various boundary conditions of the hydraulic phenomenon that is the object of this research were obtained using the following theoretical methods:

- The reflection or images method for velocity and depth

Inner Boundary: $(\; . \;)_1$ Outer Boundary: $(\; . \;)_{JMAX}$

$$(V_\theta)_0 = (V_\theta)_2 \qquad\qquad (V_\theta)_{JMAX-1} = (V_\theta)_{JMAX+1}$$
$$h_0 = h_2 \qquad\qquad h_{JMAX-1} = h_{JMAX+1} \qquad (7)$$
$$(V_r)_0 = (V_r)_2 \qquad\qquad (V_r)_{JMAX-1} = (V_r)_{JMAX+1}$$

- Linear approximations of the transverse profile of the free surface near the walls.

Inner Boundary

$(h_i)_0 = 2 \, (h_i)_1 - (h_i)_2$

$(h_i)_0 = 1.5 \, (h_i)_1 - 0.5 \, (h_i)_2$

Outer Boundary

$(h_i)_{JMAX} = 2 \, (h_i)_{JMAX-1} - (h_i)_{JMAX-2}$ (8)

$(h_i)_{JMAX} = 1.5 \, (h_i)_{JMAX-1} - (h_i)_{JMAX-2}$ (9)

- Adjustment of radial velocities at the walls to achieve a flow parallel to the boundary, using the superimposition of a single wave on the numerical solution following Abbett's basic idea (Jimenez, Chaudry[2]).

These theoretical formulas have been calibrated, adjusted (or rejected in some cases) after exhaustive laboratory testing carried out (Fernández–Bono[3]), (Poggi[4]) using the principal geometric and flow parameters.

CONVERGENCE AND STABILITY CONDITIONS

The stability of the scheme used for this work is determined by the Courant–Friedrich–Lewy condition. For equations (4) to (6) the said condition establishes that:

$$C = |\lambda_{MAX}| \, \frac{r \, \Delta\theta}{\Delta r} \leq 1 \qquad (10)$$

with

$$|\lambda_{MAX}| = \frac{|v_r \, v_\theta| + g \, h \, \sqrt{F_r^2 - 1}}{v_\theta^2 - g \, h} \qquad (11)$$

where C is the Courant number

$|\lambda_{MAX}|$ is the maximum absolute value of the characteristic slopes

Given that $|\lambda_{MAX}|$ is a local function of h, v_θ, v_r, the step size is automatically determined in order that Eq. 10 is satisfied for all the points along the r-direction.

The convergence requirement is given by

$$\Delta\theta \leq \frac{1}{r} \, \Delta r \, \sqrt{F_r^2 - 1} \qquad (12)$$

obtained from the wave propagation theory.

CHECKING AND CALIBRATION OF THE MATHEMATICAL MODEL. HYBRID MODELLING.

The verification and calibration of the mathematical model for steady–state, supercritical flow in curved circular channels as described previously is undertaken using the laboratory results gathered by B. Poggi[4] from various scale–models.

Figure 2 shows a comparison of the results calculated using the aforementioned mathematical model with the measured results gathered using the physical models.

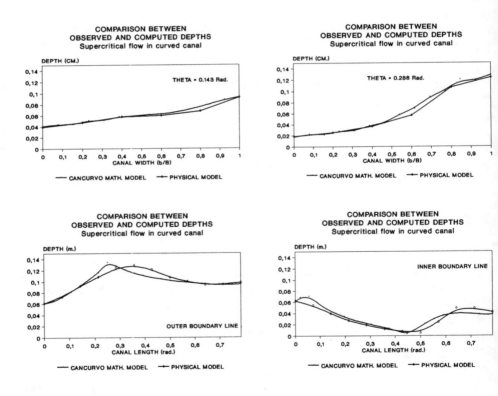

Figure 2. Comparison between observed and CANCURVO computed depths for supercritical flow in a curved canal

HYDRAULIC BEHAVIOUR AND DESIGN MODEL

The application of the CANCURVO model is in the analysis of steady, supercritical flow in curved channels connected directly to a stilling basin, and also in the interactive design of the shape of the hydraulic section which ensures that the connection creates a stable hydraulic jump in the stilling basin.

The program comprises a main routine to enter the geometric, flow and initial data and to control interactivelly the possible modifications of the initial channel design, until a totally stable hydraulic performance is achieved, and two subroutines: RAPIDA and CUENCO.

Subroutine RAPIDA analyses flow in the curved channel and determines the minimum depth (Y_{MIN}) of the transverse section at its end, while subroutine CUENCO calculates the conjugate hydraulic jump depths. Sequent supercritical depth (Y_1) is compared with Y_{MIN} to determine the formation and stability of the jump in the energy dissipation structure.

In case of instability the computational process returns to main program in order that the modelling system developer might select the appropiate design option from among the following:

– Re–design solutions, such as modify the radius of curvature, the circular angle,...

– Additive solutions, such as incorporation of one or more longitudinal dividing wall or consideration of transverse bed slope,

or a combination of the above.

Once a decision has been taken the program re–analyses the flow (or flows) in the entire system in order to stabilize hydraulic behaviour.

RELIABILITY OF HYDRAULIC BEHAVIOUR AND DESIGN MODEL

To test the reliability of the CANCURVO mathematical model, the data of a model built in the Hydraulics and Water Works Laboratory of the Polytechnical University of Valencia have been taken in order to solve a real problem (Fernández–Bono[3]).

Table 1 shows the calculated and measured results obtained from the mathematical and physical models respectively.

DATA: Q = 2 m ^{3}/sec. ,, θ = 0.2691 rad. ,, V_θ= 8.08 m/sec. ,,
$Y_{DOWNSTREAM}$= 0.60 m. ,, b = 1.5 m. ,, R_{MED}= 35 m.,,
h = 0.165 m. ,, n = 0.014 ,, α = 0.2121 ,, F_0= 6.35

Parameters	Results of physical model	Results of CANCURVO model
Y_{out} ~ Y_{inn} (m.) (channel end transverse section)	0.48 m.~ 0.048 m.	0.45 m. ~ 0.0495 m.
Z (m.) (height of stilling basin end sill)	1.30 m.	1.324 m.
Y_2 (m.) (stilling basin subcritical depth)	1.87 m.	1.90 m.
Hydraulic Jump Stability	Yes	Yes

DATA: Q = 3.7 m^3/sec. ,, $Y_{DOWNSTREAM}$= 0.87 m. ,, h = 0.247 m.

Parameters of initial solution	Results of physical model	Results of CANCURVO model
Y_{out} – Y_{inn} (m.)	0.910 m. – 0.072 m.	0.921 m. – 0.067 m.
Hyd. Jump Stability	Sweep	Sweep (Y_{min}< Y_1)
Provided solution	Two longitudinal dividing walls	Two longitudinal dividing walls
Y_{OUT} (m.)	0.47 ,, 0.46 ,, 0.45	0.471 ,, 0.465 ,, 0.458
Y_{INN} (m.)	0.36 ,, 0.34 ,, 0.32	0.371 ,, 0.355 ,, 0.318
Y_2 (m.)	2.26 m.	2.32 m.
Hydraulic Jump Stability	Yes	Yes (Y_{min} > Y_1)

Table 1. Comparison between calculated and measured corresponding results from mathematical and physical models.

CONCLUSIONS

This paper gives out a simple method for solving the hydraulic behaviour and design problems of supercritical flows in channels and spillways with circular curved plan and direct connection to stilling basins. The calculating results obtained are found to be in very good coincidence with those obtained through corresponding model experiments.

REFERENCES

1. Peterka, A.J. *Hydraulic Design of Stilling Basins and Energy Dissipators.* U.S. Bureau of Reclamation Engineering Monograph # 25, 1963

2. Jimenez, O.F., Chaudry, M. H. ' Computation of Supercritical Free–Surface Flows' *Journal of Hydraulic Engineering,* Vol.114, nº 4, pp. 377 – 395, 1988.

3. Fernández–Bono, J.F. *Estudio en Modelo Reducido del Comportamiento Hidráulico de las Rápidas 1 y 2 del Canal de la Margen Izquieda del Río Magro (Valencia).* Monografía del Laboratorio de Hidráulica y Obras Hidráulicas de la Universidad Politécnica de Valencia, 1987.

4. Poggi, B. ' Correnti Veloci nei Canali in Curva' *L'Energia Elettrica,* pp. 465 – 480, 1955.

Numerical simulation of flooding and drying in a depth-averaged boundary-fitted tidal model

R.V. Pearson, R.W. Barber
Department of Civil Engineering, University of Salford, Salford, England

ABSTRACT

This paper describes a finite-difference scheme for the solution of the shallow water equations on arbitrary non-orthogonal boundary-fitted grids. The transformed hydrodynamic equations are solved on a MAC type computational mesh which differs from conventional approaches in that both the U- and V-velocity components are prescribed at the mid-points of cell faces. Special attention is given to the simulation of the exposure and re-submergence of the inter-tidal zones which cause the flow perimeter to change shape. The versatility of model is demonstrated by examining the flow in the Humber Estuary on the east coast of England. The results indicate that the numerical scheme has considerable promise for simulating the hydrodynamics of awkwardly shaped estuaries.

INTRODUCTION

Boundary-fitted coordinate systems provide an approach which combines the best aspects of finite-difference discretisation with the grid flexibility usually associated with finite element procedures. Although numerical grid generation techniques have been thoroughly documented, few publications are yet available concerning the solution of the depth-averaged shallow water equations using curvilinear techniques. The earliest studies on the transformed non-linear shallow water equations were conducted by Johnson[1] in the U.S.A. Johnson solved the governing equations in primitive variable (U, V, ζ) form using a computational grid where both the U- and V-velocity components were represented at cell corners and the surface elevations (ζ) were calculated at cell centres. Other curvilinear models using the same grid configuration as Johnson were those of Häuser et al.[2] and Raghunath et al.[3] which solved the *linearised* shallow water expressions using an explicit technique. More recently Borthwick and Barber[4] have presented a non-orthogonal alternating-direction-implicit scheme to solve the complete non-linear shallow water equations.

The simulation of tidal processes in shallow coastal seas and estuaries presents special problems which do not occur in the modelling of large scale shelf seas. These problems stem from the existence of inter-tidal flats which are exposed and re-submerged during each tidal cycle, thereby altering the shape of the flow domain. The present scheme utilises a flooding and drying methodology similar to that used in Cartesian procedures whereby cells are removed or added to the computations by checking water surface elevation.

METHODOLOGY

Following Thompson et al.[5], the non-orthogonal boundary-fitted mesh was generated by solving a quasi-linear elliptic system:

$$\left.\begin{array}{l} \alpha\ x_{\xi\xi}\ -\ 2\beta\ x_{\xi\eta}\ +\ \gamma\ x_{\eta\eta}\ +\ J^2(P\ x_\xi\ +\ Q\ x_\eta)\ =\ 0 \\[2mm] \alpha\ y_{\xi\xi}\ -\ 2\beta\ y_{\xi\eta}\ +\ \gamma\ y_{\eta\eta}\ +\ J^2(P\ y_\xi\ +\ Q\ y_\eta)\ =\ 0 \end{array}\right\} \tag{1}$$

where

$$\alpha\ =\ x_\eta^{\ 2}\ +\ y_\eta^{\ 2}\quad,\qquad \beta\ =\ x_\xi x_\eta\ +\ y_\xi y_\eta\quad,\qquad \gamma\ =\ x_\xi^{\ 2}\ +\ y_\xi^{\ 2}\quad,$$

J is the Jacobian of the transformation given by $J\ =\ x_\xi y_\eta\ -\ x_\eta y_\xi$ and the

subscripts denote the usual shorthand notation for partial differentiation.

The functions P and Q are the so called *attraction operators* which can be used to counteract grid skewness and excessive cell size variation in regions of large boundary curvature. Equation (1) is solved iteratively using successive-over-relaxation to obtain the (x,y) coordinates of the nodes of the non-orthogonal grid in terms of the boundary-fitted coordinates (ξ,η).

The governing Cartesian hydrodynamic equations then need to be transformed into curvilinear coordinates. This transformation is performed according to the numerical mapping formulae presented by Thompson et al.[5]:

$$\left.\begin{array}{l} f_x\ =\ (\ y_\eta f_\xi\ -\ f_\eta y_\xi\ )\ /\ J \\[2mm] f_y\ =\ (\ x_\xi f_\eta\ -\ f_\xi x_\eta\ )\ /\ J \end{array}\right\} \tag{2}$$

where f denotes a differentiable function of x and y. This leads to the transformed depth-averaged continuity equation:

$$\frac{\partial \zeta}{\partial t} + \frac{1}{J}\left[y_\eta \frac{\partial (UD)}{\partial \xi} - y_\xi \frac{\partial (UD)}{\partial \eta} + x_\xi \frac{\partial (VD)}{\partial \eta} - x_\eta \frac{\partial (VD)}{\partial \xi}\right] = 0 \qquad (3)$$

whilst the non-conservative x-momentum equation is written as

$$\frac{\partial U}{\partial t} + \frac{1}{J}\left[y_\eta U \frac{\partial U}{\partial \xi} - y_\xi U \frac{\partial U}{\partial \eta} + x_\xi V \frac{\partial U}{\partial \eta} - x_\eta V \frac{\partial U}{\partial \xi}\right] - f_c V +$$

$$\frac{g}{J}\left[y_\eta \frac{\partial \zeta}{\partial \xi} - y_\xi \frac{\partial \zeta}{\partial \eta}\right] - \frac{\tau_{wx}}{\rho D} + \frac{C_f U (U^2 + V^2)^{\frac{1}{2}}}{D} + DIFFUSION = 0 \qquad (4)$$

and the non-conservative y-momentum expression is written as

$$\frac{\partial V}{\partial t} + \frac{1}{J}\left[y_\eta U \frac{\partial V}{\partial \xi} - y_\xi U \frac{\partial V}{\partial \eta} + x_\xi V \frac{\partial V}{\partial \eta} - x_\eta V \frac{\partial V}{\partial \xi}\right] + f_c U +$$

$$\frac{g}{J}\left[x_\xi \frac{\partial \zeta}{\partial \eta} - x_\eta \frac{\partial \zeta}{\partial \xi}\right] - \frac{\tau_{wy}}{\rho D} + \frac{C_f V (U^2 + V^2)^{\frac{1}{2}}}{D} + DIFFUSION = 0 \qquad (5)$$

where U and V are depth-averaged velocity components in the x- and y-directions, ζ is the surface elevation above an arbitrary datum, D (which equals $h + \zeta$) is the local water depth where h is the distance between the bed and the datum, ρ is the fluid density, g is the acceleration due to gravity, f_c is the Coriolis parameter, τ_w is the wind stress and C_f is the bed friction coefficient calculated using Manning's equation. Although the transformed expressions are more complex than their Cartesian counterparts, the curvilinear equations of motion can now be solved on a regular finite-difference mesh composed of uniformly-spaced, square cells.

The transformed governing equations (3, 4 and 5) were discretised on a staggered (ξ, η) grid where both the U- and V-velocity components were represented at the mid-points of cell faces and the surface elevations (ζ) were calculated at cell centres. This grid was chosen so as to minimise interpolation which is not theoretically compatible with the varying cell sizes in the physical domain. A one-step explicit forward time central space finite difference scheme was used to solve the equations of motion. The scheme is therefore first order accurate in time and second order accurate in space.

FLOODING AND DRYING PROCEDURE

In an estuary at high tide the entire surface may be covered by water and as the tide begins to ebb the shallower regions are exposed and ultimately the flow is often restricted to the deeper channels. Although continuously deforming time dependent boundaries are more satisfactory in that they represent the physical processes of inundation and drying more rigorously, they are much more difficult to apply in estuarine areas.   Johnson et al.[6], with reference to continuously deforming boundaries on non-orthogonal curvilinear coordinate systems, pointed out that if the areas to be flooded and dried are essentially islands then some technique to allow cells to collapse to a single point when an island is flooded would be required. Moreover, the effect of the movement of the boundaries may be to *starve* important areas of grid points. This could occur in a region which has a very complicated geometry at high tide whilst having a relatively simple geometry at low tide. In order to ensure that as the boundary deformed, the grid point distribution, cell size variation and grid orthogonality remained adequate, it would be necessary not only to change the boundary node positions in the physical domain but also to reconstruct the transformed domain. Furthermore, it would be necessary to re-interpolate the depth field each time the mesh was regenerated thereby significantly increasing the computational costs of the scheme.

In order to circumvent the problems of using a dynamic coordinate system, the present numerical scheme employs a static boundary-fitted mesh in conjunction with a flooding and drying approach whereby grid cells are removed or added to the computational domain depending upon the local water depth.   The flooding and drying technique utilised in the present study is similar to the Cartesian procedure developed by Falconer and Chen[7]:

First drying check - At the beginning of every time step, the cell centre depths are calculated from

$$DEPZ(I,J) = ZETA(I,J) + H(I,J)$$

where $DEPZ(I,J)$ is the total water depth, $ZETA(I,J)$ is the value of the surface elevation at the start of the time step and $H(I,J)$ is the distance between the bed and the datum. The water depths at the velocity positions are also required in the scheme. Thus,

$$DEPE(I,J) = [DEPZ(I,J) + DEPZ(I+1,J)]/2$$

$$DEPN(I,J) = [DEPZ(I,J) + DEPZ(I,J+1)]/2$$

where $DEPE(I,J)$ and $DEPN(I,J)$ are the total water depths at *east* and *north* positions of the staggered mesh respectively. The drying check is invoked by specifying a roughness height, RH.   If an easterly or northerly depth is calculated to be less than RH then that depth is equated to zero. A check is then made on all four side depths of each grid cell and if all four side depths are less than or equal to RH then the grid cell is effectively dry and is removed from subsequent computations.

Second drying check - This involves checking the cell centre depths. If this depth is less than RH then the cell is also assumed to be dry and is removed.

Final drying check - In this check, all wet grid cells where the cell centre depth is less than a predetermined value PRESET are considered *potentially* dry. If at least one water depth around the four sides of the grid cell is greater than RH *and* DEPZ(I,J) is less than PRESET but greater than RH then the cell will be assumed to be dry unless the flow direction from adjacent wet grid cells connected by way of a depth greater than RH is towards the potentially dry cell.   If the flow direction is out of the cell then it is removed from the computations. Numerical experimentation indicates that a suitable value of the predetermined value PRESET is typically 2 to 2.5 times the roughness height.

Following the above drying checks, all dry cells are then considered for possible inundation. In the flooding checks, a dry cell will be returned to the computational domain if *all* the following are satisfied:

(a) Any one of the four surrounding cells is wet.
(b) The total depth at the east or north position connecting the adjacent wet cell(s) and the dry cell is greater than RH.
(c) The surface elevation of the adjacent wet cell(s) is higher than that of the dry cell so that the flow direction is towards the dry cell.

It should be noted that flooding can occur from one to four sides of the dry grid cell and so many geometric combinations are possible, all of which need to be checked.

RESULTS

The numerical model was validated by examining the flow in the Humber Estuary on the east coast of England. In order to simulate the tidal currents in the estuary, it was necessary to introduce time varying surface elevations at both the open landward and seaward boundaries. The tidal curves for these boundaries were digitised at discrete intervals and then cubic spline interpolation was used to calculate the required water surface elevation at each time step.   Land/water boundaries were treated using a no-slip condition whereby $U=V=0$. Figure 1 shows the boundary-fitted coordinate system representative of the Humber Estuary together with the positions of the open boundaries whilst Figures 2 and 3 illustrate the distribution of dry cells and the velocity vectors at the mouth of the estuary at mean water level flood spring tide. The model was tested for various values of Manning's n with the closest agreement between computed and field measured results being obtained for n=0.015. Numerical experimentation was also used to determine the optimum values for the roughness height, RH and the parameter PRESET employed in the flooding and drying procedure; in the present study values of RH=0.08m and PRESET=0.16m were found to give the best results. Model simulations were always started at high tide relative to the seaward boundary with the initial velocities zero everywhere and the surface elevations across the whole hydrodynamic domain equal to the high tide surface elevation at the seaward boundary.

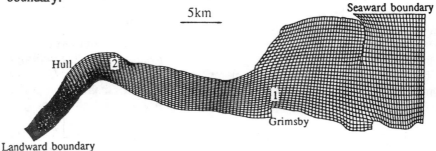

Figure 1. Boundary-fitted mesh representative of the Humber Estuary

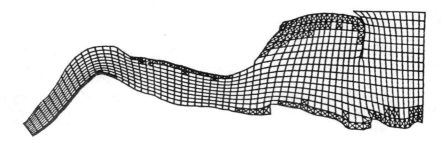

Figure 2. Dry zones at mean water level flood spring tide

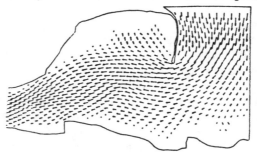

Figure 3. Velocity vectors at mean water level flood spring tide

Two intermediate sites along the estuary reach (1 and 2 in **Figure 1**) were chosen to compare the computed results with field measurements obtained by the British Transport Docks Board[8]. The resulting surface elevation profiles for both sites are shown in Figure 4 where it can be seen that the agreement between computed and measured results is very good. It is also clear from the smooth nature of the surface elevation profiles that the flooding and drying technique produces minimal boundary noise.

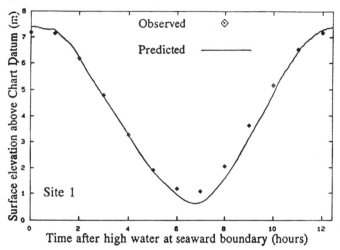

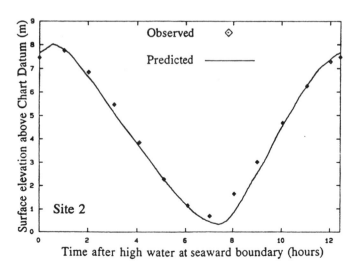

Figure 4. Comparisons of surface elevation at sites 1 and 2

CONCLUSIONS

The results indicate that the curvilinear shallow water equation solver described in this paper is capable of simulating the hydrodynamics in awkwardly shaped estuaries. A Cartesian flooding and drying scheme is used which works well and is not to the detriment of the scheme since generally not all regions adjacent to the perimeter will be dry at all states of the tide and so the advantages of the boundary fitted approach can still be realised. This hybrid methodology therefore allows the highest accuracy of boundary representation wherever possible. The method is to be preferred to using a dynamic boundary-fitted coordinate system which is both computationally expensive and difficult to implement.

REFERENCES

1.   Johnson, B.H. 'VAHM - A Vertically Averaged Hydrodynamic Model using Boundary-Fitted Coordinates', *Misc. Paper HL-80-3*, U.S. Army Engineer Waterways Experiment Station Hydraulics Laboratory, Vicksburg, Mississippi, U.S.A., 1980.

2.   Häuser, J., Paap, H.G., Eppel, D. and Mueller, A. 'Solution of Shallow Water Equations for Complex Flow Domains via Boundary-Fitted Coordinates', *Int. J. for Numerical Methods in Fluids*, Vol. 5, pp. 727-744, 1985.

3.   Raghunath, R., Sengupta, S. and Häuser, J. 'A Study of the Motion in Rotating Containers using a Boundary-Fitted Coordinate System', *Int. J. for Numerical Methods in Fluids*, Vol. 7, pp. 453-464, 1987.

4.   Borthwick, A.G.L. and Barber, R.W. 'River and Reservoir Flow Modelling using the Transformed Shallow Water Equations', *Int. J. for Numerical Methods in Fluids*, Vol. 14, pp. 1193-1217, 1992.

5.   Thompson, J.F., Thames, F.C. and Mastin, C.W. 'Automatic Numerical Generation of Body-Fitted Curvilinear Coordinate System for Field Containing Any Number of Arbitrary Two-Dimensional Bodies', *J. of Comp. Physics*, Vol. 15, pp. 299-319, 1974.

6.   Johnson, B.H., Thompson, J.F. and Baker, A.J. 'A Discussion of Adaptive Grids and their Applicability in Numerical Hydrodynamic Modelling', *Misc. Paper HL-84-4*, U.S. Army Engineer Waterways Experiment Station Hydraulics Laboratory, Vicksburg, Mississippi, U.S.A., 1984.

7.   Falconer, R.A. and Chen, Y. 'An Improved Representation of Flooding and Drying and Wind Stress Effects in a Two-Dimensional Tidal Numerical Model', *Proc. Instn. Civ. Engrs.*, Part 2, Vol. 91, pp. 659-678, 1991.

8.   British Transport Docks Board 'Collection of Field Data for the Design and Operation of the Humber Tidal Model', *Report H1*, Humber Estuary Research Committee, 1974.

x-t Plane development using mass-momentum conservation

N. Haie

Civil Engineeering Department, University of Minho, 4800 Guimarães, Portugal

ABSTRACT

A mathematical model of the flow phenomena, with the moving tip, was developed for the unsteady gradually varied flow using the complete forms of mass and momentum conservation relations, which form the non-linear hyperbolic type equations to be solved. An implicit finite-difference scheme using an Eulerian system of fluid flow led to the simulation of x-t planes of different surface flow situations. Dry, wet, and transition infiltration functions were used to describe the temporal and spatial variability of infiltration rates. Model performance for different flow regimes was verified.

INTRODUCTION

Interest in the numerical description of surface flow has been encouraged by popular concern with water resources management. Attempts which are likely to develop a more desirable outcome to describe surface flow in the literature. One of the approaches which uses the principles of fluid mechanics to solve the surface flow problem is the hydrodynamic method. This approach is based on the principles of conservation of mass and conservation of momentum, known as the Saint-Venant equations. These equations relate flow area and discharge in an open-channel flow and form a set of first order, non-linear, hyperbolic partial differential equations with no closed form solution. Their solution is more complicated by the fact that the velocity of advanced is not known a priori, and so the moving boundaries of the flow region must be found as part of the solution.

The equations can not be solved directly, but approximate solutions may be reached by numerical techniques. Three of these techniques which have been used successfully are: (1) the method of characteristics; (2) integration over oblique cells; and (3) integration over rectangular cells (Eulerian method). The third method is the focus of this paper and therefore will be summarised in more detail in the next section.

MATHEMATICAL MODEL

The hydrodynamic formulation consists of the continuity and momentum equations, e.g. Haie [1], Bautista and Wallander [2]. These equations, respectively, are:

$$\frac{\partial Q}{\partial x} + \frac{\partial A}{\partial t} + I = 0 \tag{1}$$

$$\frac{1}{g}\frac{\partial Q}{\partial t} + \frac{\partial}{\partial x}\left(p + \frac{Q^2}{Ag}\right) = A\left(S_o - S_f\right) \tag{2}$$

the infiltration rate, I , has been computed as follows:

$$I = \frac{\partial z}{\partial t} \tag{3}$$

where z , infiltrated volume per unit length, is represented by the Kostiakov Lewis infiltration function:

$$z = k\tau^a + f_o\tau \tag{4}$$

and the rest of the variables in the above equations are defined as: Q = the average flow rate; A = the cross sectional area of flow; x = the distance along the channel bed; t = the time; g =acceleration of gravity; P = hydrostatic pressure force acting on the cross section divided by the specific weight of water; S_o =channel bottom slope; S_f = the resistance slope; τ = the intake opportunity time; and k, a and f_o are empirical parameters.

The integrated form of the continuity equation can be written as:

$$\left[\overline{Q}(x + \delta x, t) - \overline{Q}(x, t)\right]\delta t + \left[\tilde{A}(x, t + \delta t) - \tilde{A}(x, t)\right]\delta x +$$
$$+ \left[\tilde{z}(x, t + \delta t) - \tilde{z}(x, t)\right]\delta x = 0 \tag{5}$$

where δt is the time increment and δx the space increment both of which can be variable. The bar over a variable shows a time average over δt; the tilde over a variable shows a distance average over the increment δx.

Assuming a constant bottom slope, the integrated form of the momentum equation (2) is as follows:

$$\frac{1}{g}\left\{\left[\tilde{Q}_{t+\delta t}-\tilde{Q}_t\right]\delta x+\left[\overline{\left(\frac{Q^2}{A}\right)}_{x+\delta x}-\overline{\left(\frac{Q^2}{A}\right)}_x\right]\delta t\right\}+\left(\overline{P}_{x+\delta x}-\overline{P}_x\right)\delta t=\left(\tilde{\overline{A}}-\tilde{\overline{D}}\right)\delta t\;\delta x$$

(6)

where $D=AS_f=$ the drag of soil surface divided by the specific weight of water.

The hydrodynamic model (5) and (6) consists of two non-linear equations in the two unknowns Q and A at a particular x and t. The development of the numerical solution of the governing equations may be divided into two general parts: (1) description of the Eulerian system of fluid flow as applied to the present model, and (2) the solution of the set of equations by the double sweep algorithm, a recursive type Gaussian elimination procedure.

In an Eulerian system, the left and right boundaries of a control volume, cell, does not move in a time increment as opposed to the oblique cell method of Katopodes and Strelkoff [3]. The Eulerian approach is simpler to formulate and can be depicted in figures 1 and 2. On each time step, the solution is obtained at a sequence of points x_k ($k=1,2,...,N$; $N=I+1$, where k is the space index, $I=1,2,3,...$ is the time index and $N=k$ at the downstream boundary). At the beginning of the time step, t, the surface and subsurface areas are A_J and Z_J at station x_{k-1}, and the surface and subsurface areas are A_M and Z_M, respectively, at station x_k. At this moment in time Q_J is the discharge flowing into the cell at x_{k-1} and Q_M is the discharge flowing out of the cell at x_k. At the end of the time step, $t+\delta t$, the surface and subsurface areas are A_L and Z_L respectively at station x_{k-1}, and A_R and Z_R at x_k. The discharges are Q_L and Q_R at x_{k-1} and x_k, respectively.

The two equations of hydrodynamic contain four unknowns, A_L, Q_L, A_R and Q_k, when they are applied to a cell $JMLR$ of figure 1. This is due to the fact that all the variables of the previous time line, JM, and all the Z values of the current time line, LR, are known. Applying the two equations to the other cells yield two more unknowns for each cell or a total of 2N unknowns and

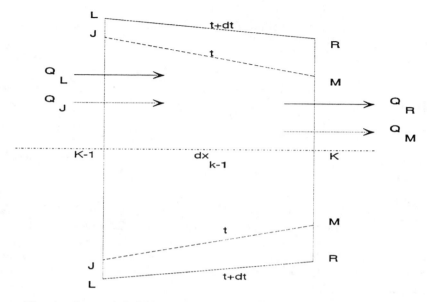

Fig. 1 - General fluid element at the beginning and end of a time step

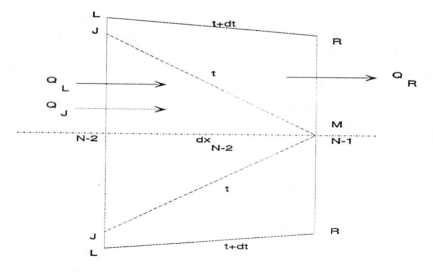

Fig. 2 - Computational cells before the moving tip cell

(2N-2) equations for a given time line, $t + \delta t$. The addition of boundary conditions, upstream and downstream, eliminates two of the unknowns and makes the solution of the equations possible.

The second part, the solution of the set of equations by the double sweep algorithm, can be found in numerous references, e.g. Strelkoff [4].

Using the model for the surged flow systems (like surface irrigation surged management systems) poses some special problems like the spatial and temporal variability of infiltration. The first surge advances over a dry section. This is a limited case of the continuous flow situation. The subsequent surges advance over both wet and previously dry sections. Two Kostiakov-Lewis functions for these two sections were used. For the second wetting areas, an infiltration transition function was employed.

VERIFICATION

In this section, the performance of the model is illustrated in 2 major parts: (1) verification with continuous flow; (2) verification with surged flow.

Four different sets of data have been utilised in this study as summarised in table 1. The first come from the Colorado State University, e.g. Haie [1]. The data were collected from a Colorado location, the Benson farm. The length of the furrows in Benson farm was 625 meters with a clay-loam soil and 0.44 percent slope. This set of data is limited to the continuous flow conditions. The second set of data comes from the Arizona precision border data on bare soil as published by Roth et al. [5]. The length of the borders was 91.4 meters with 0.46 meters of sandy loam soil overlying sand and 0.1 percent slope. This set contains continuous border irrigation data. The third data set was estimated from Chow [6], for a continuous flow of water in a lined canal, to give a wider range of possibilities to the model. Although it still needs a more thorough verification for canals, this example shows that the model can easily be adopted to other conditions. Finally, the fourth data set comes from the Utah State University. These data were collected by a research group, including the author as part of a project to study surge flow phenomena. The data are from a location near Flowell, Utah. The length of the furrows was 360 meters with a sandy-loam soil and 0.8 percent slope. This set contains surged furrow irrigation data. Figures 3 through 6 show the x-t trajectories simulated by the hydrodynamic model and the observed field data.

CONCLUSIONS

Hydrodynamic development of surface flow started with the simulation of the advance trajectories for the continuous flow situation. Then the model was modified to handle surge flow modeling. Dry, wet and transition infiltration functions were used to describe the temporal and spatial variability of infiltration rates under surge flow regimes. Model performance over a relatively wide range of field conditions showed that in all cases the observed and simulated advance agree closely. One of the issues during the development was the definition of the moving tip. Although this topic, among others, needs more attention, in general, the model promises a robust tool for design and simulation.

Table 1 - Input Data

Model Input Parameters	Benson 1-1-5	Arizona 9-B	Chow Canal	Flowell WF
Inflow rate (lps)	2.776	2.406	11000	2.0
Field Length (m)	625	91.4	600	360
Field Slop (m/m)	.0044	0.001	0.002	0.008
Mannings roughness	.03	0.035	0.025	0.04
Time of cutoff (min)	320	50	--	*
Furrow geometry:				
$B = C\,y^M$ C	2.244	1.0	19	2.952
$B = C\,y^M$ M	0.576	0.0	0.45	0.866
Kostiakov-Lewis intake function:				**
k	0.02771	.01427	0.0	0.0028
a	0.0071	0.358	0.0	0.534
f_0	.000209	0.0	0.0	0.000222

* Cycle Time = 80 min; Cycle Ratio = 0.5

** Surge flow intake: $k_s = 0.00459$; $a_s = 0.356$; $f_{0s} = 0.00018$

REFERENCES

1. Haie, N. 'Hydrodynamic Simulation of Continuous and Surged Surface Flow.' Ph.D. thesis, Utah State University, Logan, Utah, 1984.
2. Bautista, E. and Wallender, W.W. 'Hydrodynamic Furrow Irrigation Model with Specified Space Steps.' Journal of Irrigation and Drainage Engineering, ASCE, Vol.118, No.3, pp. 450 - 465, 1992.
3. Katapodes, N.D. and Strelkoff, T. 'Hydrodynamics of Border Irrigation - A Complete Model.' Journal of Irrigation and Drainage Engineering, ASCE, Vol.103, No.IR3, pp. 309 - 324, 1977.
4. Strelkoff, T. 'EQSWP: Extended Unsteady-Flow Double-Sweep Equation Solver.' Journal of Hydraulic Engineering, ASCE, Vol.118, No.5, pp. 735 - 742, 1992.
5. Roth, R.L., Fonken, D.W., Fangmeier, D. and Atchison, K.T. 'Data for Border Irrigation Models.' Transactions of the ASAE, Vol.17, No.1, pp. 157 - 161, 1974.
6. Chow, V.T. 'Open Channel Hydraulics.' Chapter 10, Methods of Computation, pp. 249 - 296, McGraw-Hill Kogakusha, Tokyo and New Delhi, 1959.

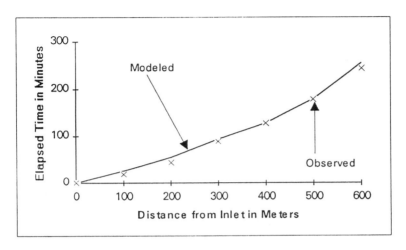

Fig. 3 - Observed and modeled advance for Benson 1-1-5

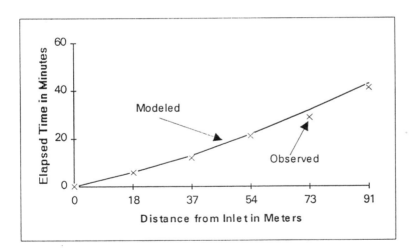

Fig. 4 - Observed and modeled advance for Arizona 9-B

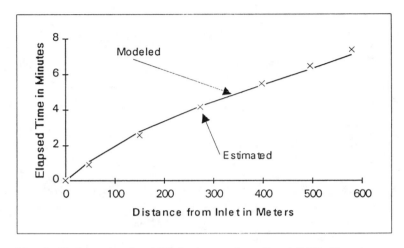

Fig. 5 - Estimated and modeled advance for a Canal (V.T. Chow)

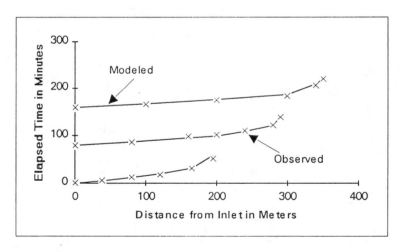

Fig. 6 - Observed and modeled surges for Utah FWF

SECTION 8: SOLIDIFICATION AND MELTING

Effectiveness NTU performance of finned PCM storage unit

K.A.R. Ismail, M.M. Gonçalves

UNICAMP-FEM-DETF, C.P. 6122, 13081-970 Campinas, SP, Brazil

ABSTRACT

This paper presents a mathematical model based upon two dimensional formulation of the phase change heat transfer problem around externally finned tube immersed in the PCM while the working fluid flows through it. The energy equation is written in its enthalpic form and the heat and flow processes are coupled by an energy balance on the fluid element flowing inside the tube. The numerical solution is based upon the control volume technique and ADI finite difference representation. The results obtained show the effect of the geometrical parameters such as number of fins, fin length, compactness ratio and the fin thickness on the solidified mass, NTU and effectiveness.

INTRODUCTION

Analytical solutions to the heat transfer problem with phase change although very important are limited to very special cases of little practical interest. Many semi–analytical methods were proposed including the integral method, moving heat source method and perturbation methods.

Various numerical methods were proposed for the solution of heat transfer problem with phase change. These methods can be conveniently divided into strong numerical solutions where finite difference or finite element techniques are used in the strong formulation of the process, localizing the interface and the temperature distribution in each step or using special transforms to immobilize the interface.

The other group called weak numerical methods in which the explicit attention in following the interface is avoided.

The main advantage of the enthalpic formulation is that one

basic equation is used to represent the whole region solid and liquid and no modification in the numerical scheme is necessary to handle the interface region. Again the formulation is equaly applicable for the case of PCM fixed and unique fusion temperature as well as for the case of fusion over a temperature range. Because of these advantages these methods are widely.

Of particular interest to the present study is the work due to Sparrow et al [2] on a tube with four fins in which they observed the presence of natural convection in the liquid phase which can lead to interrupting or delaying the solidification process. Bathelt and Viskanta [3], studied the case of storage in PCM using a tube with three fins and studied the influence of the geometrical arrangement of the fins on the fusion front and the presence of natural convection. Shamsundar and Srimiver san [4], presented charts of NTU and ε for a storage unit of the shell-tube type. Ismail and Alves [5] and [6] presented various studies on phase change problems with finned tubes including NTU and ε charts for engineering calculations. Ismail [7] presented numerical and experimental results for various finned tube configurations suitable for PCM storage. Padmanabhan and Krishma [8] studied the heat transfer process around a cylinder with axial fins.

In the present work the mathematical model is based upon two dimensional formulation of the phase change problem around externally finned cylinder immersed in the PCM as in Fig.1. The heat conduction equation is written in its enthalpic form and the heat and flow problems were coupled by an energy balance on the fluid element flowing inside the tube. The numerical solution of the energy equation was based upon the control volume technique and the ADI scheme.

FORMULATION OF THE PROBLEM

In this formulation it is assumed that the heat transfer process is dominated by conduction, the sensible heat of the PCM is negligible compared to its latent heat, the fluid temperature at inlet is constant, constant heat transfer coefficient between the fluid and the tube wall, the phase change occurs over a range of temperature. Because of the symmetry of the problem the representative domain can be considered as in Fig.2.

Considering the above simplification and following Bonacina's method [1], it is possible to write the heat conduction equation.

$$\bar{C}(T) \frac{\partial T}{\partial t} = \frac{1}{r} \frac{\partial}{\partial r} (r\bar{k}(T) \frac{\partial T}{\partial r}) + \frac{1}{r} \frac{\partial}{\partial \theta} (\frac{\bar{k}(T)}{r} \frac{\partial T}{\partial \theta}) \qquad (1)$$

applicable for the solid, liquid and fin region by substituting the appropriate values for $\bar{C}(T)$ and $\bar{k}(T)$ as in Bonacina [1].

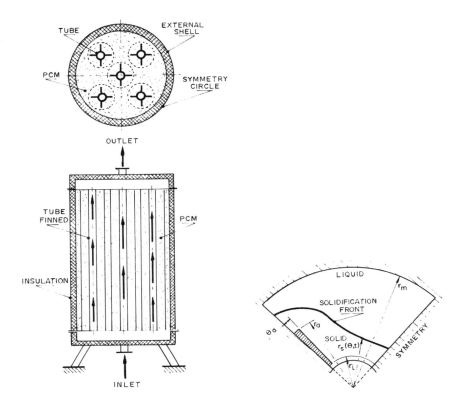

Figure 1. PCM storage unit.   **Figure 2. Symmetry region.**

The boundary, initial and final conditions associated with the above equations are:

$$\frac{\partial T}{\partial r}\bigg|_{r = r_i} = \frac{h}{k} (T(r_i, \theta, t) - T_b)$$

$$\frac{\partial T}{\partial r}\bigg|_{r = r_m} = 0 \quad j \quad \frac{\partial T}{\partial \theta}\bigg|_{\theta = 0} = 0 \quad j \quad \frac{\partial T}{\partial \theta}\bigg|_{\theta = \theta_m} = 0 \tag{2}$$

$$T(r,\theta,0) = T_m^+ \quad j \quad T(r,\theta,t_f) = T_m^-$$

where $T_m^+ - T_m^- = 2\Delta T$, T_b is fluid bulk temperature, T_m is the phase change temperature, T_m^+ is the phase change temperature for the liquid phase, T_m^- is the phase change temperature for the solid, $2\Delta T$ is the phase change range and h is convective heat transfer coefficient.

The system of equations (1) and (2) represent the conduction dominated phase change problem. In the case of a working fluid flowing in the finned tube, the phase change problem must be coupled to the flow problem by considering energy balance between the fluid and the phase change problem.

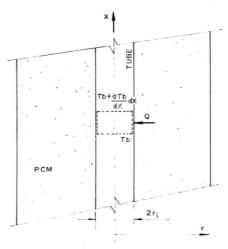

Figure 3. Energy balance on a fluid element.

Performing an energy balance between the fluid and the PCM one can obtain

$$\dot{q} = \dot{m}_b \, c_b \, \frac{dT_b}{dx} \qquad (3)$$

where $\dot{m}_b = \rho_b \pi r_i^2 \, \bar{u}$ and $\bar{u} = \frac{dx}{dt}$

Hence equation (3) can be written as

$$\frac{d(T_m^+ - T_b)}{(T_m^+ - T_b)} = -2 \, B_i \, C_{sf} \, \Gamma \, d\tau \qquad (4)$$

where $C_{sf} = C_s/(\rho_b \, C_b)$ = ratio of specific heats, C_b = the fluid specific heat and $\Gamma = \dot{q}/\dot{q}_{max}$ = the dimensionless heat flux. Note that $\dot{q} = 2\pi \, r_i \, k_s \, \partial T/\partial r$ = heat flux and $\dot{q}_{max} = 2\pi \, r_i \, h \, (T_m^+ - T_o)$ = maximum heat flux.

Integrating equation (4) one can obtain the local bulk temperature of the

$$T_b(\tau) = T_m^+ - \exp \, [-2B_i C_{sf} \int \Gamma \, d\tau + \ln(T_m^+ - T_b(0)9] \qquad (5)$$

where the dimensionless time τ is determined from

$$\tau = \mu^* \, x^*/(Re \, Pr \, \rho^*) \qquad (6)$$

where

$Pr = C_s \, \mu_\ell/k_s$ is the Prandtl number for the solid phase;

$Re = \rho_b \, \bar{u} \, r_i/\mu_b$ is the Reynold number;

$u^* = \mu_\ell/\mu_b$ is the relative viscosity;

$\rho^* = \rho_s/\rho_b$ is the relative density;

$x^* = x/r_i$ is the dimensionless axial position along the tube measured from the entry position of the tube.

Define the effectiveness as the ratio of real heat flux to the maximum heat flux one can write

$$\varepsilon = \dot{q}/\dot{q}_{max} = \Gamma \tag{7}$$

where

$$\dot{q} = \frac{\dot{m}_b \; C_b}{x} \; [T_b(x) - T_b(0)]$$

$$\dot{q}_{max} = 2\pi r_i h \; [T_m^+ - T_b(0)]$$

with x as the position of the fluid element along the axis of the tube.

Hence

$$\varepsilon = \frac{\dot{m}_b \; C_b}{2\pi r_i xh} \; [\frac{T_b(x) - T_b(0)}{T_m^+ - T_b(0)}] = \quad \text{the effectiveness} \tag{8}$$

and the (NTU) number of thermal units as

$$NTU = 2\pi r_i xh/(\dot{m}_b \; C_b) \tag{9}$$

NUMERICAL TREATMENT

The system of equations and the associated boundary conditions were solved numerically by using the control volume finite difference method due to Patankar [18] and the ADI numerical scheme. Various numerical tests were realized to establish the optimum grid in both the radial and circumferential directions.

It was found that 30 radial points and 30 circumferential ones gave best results.

DISCUSSIONS

Figure 4 shows the variation of solidified mass for the time increment $\tau = 0,1$ as function of the number of fins. As can be seen the increases in the number of fins leads to increase in the solidified mass. The effects on the effectiveness and NTU of the storage unit are shown in Fig.5.

The compactness ratio CR defined as $\dfrac{r_m - r_i}{r_i}$ has an adverse effect on the solidified mass as can be verified from Fig. 6.

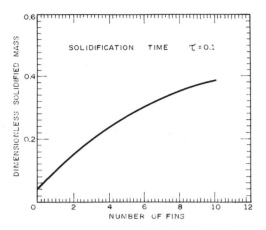

Figure 4. Effect of number of fins.

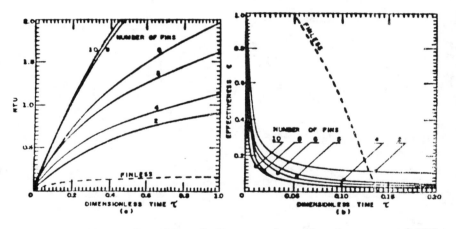

Figure 5. Effect of number of fins on the effectiveness and NTU.

The increase of CR above about 5 does not seem to effect the solidification any further. Figure 7 shows the effect of CR on the effectiveness and NTU of the storage unit as compared to the finless one.

Variation of the solidified mass with the variation of the fin length is shown in Fig.8. The figure indicates that for values of dimensionless fin length above 10, the solidified mass seems to be affected very little.

The thickness of the fin seems to affect very little the solidified mass, ε and NTU of the storage unit and the curves are omitted for brevity.

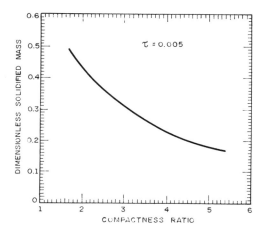

Figure 6. Effect of compactness ratio.

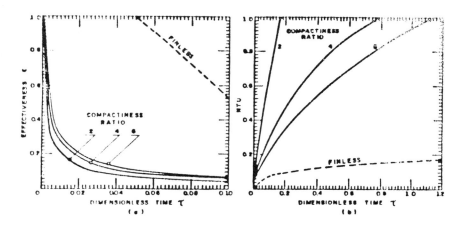

Figure 7. Effect on the compactiness ratio on ε and NTU.

CONCLUSIONS

This study indicates that the proposed model and the numerical approach are adequate to simulate the effects of the geometrical parameters on the performance of a latent heat storage unit with finned tubes. The curves of NTU and effectiveness are helpful for design purposes.

REFERENCES

1.   Bonacina et alli. 'Numerical Solution of Phase Change Problems'. International Journal of Heat and Mass Transfer, 16 (1825-1832), 1973.

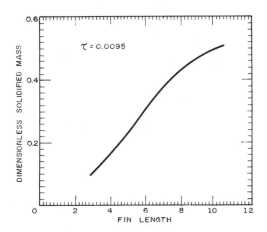

Figure 8. Effect of fin length.

2. Sparrow, E.M. et alli. 'Freezing on a Finned Tube for Either Conduction-Controlled on Natural Convection Controlled Heat Transfer, Int. J. Heat Mass Transfer, 24, (273-284), 1981.

3. Bathelt, A.G. and Viskanta, R. 'Heat Transfer and Interface Motion During Melting and Solidification Around a Finned Heat Source/Sink., 1981.

4. Shamsundar, N. and Srimivesan, R. 'Effectiveness NTU Charts for Heat Recovery from Latent Heat Storage Units', J. Solar Engineering, 192(263-271), 1980.

5. Ismail, K.A.R. and Alves, C.L. 'Analysis of Shell Tube PCM Storage System', 8th Int. Heat Transfer Conf., S. Francisco, California, USA, 1986, paper nº FM-10, pp. 1781-1786.

6. Ismail, K.A.R. and Alves, C.L. 'Numerical Solutions of Finned Geometries Immersed in Phase Change Material', ASME 26th Nat. Heat Transfer Conf., Philadelphia, USA, HTD, 109(31-36), 1989.

7. Ismail, K.A.R. 'Possible Finned Geometries for PCM Thermal Storage Units', Heat Transfer 90, 17-19 July, Southampton, UK, pp. 55-56, 1990.

8. Padmanabhan, P.V. and Krishma, M.V. 'Outward Phase Change in a Cylindrical Annulus with Axial Fins on the Inner Tub.', Int. J. Heat Mass Transfer, 29(12), pp. 1855-1868, 1986.

9. Patankar, S.V. 'Numerical Heat Transfer and Fluid Flow', Hemisphere Publishing Corporation, 1980.

Fusion of PCM in finned plane cavities

K.A.R. Ismail, M.R.B. Trullenque

UNICAMP-FEM-DETF, C.P. 6122, 13081-970 Campinas, SP, Brazil

ABSTRACT

This paper presents a simplified two dimensional model for the fusion (solidification) of PCM in a rectangular cavity with internal fins. The formulation of the model follows Voller's approach. The results of the model were compared with available experimental and numerical data and the agreement was found good. Geometrical parameters of the cavity such as width, length of fin, thickness of fin and thickness of top and bottom were investigated. Also operational paremeters such as the magnitude of the heat flux and its frequency were also analysed.

INTRODUCTION

Equipment for the thermal control with phase material (PCM) have received much interest in recent years due to its immediate applications in the field of thermal control and cooling of electrical and electronic equipments. Various geometries were proposed and solved analitically, numerically and experimentally resulting in a real advance in this area. The use of finned geometry was initially proposed by Abhat [1] and later by Humphries and Griggs [6].

The pionner analytical solutions to the phase change problem were reported by Lamé and Claperyon [7] in 1831 and Stefan [11] in 1891. Since then many analytical, semi analytical and particularly numerical methods were proposed. The analytical methods in general were developed for simple geometries with initial and boundary conditions of little practical use. The semi analytical and approximate methods can incorporate more realistic boundary and initial conditions and hence can handle more practical situations. Such methods include the Integral method due to Goodman [4], Refined Integral method due to Bell [2], method of moving heat source and perturbation methods [5, 9]. Many numerical solutions for the problem of heat transfer

with phase change were reported such as Bonacina methods [3] ,
Shamsundar and Sparrow's method [10], Voller's [12] and others,
in wich the convection effects were included and analysed. The
main objective of the present study is to develop a simplified
two dimensional model to handle the phase change problem
controlled by conduction in a finned cavity and to be able to
investigate the geometrical and operational parameters and
their effects on the thermal performance of the cooling unit.

FORMULATION OF THE PROBLEM

The physical model considered in this work is shown in Fig. 1,
where the finned rectangular cavity contains the PCM, heat is
received from the top and dissipated from the bottom of   the
unit using either natural or forced convection. Due to symmetry
of the problem the half cavity shown in Fig. 2 is   considered
for sake of the analytical and numerical formulation.   The
problem is considered two dimensional with constant   physical
properties for the metal and PCM. Also only conduction   is
considered as the mean of heat transfer in the PCM.   The
metallic enclosure and fins are supposed to be of   aluminium
whose relevant properties are:

- Density 2707 kg/m^3
- Specific heat 0.88 kJ/kg^{o}C
- Thermal conductivity 160.9 W/m^{o}C

The PCM adopted for this study is Poliethileneglycol 600,
whose relevant properties are:

- Density 1100 kg/m^3
- Thermal conductivity 0.160 W/m^{o}C
- Specific heat 2260 J/kg^{o}C
- Latent heat 146 kJ/kg
- Phase change temperature range 20–25°C
- Coefficient of thermal expansion 0.0075^{o}C^{-1}
- Compatible with aluminium

Considering only heat transfer by conduction in the   PCM,
the total energy can be expressed by

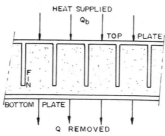

Fig. 1. Layout of the problem cooler

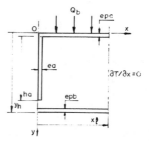

Fig. 2. Details of the problem domain

$$H = h + \delta H \tag{1}$$

where h is the sensible enthalpy and δH is the latent heat. Considering a linear relation between the latent heat and the temperature in the form,

$$\Delta H = \begin{matrix} 0 & -\varepsilon > \\ L/2\varepsilon\,(T + \varepsilon) & -\varepsilon \leq T \leq \varepsilon \\ L & T > \varepsilon \end{matrix} \tag{2}$$

where ε is half the PCM temperature fusion range and L is the latent heat of fusion. Considering that the sensible enthalpy is cT where c is the specific heat, one can write the two dimensional heat conduction equation for this problem as:

$$\rho c\,\frac{\partial T}{\partial t} = k\,\frac{\partial^2 T}{\partial x^2} + k\,\frac{\partial^2 T}{\partial y^2} + F \tag{3}$$

where

$$F = -\rho\,\frac{\partial \Delta H}{\partial t} \tag{4}$$

is the heat source term. The initial and boundary conditions for this problem are:

. $x = 0$ and $x = x_1$, $k\,\dfrac{\partial T}{\partial x} = 0$ \hfill (5)

. $y = y_h$, $k\,\dfrac{\partial T}{\partial y} = 0$ \hfill (6)

. for the case natural convection

$y = y_h$, $-k\,\dfrac{\partial T}{\partial y} = h_c\,(T_w - T_\infty)$ \hfill (7)

. Q_b , in $y = 0$, $-k\,\dfrac{\partial T}{\partial y} = Q_b$ \hfill (8)

. for $t = 0$, $t = -\varepsilon$ \hfill (9)

NUMERICAL TREATMENT

The heat conduction equation and the associated initial and boundary conditions were discretized using the control volume technique due to Patankar [8] in an implicit form resulting in a system of algebraic equations which were solved by the line by line method. The convergence of this method is relatively fast and the precision is good. The domain of the numerical solution was divided into 7 points along the x direction and 8 points along the y direction. This combination resulted in small CPU values and good precision as can be verified from the comparisons with available experimental results in   Fig. 3

and numerical results in Fig. 4.

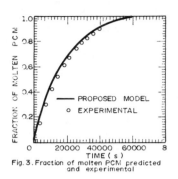

Fig. 3. Fraction of molten PCM predicted
and experimental

Fig. 4. Comparison of present model with
Humpheries model [6]

RESULTS AND DISCUSSIONS

In order to investigate the effects of the geometrical   and
operational parameters of the unit on the temperature   of   the
base at the end of fusion, on the time necessary for   complete
fusion and on the ratio (latent heat)/(heat supplied),   we
adopted a standard configuration and a reference heat flux   for
the half cavity as follows:

. Internal height hp = 0.020 m
. Width lp = 0.005 m
. Fin height hpa = 0.020 m
. Bottom plate thickness epc = 0.001 m
. Reference heat flux Qb1 = 469.83 W/m²

The time for complete fusion as function of the heat   flux
rate for the standard configuration is shown in Fig. 5.   As can
be verified the dimensionless time is largely reduced by   the
increase in the heat flux rate.

Variation of the top plate temperature as function of   the
heat flux rate for the standard configuration is   shown   in
Fig. 6. As can be seen the top plate temperature is found   to
increase with the increase in the heat flux rate.

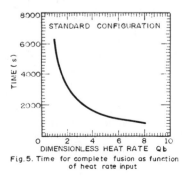

Fig. 5. Time for complete fusion as function
of heat rate input

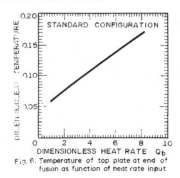

Fig. 6. Temperature of top plate at end of
fusion as function of heat rate input

The temperature distribution along the y-axis for the position $x = x_1$ for the case of a cell of the same geometry as the standard but without fins is found to increase with time as in Fig. 7, while if the cell is finned the temperature field remains almost unchanged, as in Fig. 8. This indicates the necessity of the fins as means of enhancing the heat transfer process within the PCM in the cell.

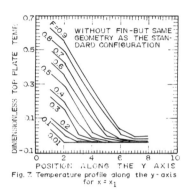

Fig. 7. Temperature profile along the y-axis for $x = x_1$

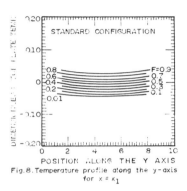

Fig. 8. Temperature profile along the y-axis for $x = x_1$

In this study we considered the variation of the width of the unit $\ell^* = 1; 2; 4$, the variations of the lenth of the fin $h^* = ha/hpa = 0; 0.5; 0.75; 10.0$, the variations of the fin thickness $ea^* = ea/epa = 0.125; 0.25; 0.5; 1$, the variations of the thickness of the bottom and top plates $eb^* = eb/epb = 0.5; 1.0; 1.5$ and the variation of the ratio of the heat flux supplied $Qb^* = Qb/Qb1$.

Because of the massive amount of graphs we only present some samples of the results as the available space permits and comment the general conclusions. The values are referred to the standard configuration values to facilitate the analysis. These ratio values are defined as:

- $\ell^* = \ell/\ell p$
- $h^* = ha/hpa$
- $ea^* = ea/epa$
- $e_b^* = eb/epb$
- $e_c^* = ec/epc$
- $Q^* = Qb/Qb_1$
- $t^* = t/tp$
- $T^* = T/Tp$
- $Qr = Q\ell/Ein$
- $Qr^* = (Q\ell/Ein)/(Q\ell/Ein)_p$

Figures 9 and 10 illustrate the effect of the variation of the width of the cell on the temperature of the top plate at the end of fusion, time necessary to complete the fusion and finally on the ratio of latent heat to heat supplied.

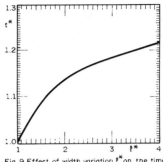

Fig. 9. Effect of width variation l^* on the time
ratio for complete solidification t^*

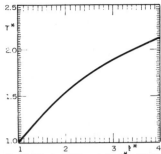

Fig. 10. Effect of width variation l^* on the ratio
of temperature at the end of solidification T^*

As can be seen the effect of the variation of the width of the cell is to increase the complete fusion time, increase the temperature of the top plate and reduce the ratio of latent heat/heat supplied at the top plate. Effect of varying the fin length is found to decrease the time for complete fusion and to reduce the top plate temperature at the end of complete fusion and to increase the ratio of latent heat/heat supplied as can be seen in Fig. 11 and 12.

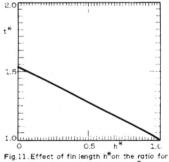

Fig. 11. Effect of fin length h^* on the ratio for
complete solidification t^*

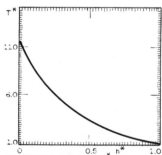

Fig. 12. Effect of fin length h^* on the ratio of
temp. at the end of solidication T^*

The variation of fin thickness is found to decrease the time to complete fusion and reduce the temperature at the end of complete fusion.

In summary it is found that the time necessary to complete melting increase with the increase of the cavity width, decreases greatly with the increase of fin heigth, decreases moderately with increase in fin base and top thickness.

The temperature of the top plate at the end of melting is found to increase with the increase of fin length and slightly decreases with the increase in the thickness of the fin, top and bottom plates.

The transient variation of the heat flux seems to affect

little the temperature of the top plate at the end of melting and also the time necessary to complete the melting process.

CONCLUSIONS

The results of the simplified model proposed to investigate rectangular cavities filled with PCM used as cooling unit for electronic equipment with constant or variable heat flux is found to compare well with experimental data available. It was also demonstrated that the model permits quick investigation of the effects of the geometrical parameters of the unit and the operational variables on the performance of the PCM cooling unit.

Acknowledgements

The authors wish to acknowledge the National Council for Research, CNPq, for the financial support, Mrs. Sonia A. G. Oliveira for the careful typing and Mr. Wilton Furquim for the drawings.

REFERENCES

1. A. Abhat, 1978, Latent Heat Thermal Storage in the Temperature Range 20–80°C, First Seminar on Solar Energy Storage; Thermal Storage, Trieste-Miramare, Italy, Sept.

2. Bell, G.E., 1978, A Refinement of the Heat Balance Integral Method Applied to a Melting Problem, Int. J. Heat Mass Transfer, Vol. 21, pp. 1357–1362.

3. Bonacina, C., Comini, G., Fasano, A. & Primicerio, M., 1973, Numerical Solution of Phase-Change Problems, Int. J. Heat Mass Transfer, Vol. 16, pp. 1825–1832.

4. Goodman, T. & Shea, J.J., 1960, The Melting of Finite Slabs, Trans. ASME, J. Applied Mechanisms, Vol. 32, pp. 16–24.

5. Huang, C. & Shih, Y., 1975, Perturbation Solutions for Planar Solidification of a Saturated Liquid with Convection at the Wall, Int.J. Heat Mass Transfer, Vol.18, pp.689–695.

6. Humphries, W.R. & Griggs, E.I., 1977, Design Handbook for Phase Change Thermal Control and Energy Storage Devices, NASA-TP-1074.

7. Lamé, G. & Claperyon, B.P., 1831, Ann.Chem.Phys., Vol. 47, pp. 250–256.

8. Patankar, S.V., 1980, Numerical Heat Transfer and Fluid Flow, 1$\underline{st}$ ed., pp. 1–77, McGraw-Hill, Book Company, USA.

9. Sen, A.K., 1978, Perturbation Solution for the Shape of a Solidification Interface Subjected to a Spacially Periodic Heat Flux, Trans.ASME, J.Heat Transfer, Vol.109, pp.835–840.

10. Shamsundar, N. & Sparrow, E.M., 1975, Analysis of Multidimensional Conduction Phase Change via the Enthalpic Method, Trans. ASME, J. Heat Transfer, Vol. 97, pp.333–340.

11. Stefan, J., 1891, Ann. Phys. Chemie (Wiedemannsche Annalen), Vol. 42, pp. 269–286.

12. Voller, V.R., 1985, Implicit Finite-Difference Solutions of the Enthalpy Formulation of Stefan Problems, IMA J. of Numerical Analysis, Vol. 5, pp. 201–214.

Ablation problems using a finite control volume technique

B.F. Blackwell, A.L. Thornton, R.E. Hogan
Engineering Sciences Center 1500, Sandia National Laboratories, Albuquerque, NM 87185, USA

ABSTRACT

An element based finite control volume procedure is applied to the solution of ablation problems for 2-D axisymmetric geometries. A mesh consisting of four node quadrilateral elements was used. The nodes are allowed to move in response to the surface recession rate. The computational domain is divided into a region with a structured mesh with moving nodes and a region with an unstructured mesh with stationary nodes. The mesh is constrained to move along spines associated with the original mesh. Example problems are presented for the ablation of a realistic nose tip geometry exposed to aerodynamic heating from a uniform free stream environment.

INTRODUCTION

Early attempts at solving ablation problems utilized 1-D finite difference techniques on a grid that allowed the surface node to move while keeping the interior nodes fixed in space. When the surface node became sufficiently close to its nearest neighbor node, it was removed from the computational domain. The work of Brogan[1] was typical of this approach. When nodes were removed from the computational domain, perturbations in recession rate (and possibly surface temperature) commonly occurred. Moyer and Rindal[2] circumvented this problem by attaching a coordinate system to the receding surface; all nodes moved with the velocity of the ablating surface, with the exception of the last ablating node which was stationary. The Charring Materials Ablation (CMA) code that resulted from this work is still used extensively throughout the aerospace industry. Enhancements to this translating grid technique were reported by Blackwell[3]. While the translating grid technique works quite well for 1-D geometries, it is not readily extendable to multi-dimensions.

Landau[4] introduced the concept of a 1-D contracting finite difference grid in which the computational domain shrinks while keeping the number of nodes in the ablator fixed. This was accomplished by introducing a spatial coordinate transformation that mapped the remaining ablator thickness into the domain $0 \leq \eta \leq 1$ where $\eta = 1$ is always the ablating surface and $\eta = 0$ is the fixed surface. The resulting mesh moves with a local velocity of $\eta \dot{s}$; the ablating surface velocity is $\dot{s}$ while the last ablator nodal velocity is zero. Additional refinements of this one-dimensional method have been presented in Blackwell and Hogan[5].

Several authors have utilized Landau-like transformations to solve two- and three-dimensional ablation problems; see References 6-11 for a representative sampling. The resulting transformed energy equation is more complicated than the original partial differential equation because of the addition of convection like terms due to the moving grid and other geometry change related terms. Finite difference techniques applied to a regular mesh were used to solve the resulting energy equation. Although the above works can handle reasonably complex exterior geometries, they all suffer from the inability to simultaneously model the complicated interior geometries of realistic nose tips.

Element-based methods have been more successful in modeling conduction phenomena in geometrically complex objects than have finite difference, structured grid based methods. Hogge and Gerrekens[12] applied the finite element method to 1-D ablation problems with pyrolysis; a deforming mesh based on penetration depth concepts was utilized. Chin[13] applied the finite element method to 1- and 2-D ablation problems with pyrolysis using a fixed mesh. In comparing his results with the CMA[2] code, oscillations occurred in the surface energy balance terms. It is likely that these oscillations were due to surface elements being removed from the mesh just as were those oscillations reported in Brogran[1]. Hogge and Gerrekens[14] applied the finite element method to 2-D nose tip geometries. A regular mesh was applied to the material region experiencing ablation with one set of mesh lines approximately parallel to the ablating surface. The other mesh lines were formed by straight line rays or spines. For a given ray, the surface node moves a distance $\dot{s} \Delta t$ in the direction of the local surface (inward) normal. All other nodes along this ray are moved proportionally with the last ablating node (for this ray) being fixed in space. This causes the rays to rotate with time and contract their length; however, the rays still remain straight lines. In the nose tip examples they presented, the initial mesh of the tip region was constructed based on a cylindrical coordinate system. This precludes ablation depths greater than one nose radius, which is unrealistic for small nose radius ballistic reentry vehicles.

In the work presented, an element-based numerical method was adopted because of the desire to solve problems with complicated internal geometries. However, it will not be the method of weighted residuals approach used in the traditional finite element method. Instead, energy will be conserved on control volumes of finite size. Additional details on this Finite Control Volume (FCV) method are given in Blackwell and Hogan[15].

DEVELOPMENT OF BASIC EQUATIONS

The starting point for our development is the integral form of conservation of energy on a moving and deforming control volume

$$\frac{d}{dt}\iiint_{\mathcal{V}}\rho e\, d\mathcal{V} + \iint_{A} dA\cdot\dot{q} - \iint_{A}\rho i V_{b}\cdot dA = 0. \tag{1}$$

where V_{b} is the local element velocity. The three terms above represent energy storage, heat conduction, and "apparent" convection of energy due to the mesh motion, respectively. For a solid, the internal energy e is approximately equal the enthalpy i. In order to move the time derivative inside the integral sign in Equation (1), Leibnitz rule[16] will be applied

$$\frac{d}{dt}\iiint_{\mathcal{V}}\rho e\, d\mathcal{V} = \iiint_{\mathcal{V}}\frac{\partial}{\partial t}(\rho e)\, d\mathcal{V} + \iint_{A}\rho e V_{b}\cdot dA \tag{2}$$

Applying Equation (2), the energy equation becomes

$$\iiint_{\mathcal{V}}\frac{\partial}{\partial t}(\rho e)\, d\mathcal{V} + \iint_{A} dA\cdot\dot{q} = 0 \tag{3}$$

Blackwell and Hogan[15] solved Equation (1) using the FCV procedure on a four node quadrilateral mesh for non-ablating problems (stationary mesh) with a bilinear temperature profile; this technique was extended to moving mesh problems. Since the discretization of the conduction term for this work is identical for that of Reference 15, the details will not be repeated here.

In the discretization of the energy storage term in Equation (3), we assumed the density was constant over each element and that $e = C_{v}T$. Expressing the elemental temperature distribution using the element shape function and nodal temperatures, the storage term becomes

$$\iiint_{\mathcal{V}} \frac{\partial T}{\partial t} d\mathcal{V} = \iiint_{\mathcal{V}} \frac{\partial}{\partial t} \begin{bmatrix} N_1 & N_2 & N_3 & N_4 \end{bmatrix}^{(e)} \begin{bmatrix} T_1 \\ T_2 \\ T_3 \\ T_4 \end{bmatrix}^{(e)} d\mathcal{V} \tag{4}$$

For stationary mesh problems, the shape functions are independent of time; however, they are time dependent for a moving mesh. Following Lynch and Gray[17] and Lynch and O'Neill[18], the shape function derivatives can be computed from

$$\frac{dN_i}{dt} = \frac{\partial N_i}{\partial t} + V_b \cdot \nabla N_i = 0 \tag{5}$$

Within a moving element, the shape function total derivative is zero while the partial derivative with respect to time is non-zero. Expanding Equation (4), the energy storage term becomes

$$\iiint_{\mathcal{V}} \frac{\partial T}{\partial t} d\mathcal{V} = \iiint_{\mathcal{V}} \begin{bmatrix} \frac{\partial N_1}{\partial t} & \frac{\partial N_2}{\partial t} & \frac{\partial N_3}{\partial t} & \frac{\partial N_4}{\partial t} \end{bmatrix}^{(e)} \begin{bmatrix} T_1 \\ T_2 \\ T_3 \\ T_4 \end{bmatrix}^{(e)} d\mathcal{V}$$

$$+ \iiint_{\mathcal{V}} \begin{bmatrix} N_1 & N_2 & N_3 & N_4 \end{bmatrix}^{(e)} \frac{d}{dt} \begin{bmatrix} T_1 \\ T_2 \\ T_3 \\ T_4 \end{bmatrix}^{(e)} d\mathcal{V} \tag{6}$$

The first term is the contribution due to the moving mesh while the second term is the stationary mesh energy storage term. The details of the numerical integration of the second term are given in Blackwell and Hogan[15]; the first term was evaluated using a similar technique.

MESH MOTION ALGORITHM

The computational domain for a nose tip will be divided into two regions. The first region (ablating) contains moving elements and must be slightly larger than the maximum anticipated ablation; within this region, a structured mesh was utilized. The second region will be the remainder of the nose tip; its mesh is stationary but may be unstructured. Figure 1 shows a typical nose tip mesh with the structured grid for the moving region and the unstructured grid for the stationary region. The location of the interface between the ablating and non-ablat-

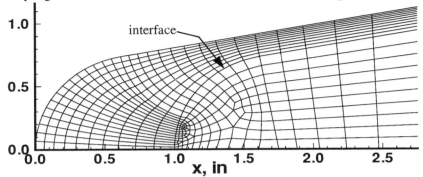

Figure 1. Schematic of initial mesh showing moving and stationary regions.

ing regions is somewhat arbitrary provided the thickness of the ablating region does not shrink to zero. The mesh lines that intersect the ablating surface will be called rays or spines and the mesh will be constrained to move along them. Figure 2 is a schematic of the mesh motion algorithm that will be utilized. The unit

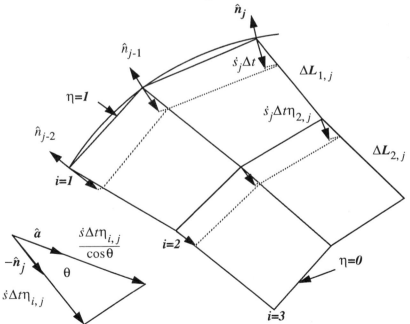

Figure 2. Schematic of mesh motion algorithm.

vector $\hat{a}$ lies along the spines while the unit vector $\hat{n}_j$ is the surface normal for the j'th spine. The variable η is a Landau type variable that gives the distance from th non-ablating boundary as a fraction of the total spine length and is computed from

$$\eta_{i,j} = 1 - \frac{1}{L_j} \sum_{k=1}^{i-1} \Delta L_{k,j} \quad ; \quad L_j = \sum_{k=1}^{l} \Delta L_{k,j}$$

The η values are calculated for the initial mesh and do not change with subseque mesh motion. For a rectangular mesh with recession parallel to one of the coordina directions or 1-D geometries, η is identical to the spatial coordinate transformation i troduced by Landau[4]. The motion in the direction of the spine will always be great than or equal to the motion in the normal direction; see the inset in Figure 2.

COMPUTATIONAL RESULTS

To demonstrate the validity of this mesh motion algorithm, the nose tip given in Figu 1 was exposed to a uniform free stream environment. The Reynolds number was suff ciently low that the boundary layer remained laminar. The nose tip material was grap ite and temperature dependent thermal properties were used. The boundary conditio used were a specified temperature and recession rate as a function of time. Figure 3 pr sents the nose tip shape, deformed mesh, and isotherms for four different times. Th isotherm interval is 500 R with a maximum temperature of 7500 R. The mesh motic algorithm performed quite well. In practice, the aerodynamic heating distribution vari as the nose tip changes shape; this effect was ignored in this calculation. Future wo will include simulations involving turbulent heat transfer on the spherical portion of th nose tip and inclusion of more realistic surface energy balance relationships.

REFERENCES

1 . Brogan, J. J., 'A Numerical Method of Solution for Heat Conduction in Composi Slabs with a Receding Surface,' LMSD 288204, Lockheed Missiles and Space Div sion, Lockheed Aircraft Corp., Sunnyvale, CA, January 1960.

2 . Moyer, C. B. and Rindal, R. A., 'An Analysis of the Coupled Chemically Reactir Boundary Layer and Charring Ablator, Part II, Finite Difference Solution for the I Depth Response of Charring Materials Considering Surface Chemical and Energy Ba ances,' NASA CR-1061, June, 1968.

3 . Blackwell, B. F., 'Numerical Prediction of One-Dimensional Ablation Using a F nite Control Volume Procedure with Exponential Differencing,' Numerical He Transfer, Vol. 14, pp.17-34, 1988.

4 . Landau, H. G., 'Heat Conduction in a Melting Solid,' Quarterly of Applied Mat Vol. VIII, No. 1, pp. 81-94, 1950.

5 . Blackwell, B. F. and Hogan, R. E., 'One-Dimensional Ablation Using Land Transformation and Finite Control Volume Procedure,' submitted to Journal of The mophysics and Heat Transfer, 1993.

6 . Popper, L. A. and Toong, T. Y., 'Three-Dimensional Ablation Considering Shap Changes and Internal Heat Conduction,' AIAA Paper No. 70-199, Presented at AIA 8th Aerospace Sciences Meeting, NY, NY, January 19-21, 1970.

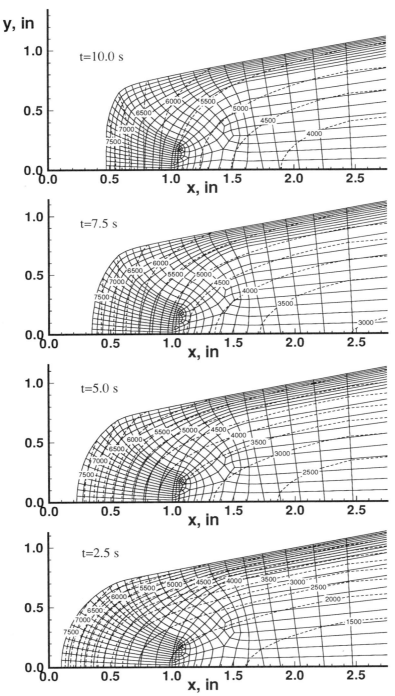

Figure 3. Computational results for 2.5, 5.0, 7.5, and 10.0 s.

7 . Chin, J. H., 'Shape Change and Conduction for Nosetips at Angle of Attack,' AIAA Journal, Vol. 13, No. 5, pp. 599-604, May 1975.

8 . Rafinejad, D. and Kendall, R. M., 'Transient Conduction and Shape Change Calculation of Three-Dimensional Nose Tips,' AIAA Paper No. 76-168, Presented at AIAA 14th Aerospace Sciences Meeting, Washington, DC, January 26-28, 1976.

9 . King, H. H. C, Muramoto, K. K., Murray, A. L., and Pronchick, S. W., 'ABRES Shape Change Code (ASCC 86), Technical Report and User's Manual,' BMO TR-87-57, Headquarters Ballistic Missile Office/MYES, Norton AFB, CA, December, 1986.

10 . Cai, T. and Hou, X., 'A Simple Method for Tackling Moving Boundary in Numerical Simulation of Temperature Response of the Solid Rocket Motor,' AIAA Paper No. 88-0083, Presented at AIAA 26th Aerospace Sciences Meeting, Reno, NV, January 11-14, 1988.

11 . Muramoto, K. K., Squire, T. H., and Thompson, C. F. Jr., 'A Thermal Analysis Code for Three-Dimensional Wing Leading Edges,' AIAA Paper No. 91-1354, Presented at AIAA 26th Thermophysics Conference, Honolulu, Hawaii, June 24-26, 1991.

12 . Hogge, M. and Gerrekens, P., 'One-Dimensional Finite Element Analysis of Thermal Ablation with Pyrolysis,' Computer Methods in Applied Mechanics and Engineering, Vol. 33, pp. 609-634, 1982.

13 . Chin, J. H., 'Charring Ablation by Finite Element,' Numerical Methods in Thermal Problems II, Edited by R. W. Lewis, K. Morgan, and B. A. Schrefler, Pineridge Press, Swansea, Wales, pp. 218-229, 1982.

14 . Hogge, M. and Gerrekens, P., 'Two-Dimensional Deforming Finite Element Methods for Surface Ablation,' AIAA Journal, Vol. 23, No. 3, pp. 465-472, 1985.

15 . Blackwell, B. F. and Hogan, R. E. 'Numerical Solution of Heat Conduction Problems Using a Finite Control Volume Technique, Journal of Thermophysics and Heat Transfer, Vol. 7, No. 2, April-June 1993.

16 . Bird, R. B., Stewart, W. E., and Lightfoot, E. N., 'Transport Phenomena,' John Wiley & Sons, Inc., New York, p. 732, 1960.

17 . Lynch, D. R. and Gray, W. G., 'Finite Element Simulation of Flow in Deforming Regions,' Journal of Computational Physics, Vol. 36, pp. 135-153, 1980.

18 . Lynch, D. R. and O'Neill, K., 'Continuously Deforming Finite Elements for the Solution of Parabolic Problems, With and Without Phase Change,' International Journal for Numerical Methods in Engineering,' Vol. 17, pp. 81-96, 1981.

Application of the dual reciprocity boundary element method on Stefan problems

B.Šarler, A. Košir

Jožef Stefan Institute, University of Ljubljana, Ljubljana, Slovenia

ABSTRACT

This paper describes the application of the dual reciprocity boundary element method for the solution of Stefan problem that appears when treating multidimensional Fourier conduction melting and solidification in rigid systems. The physical model is based on the mixture continuum formulation and includes temperature dependent thermal conductivities and specific heats of the solid and liquid phase. Phase-change could take place at distinct melting temperature or continuously on a solidus-liquidus temperature interval. The resulting governing equation is reformulated by the Kirchhoff transform and cast in the latent heat source term shape. Boundary element method solution procedure is structured by the Green's function of the Laplace equation and by the dual reciprocity boundary-only representation of domain integrals based on the $1 + r$ space splines. The highly non-linear source term updating is made following the recently deduced efficient Voller and Swaminathan scheme. The numerical solution is constructed by straight line boundary elements with constant space and linear time splines. The sensitivity of the solution with respect to space-time discretization was investigated on a two-phase Rathjen and Jiji's analytical solution for the solidification of an infinite rectangular corner.

INTRODUCTION

The research of the solid-liquid phase change involves interdisciplinary theoretical, experimental, and computational modelling of phase transformation kinetics, solid mechanics, and transport phenomena. It has an important impact on many basic-science, engineering, and medical developments. An overview of the discipline could be found in [1]. A data base of relevant references, including several key words is listed in [2].

Due to the demonstrated [3] suitability of the Boundary Element Method (BEM) for discrete approximative solution of nonlinear transport phenomena models, a great interest also exists to enable this method to cope with melting and solidification. A comprehensive survey of the related BEM applications is published in [4].

The principal incitement for present work was an advanced numerical solution of the boundary-domain integral equation describing the mixture continuum formulation [5] of the energy transport based on a simple conduction governed monoconstituent sub-model.

This equation was deduced in [6] and forms a part of the Laplace equation fundamental solution structured boundary-domain integral equations of the general mixture continuum formulation for the extremely non-linear coupled transport of mass, energy, momentum, and species during melting and solidification.

FORMULATION

Geometry and Material Properties

Consider a connected fixed domain Ω with boundary Γ occupied by a rigid phase change material described with the density ρ_0 the temperature dependent specific heat $c_{\mathcal{P}}$ and the thermal conductivity $k_{\mathcal{P}}$ of the solid $\mathcal{P} = s$ and the liquid $\mathcal{P} = \mathcal{L}$ phase, and the specific latent heat of solid-liquid phase change $H_{\mathcal{M}}^0$.

Governing Equation

The mixture continuum formulation of the energy transport for the assumed system is

$$\rho_0 \frac{\partial}{\partial t}(f_S H_S + f_{\mathcal{L}} H_{\mathcal{L}}) = -\nabla \cdot (f_S \mathbf{F}_S + f_{\mathcal{L}} \mathbf{F}_{\mathcal{L}}) + f_S q_S + f_{\mathcal{L}} q_{\mathcal{L}}, \quad f_S + f_{\mathcal{L}} = 1. \quad (1)$$

Function $f_{\mathcal{P}}$ presents the temperature dependent volume fraction, $H_{\mathcal{P}}$ the specific enthalpy, $\mathbf{F}_{\mathcal{P}}$ heat flux, and $q_{\mathcal{P}}$ heat source of the phase $\mathcal{P}$. Heat sources could depend arbitrary on temperature and independent time and position variables. Due to the local thermal equilibrium between the phases, the mixture temperature T and the phase temperatures T_S and $T_{\mathcal{L}}$ are equal.

Constitutive equations for the two heat fluxes are based on the Fourier relation

$$\mathbf{F}_S = - k_S \nabla T, \quad \mathbf{F}_{\mathcal{L}} = - k_{\mathcal{L}} \nabla T, \quad (2)$$

and the enthalpy-temperature relationship is defined as

$$H_S = c_S(T_H) T_H + \int_{T_H}^{T} c_S(\theta)\, d\theta, \quad H_{\mathcal{L}} = c_{\mathcal{L}}(T_H) T_H + \int_{T_H}^{T} c_{\mathcal{L}}(\theta)\, d\theta + H_{\mathcal{M}}^0, \quad (3)$$

with T_H representing the enthalpy reference temperature. The governing equation could be rewritten in the following latent heat source term form

$$\rho_0\, c\, \frac{\partial T}{\partial t} = \nabla \cdot (k \nabla T) + q - \rho_0 \frac{dH_{\mathcal{M}}}{dT} \frac{\partial T}{\partial t}, \quad (4)$$

with

$$q = f_S q_S + f_{\mathcal{L}} q_{\mathcal{L}}, \quad \frac{dH_{\mathcal{M}}}{dT} = (H_{\mathcal{L}} - H_S) \frac{df_{\mathcal{L}}}{dT} = - (H_{\mathcal{L}} - H_S) \frac{df_S}{dT}. \quad (5)$$

The thermal conductivity k and the specific heat c of the mixture are defined as

$$k = k_0 + k_T = f_S k_S + f_{\mathcal{L}} k_{\mathcal{L}}, \quad c = c_0 + c_T = f_S c_S + f_{\mathcal{L}} c_{\mathcal{L}}. \quad (6)$$

Constants k_0, c_0 present mean values, and functions k_T, c_T temperature behaviour of the respective mixture quantities.

Initial and Boundary Conditions

We seek the solution of the governing equation for mixture temperature at final time $t = t_0 + \Delta t$, where t_0 presents initial time and Δt positive time increment. The solution is constructed by the initial and boundary conditions that follow.

The initial temperature $T(\mathbf{p}, t_0)$ at point with position vector $\mathbf{p}$ and time t_0 is defined through known function T_0

$$T(\mathbf{p}, t_0) = T_0; \quad \mathbf{p} \in \Omega \oplus \Gamma. \quad (7)$$

The boundary Γ is divided into not necessary connected parts Γ^D, Γ^N, and Γ^R

$$\Gamma = \Gamma^D \oplus \Gamma^N \oplus \Gamma^R, \quad (8)$$

with Dirichlet, Neumann, and Robin type of boundary conditions respectively. These boundary conditions are at point $\mathbf{p}$ and time $t_0 \le t \le t_0 + \Delta t$ defined through known functions T_Γ, F_Γ, and h

$$T(\mathbf{p}, t) \;=\; T_\Gamma; \;\; \mathbf{p} \in \Gamma^D, \tag{9}$$

$$-k\,\nabla T(\mathbf{p}, t) \cdot \mathbf{n}_\Gamma(\mathbf{p}) \;=\; F_\Gamma; \;\; \mathbf{p} \in \Gamma^N, \tag{10}$$

$$-k\,\nabla T(\mathbf{p}, t) \cdot \mathbf{n}_\Gamma(\mathbf{p}) \;=\; h\,[\,T(\mathbf{p}, t) - T_\Gamma\,]; \;\; \mathbf{p} \in \Gamma^R, \tag{11}$$

where the heat transfer coefficient h and other known functions are allowed to depend arbitrary on thermal field. The outward pointing normal on Γ is denoted by $\mathbf{n}_\Gamma(\mathbf{p})$. Constraint

$$T_0 = T_\Gamma; \;\; \mathbf{p} \in \Gamma^D, \;\; t = t_0, \tag{12}$$

is required for the problem to be well-posed.

Governing Discretization Equation

The equation (4) is rewritten into boundary-domain integral shape by the introduction of the Kirchhoff variable

$$\mathcal{T} = T_T + \int_{T_T}^{T} \frac{k(\theta)}{k_0}\, d\theta = T + \int_{T_T}^{T} \frac{k_T(\theta)}{k_0}\, d\theta, \tag{13}$$

with T_T denoting the Kirchhoff variable reference temperature, and by weighting it over space-time $[\Omega] \times [t_0, t_0 + \Delta t]$ with the fundamental solution of the Laplace equation $T^*(\mathbf{p}; \mathbf{s})$. After lengthy procedure, detailed in [7], the following boundary-domain integral expression is obtained

$$\int_\Omega \rho_0\, c_0\, \mathcal{T}(\mathbf{p}, t_0 + \Delta t)\, T^*(\mathbf{p}; \mathbf{s})\, d\Omega - \int_\Omega \rho_0\, c_0\, \mathcal{T}(\mathbf{p}, t_0)\, T^*(\mathbf{p}; \mathbf{s})\, d\Omega$$

$$= \int_{t_0}^{t_0+\Delta t} \int_\Gamma k_0\, T^*\, \nabla \mathcal{T} \cdot d\Gamma\, dt - \int_{t_0}^{t_0+\Delta t} \int_\Gamma k_0\, \mathcal{T}\, \nabla T^* \cdot d\Gamma\, dt + \int_{t_0}^{t_0+\Delta t} c^*(\Omega, \mathbf{s})\, k_0\, \mathcal{T}(\mathbf{s}, t)\, dt$$

$$+ \int_{t_0}^{t_0+\Delta t} \int_\Omega \left[q + Q\, \frac{\partial \mathcal{T}}{\partial t} \right] T^*\, d\Omega\, dt; \quad Q = \rho_0 \left[c_0 - \frac{k_0}{k} \left(c + \frac{dH_\mathcal{M}}{dT} \right) \right],$$

$$c^*(\Omega, \mathbf{s}) = \int_\Omega \nabla^2 T^*(\mathbf{p}; \mathbf{s})\, d\Omega, \quad T_2^*(\mathbf{p}; \mathbf{s}) = \frac{1}{2\pi} \log \frac{r_0}{|\mathbf{p} - \mathbf{s}|}, \quad T_3^*(\mathbf{p}; \mathbf{s}) = -\frac{1}{4\pi} \frac{\mathbf{p} - \mathbf{s}}{|\mathbf{p} - \mathbf{s}|^3}. \tag{14}$$

Functions T_2^* and T_3^* represent the two and the three dimensional planar symmetry form of the fundamental solution T^*. Equation (14) is solved by the related Kirchhoff transformed initial and boundary conditions

$$\mathcal{T}(\mathbf{p}, t_0) \;=\; \int_{T_T}^{T_0} \frac{k}{k_0}\, d\theta; \;\; \mathbf{p} \in \Omega \oplus \Gamma, \tag{15}$$

$$\mathcal{T}(\mathbf{p}, t) \;=\; \int_{T_T}^{T_\Gamma} \frac{k}{k_0}\, d\theta; \;\; \mathbf{p} \in \Gamma^D, \tag{16}$$

$$-k_0\, \nabla \mathcal{T}(\mathbf{p}, t) \cdot \mathbf{n}_\Gamma(\mathbf{p}) \;=\; F_\Gamma; \;\; P \in \Gamma^N, \tag{17}$$

$$-k_0\, \nabla \mathcal{T}(\mathbf{p}, t) \cdot \mathbf{n}_\Gamma(\mathbf{p}) \;=\; h\,\Big[\,\mathcal{T}(\mathbf{p}, t) - T_\Gamma - \int_{T_T}^{T[\mathcal{T}(\mathbf{p},t)]} \frac{k_T}{k_0}\, d\theta\,\Big]; \; P \in \Gamma^R. \tag{18}$$

SOLUTION PROCEDURE

Transformation of Domain Integrals into Boundary Integrals

The solution procedure is based on the Dual Reciprocity Method (DRM) [8] that handles the boundary-domain integral equation of the type (14) through the calculation of the boundary integrals only.

An arbitrary function $\mathcal{F}(\mathbf{p}, t)$ is approximated over the domain Ω with $n = 1, 2, \ldots, N$ space $\Psi_n^p(\mathbf{p})$ and time splines $\Psi_n^t(t)$

$$\mathcal{F}(\mathbf{p}, t) \approx \Psi_n^p(\mathbf{p}, t)\,\Psi_n^t(t), \quad \mathcal{F}(\mathbf{p}_m, t) = \Psi_{nm}^p\,\Psi_n^t(t), \quad \Psi_n^t(t) = [\Psi_{nm}^p]^{-1}\mathcal{F}(\mathbf{p}_m, t). \quad (19)$$

The Einstein summation is used in this text wherever possible.

Using the Green's second identity and the definition for the functions $\hat{\Psi}_p^n$ the domain integral of function $\mathcal{F}(\mathbf{p}, t)$ weighted with the Green function T^* over Ω approximately transforms into a series of N integrals over its boundary

$$\int_\Omega \mathcal{F}(\mathbf{p}, t)\,T^*(\mathbf{p}; \mathbf{s})\,d\Omega \approx \int_\Omega \Psi_n^p(\mathbf{p})\,\Psi_n^t(t)\,T^*(\mathbf{p}; \mathbf{s})\,d\Omega$$

$$= \left[\int_\Gamma T^*(\mathbf{p}; \mathbf{s})\,\nabla\hat{\Psi}_n^p(\mathbf{p})\cdot d\Gamma - \int_\Gamma \hat{\Psi}_n^p(\mathbf{p})\,\nabla T^*(\mathbf{p}; \mathbf{s})\cdot d\Gamma + c^*(\Omega, \mathbf{s})\,\hat{\Psi}_n^p(\mathbf{s})\right][\Psi_{nm}^p]^{-1}\mathcal{F}(\mathbf{p}_m, t);$$

$$\nabla^2\hat{\Psi}_n^p(\mathbf{p}) = \Psi_n^p(\mathbf{p}). \quad (20)$$

The efficiency of the transformation (20) strongly depends on the choice of the splines Ψ_n^p which is not unique. We select the form

$$\Psi_n^p(\mathbf{p}) = \sum_{i_\Psi=0}^{I_\Psi} |\mathbf{p} - \mathbf{p}_n|^{i_\Psi}, \quad \hat{\Psi}_n^p(\mathbf{p}) = \sum_{i_\Psi=0}^{I_\Psi} \frac{|\mathbf{p} - \mathbf{p}_n|^{i_\Psi+2}}{(i_\Psi + 2)(i_\Psi + I_{\dim})}, \quad (21)$$

with $I_\Psi = 1$, as suggested by Partridge and Brebbia [9]. Parameter $I_{\dim} = 2$ stands for problems defined in two, and $I_{\dim} = 3$ for problems defined in three dimensions.

Nonlinear Source Term Updating, Time and Space Discretization

The numerical solution of the nonlinear integral equation (14) inherently requires timestep iterations. The recently developed robust and accurate Voller and Swaminathan scheme [10] has been used for the iterative updating of the nonlinear source term. Its DRM adapted essentials of the scheme could be perceived from the equation (28).

The governing discretization equation (14) is discretized by the introduction of the linear time splines over the time interval $[t_0, t_0 + \Delta t]$. The boundary is discretized by N_Γ boundary elements Γ_k with piecewise straight-line geometry and piecewise constant space splines. The first N_Γ points $\mathbf{p}_n$ in the splines (21) coincide with the nodes (geometric centers) of the boundary elements, and the last N_Ω points are arbitrary distributed in Ω. All subsequently involved boundary integrals have been evaluated analytically.

Setup of Algebraic Equations System

The equation (14) is solved by constructing an algebraic equation system of $j = 1, 2, \ldots, N$ equations. These equations are obtained by writing the discretized form of equation (14) for source point $\mathbf{s}$ to coincide with the nodal points $\mathbf{p}_n$. The deduced system of algebraic equations could be cast in a symbolic form

$$\mathbf{F}_{jm}^{t_0+\Delta t\,i}\,T^i(\mathbf{p}_m, t_0 + \Delta t) + \mathbf{T}_{jm}^{t_0+\Delta t}\cdot\nabla T^i(\mathbf{p}_m, t_0 + \Delta t)$$

$$= \mathbf{F}_{jm}^{t_0}\,T(\mathbf{p}_m, t_0) + \mathbf{T}_{jm}^{t_0}\cdot\nabla T(\mathbf{p}_m, t_0) + \mathbf{q}_{jm}^{t_0+\Delta t}\,q(\mathbf{p}_m, t_0 + \Delta t) + \mathbf{q}_{jm}^{t_0}\,q(\mathbf{p}_m, t_0), \quad (22)$$

which has to be rearranged according to the boundary condition types before the solution. Superscript i denotes the value of quantity at i-th iteration. The matrix elements are defined by

$$F_{jm}^{t_0+\Delta t\, i} = \Psi_{jn}\,[\Psi_{n\underline{m}}^p]^{-1}\left[\rho_0\,c_0 - Q_{t_0+\Delta t\,\underline{m}}^i + \frac{1}{2}\left(\frac{dQ}{dT}T\right)_{t_0+\Delta t\,\underline{m}}^i\right]$$

$$+ \delta_{km}\frac{\Delta t\,k_0}{2}\int_{\Gamma_k}\nabla T^*(\mathbf{p};\mathbf{s}_j)\cdot d\Gamma - \delta_{jm}\frac{\Delta t\,c^*(\Omega,\mathbf{s}_j)\,k_0}{2}, \tag{23}$$

$$F_{jm}^{t_0} = \Psi_{jn}\,[\Psi_{n\underline{m}}^p]^{-1}\left[\rho_0\,c_0 - Q[T(\mathbf{p}_{\underline{m}},t_0)] + \frac{1}{2}\frac{dQ}{dT}[T(\mathbf{p}_{\underline{m}},t_0)]\,T(\mathbf{p}_{\underline{m}},t_0)\right]$$

$$- \delta_{km}\frac{\Delta t\,k_0}{2}\int_{\Gamma_k}\nabla T^*(\mathbf{p};\mathbf{s}_j)\cdot d\Gamma + \delta_{jm}\frac{\Delta t\,c^*(\Omega,\mathbf{s}_j)\,k_0}{2}, \tag{24}$$

$$\mathbf{T}_{jm}^{t_0+\Delta t} = -\mathbf{T}_{jm}^{t_0} = -\delta_{km}\frac{\Delta t\,k_0}{2}\int_{\Gamma_k}T^*(\mathbf{p};\mathbf{s}_j)\,d\Gamma, \tag{25}$$

$$q_{jm}^{t_0+\Delta t} = q_{jm}^{t_0} = \Psi_{jn}\,[\Psi_{n\underline{m}}^p]^{-1}\frac{\Delta t}{2}, \tag{26}$$

$$\Psi_{jn} = \left[\sum_{k}^{N_\Gamma}\int_{\Gamma_k}T^*(\mathbf{p};\mathbf{s}_j)\,\nabla\hat{\Psi}_n^p(\mathbf{p})\cdot d\Gamma - \sum_{k}^{N_\Gamma}\int_{\Gamma_k}\hat{\Psi}_n^p(\mathbf{p})\,\nabla T^*(\mathbf{p};\mathbf{s}_j)\cdot d\Gamma + c^*(\Omega,\mathbf{s}_{\underline{j}})\,\hat{\Psi}_n^p(\mathbf{s}_{\underline{j}})\right]. \tag{27}$$

The value of $Q_{t_0+\Delta t\,m}$ at $(i+1)$-th iteration level is obtained through the values at i-th and $(i-1)$-th iteration level

$$Q_{t_0+\Delta t\,m}^{i+1}$$

$$= Q[T^i(\mathbf{p},t_0+\Delta t)] + \frac{dQ}{dT}[T^i(\mathbf{p}_m,t_0+\Delta t)]\,[T^i(\mathbf{p}_m,t_0+\Delta t) - T^{i-1}(\mathbf{p}_m,t_0+\Delta t)],$$

$$\left(\frac{dQ}{dT}T\right)_{t_0+\Delta t\,m}^{i+1} = \frac{dQ}{dT}[T^i(\mathbf{p}_m,t_0+\Delta t)]\,[2\,T^i(\mathbf{p}_m,t_0+\Delta t) - T^{i-1}(\mathbf{p}_m,t_0+\Delta t)]. \tag{28}$$

The timestep iterations are stopped when the absolute Kirchhoff variable difference of the two successive iterations does not exceed some predetermined positive margin T_δ in any of the meshpoints $\mathbf{p}_m$.

NUMERICAL EXAMPLE

Solidification of an Infinite Rectangular Corner

A comparison with the standard two-dimensional planar symmetry two-phase Rathjen and Jiji's [11] quasi-analytical solution is chosen to benchmark the deduced solution procedure. It represents a solidification of a planar semi-infinite rectangular corner with cartesian coordinates $X \geq 0\,[\mathrm{m}]$, $Y \geq 0\,[\mathrm{m}]$ approximated by a finite square region $0\,[\mathrm{m}] \leq X \leq 1.5\,[\mathrm{m}]$ and $0\,[\mathrm{m}] \leq Y \leq 1.5\,[\mathrm{m}]$. It is initially filled with material at constant temperature $T_0 = 1.3\,[\mathrm{K}]$. Dirichlet boundary conditions with $T_\Gamma = 0\,[\mathrm{K}]$ are imposed on boundaries $X = 0\,[\mathrm{m}]$ and $Y = 0\,[\mathrm{m}]$. Boundary conditions at $X = 1.5\,[\mathrm{m}]$ and $Y = 1.5\,[\mathrm{m}]$ are approximated by Neumann type ones with $F_\Gamma = 0\,[\mathrm{W}/(\mathrm{m\,K})]$. The material properties are $\rho_0 = 1\,[\mathrm{kg/m^3}]$, $c_S = c_L = 1\,[\mathrm{J}/(\mathrm{kg\,K})]$, $k_S = k_S = 1\,[\mathrm{W}/(\mathrm{m\,K})]$, $H_{\mathcal{M}}^0 = 0.25\,[\mathrm{J/kg}]$ with melting temperature $T_{\mathcal{M}}^0 = 1\,[\mathrm{K}]$. Distinct phase change is for computational purposes approximated by a narrow continuous range from $T_S^0 = T_{\mathcal{M}}^0 - \Delta T_{\mathcal{M}}^0$ to $T_{\mathcal{L}}^0 = T_{\mathcal{M}}^0 + \Delta T_{\mathcal{M}}^0$ with $\Delta T_{\mathcal{M}}^0 = 0.01\,[\mathrm{K}]$.

$$f_{\mathcal{L}} = \begin{cases} 0; & T < T_S^0, \\ (T - T_S^0)/(T_{\mathcal{L}}^0 - T_S^0); & T_S^0 \leq T \leq T_{\mathcal{L}}^0, \\ 1; & T > T_{\mathcal{L}}^0. \end{cases} \tag{29}$$

meshes	N_Γ	N_Ω	N	
^1M	20	25	45	
^2M	40	100	140	
^3M	60	225	285	
timesteps				Δt[s]
$^1\Delta t$				0.01
$^2\Delta t$				0.002
$^3\Delta t$				0.001

Table 1: Discretization parameters used in calculations.

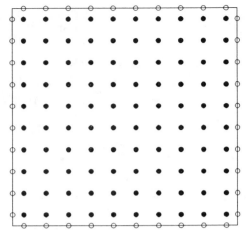

Figure 1: Arrangement of the mesh ^2M. Boundary nodes are denoted with o and the domain nodes with •. Meshes ^1M and ^3M have similar displaced configuration.

The numerically obtained temperatures $T_{cal} = \Psi_n^p(\mathbf{p})\,\Psi_n^p(t)$ have been compared with the solution from [11] in $N_{com} = 10201$ uniform meshpoints $\mathbf{p}_{com}$ (these points coincide with the crossections of the lines $Y = const.$ and $X = const.$ in Figure 2). The maximum T_{max} absolute error and the average T_{ave} absolute error of the numerical solution are

$$T_{max} = \max |T_{cal}(\mathbf{p}_{com\,n}, t) - T_{ana}(\mathbf{p}_{com\,n}, t)|; \quad n = 1, 2, \ldots, N_{com}, \tag{30}$$

$$T_{ave} = \frac{1}{N_{com}} \sum_{n=1}^{N_{com}} |T_{cal}(\mathbf{p}_{com\,n}, t) - T_{ana}(\mathbf{p}_{com\,n}, t)|. \tag{31}$$

CONCLUSIONS

This paper presents the first attempts to computationally solve a multidimensional moving boundary problem through calculations that reduce to the integration of the fixed boundary quantities only. The results preliminary confirm the suitability of the described method for coping with such Stefan type of problems.

In addition, complementary benchmarking of the developed method is needed. It will concentrate on the one-phase classical Stefan problem recalculations and research of the solution sensitivity with respect to the Stefan number for both one- and two-phase problems and will include all aspects as treated in the excellent Dalhuijsen and Segal's study [12].

The principal advantages of the method are the ease of the implementation of the different boundary condition types, straightforward mesh generation, sequel elimination of large data handling, and the potential ability to easily cope with geometrically moving boundaries as well.

The main disadvantage of the method is the resulting large algebraic system of equations, since the domain meshpoints have to be present. This unfavourable property could be set out efficiently by substructuring technique in combination with the adaptive strategy, that are both under development.

The convective term will be included in the future upgradings, thus enabling us to solve the complete energy transport equation in the discussed context.

discretization	$^1M\,^2\Delta t$	$^2M\,^1\Delta t$	$^2M\,^2\Delta t$	$^2M\,^3\Delta t$	$^3M\,^2\Delta t$
$T_{\max}$ [K]	0.268	0.366	0.196	0.098	0.075
T_{ave} [K]	0.059	0.035	0.021	0.012	0.019

Table 2: Absolute error in the numerically calculated temperatures for different space-time discretizations at time $t = 0.1$ [s]. The Table shows convergence of the method with the shorter timesteps and finer meshes. The timestep iteration margin T_δ used in calculations is 0.002 [K]. The computer time for solving one iteration on mesh ^1M, ^2M, and ^3M is approximately 45, 200, and 1000 CPU seconds respectively on 25 MHz PC i486 based compatible with NDP Fortran 77 compiler.

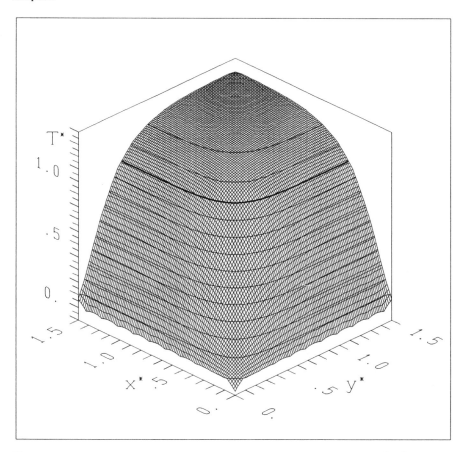

Figure 2: Axonometric view of the interpolated solution for the discretization $^2M\,^2\Delta t$. The bold isotherm represents the solid-liquid interphase boundary and the dimensionless scales are simply $T^* = T/(1\,[K])$, $X^* = X/(1\,[m])$, and $Y^* = (Y/1\,[m])$. The positions of the maximum errors are in the corners of the square.

Acknowledgement

The work described in this paper is a part of the project Computational Mechanics of Melting and Solidification. The authors would like to acknowledge *Ministry for Science and Technology, Republic of Slovenia* for financial support. Additionally, the authors wish to thank *International Bureau, Research Centre Jülich, FRG* for partial funding through the project Computational Modelling of Solid-Liquid Phase Change Systems. The application of the described method will present a part of the continuous casting process simulator of the following Slovenian companies *IMPOL, Mariborska Livarna Maribor, Steelworks Jesenice* and *TALUM*.

REFERENCES

[1] Yao, L.S. and Prusa, J. Melting and Freezing, Hartnett, J.P. (ed.), Advances in Heat Transfer Vol.19, Academic Press, New York, pp.1-95, 1989.

[2] Šarler, B. Bibliography on Stefan problem 1992, Technical report IJS-DP-6561, "Jožef Stefan" Institute, Ljubljana, 1992.

[3] Wrobel, L.C., Brebbia, C.A. An Overview of Boundary Element Applications to Nonlinear Heat Transfer Problems, Wriggers, P., Wagner, W. (eds.), Nonlinear Computational Mechanics - State of the Art, Springer-Verlag Berlin and New York, pp.226-239, 1991.

[4] Šarler, B., Mavko, B. and Kuhn, G. Chapter 16: A Survey of the Attempts for the Solution of Solid-Liquid Phase Change Problems by the Boundary Element Method, Wrobel, L.C. and Brebbia, C.A. (eds.) Computational Methods for Free and Moving Boundary Problems in Heat and Fluid Flow, Computational Engineering Series, Computational Mechanics Publications and Elsevier Applied Science, Southampton and London, 1993, (in print).

[5] Bennon, W.D. and Incropera, F.P. A continuum model for momentum, heat and species transport in binary solid-liquid phase change systems - I.Model formulation, Int.J.Heat Mass Transfer, Vol.30, pp.2161-2170, 1987.

[6] Šarler, B., Mavko, B. and Kuhn, G. A BEM formulation for mass, momentum, energy and species transport in binary solid-liquid phase change systems, Z.Angew.Math.Mech., Vol.73, 1993, (accepted for publication).

[7] Šarler, B., Mavko, B. and Kuhn, G. Mixture continuum formulation of convection-conduction energy transport in multidimensional multiconstituent solid-liquid phase change systems for BEM solution techniques, Eng.Anal., Vol.10, 1993, (accepted for publication).

[8] Partridge, P.W., Brebbia, C.A. and Wrobel, L.C. The Dual Reciprocity Boundary Element Method, Computational Mechanics Publications and Elsevier Applied Science, Southampton and London, 1991.

[9] Partridge, P.W. and Brebbia, C.A. Computer implementation of the BEM dual reciprocity method for the solution of general field equations, Comm.Appl.Num.Meth., Vol.6, pp.83-92, 1990.

[10] Voller, V.R. and Swaminathan, C.R. General source-based method for solidification phase change, Num.Heat Transfer, Vol.19B, pp.175-189, 1991.

[11] Rathjen, K.A. and Jiji, L.M. Heat conduction with melting or freezing in a corner, J.Heat Transfer, Vol.93, pp.101-109, 1971.

[12] Dalhuijsen A.L. and Segal, A. Comparison of finite element techniques for solidification problems, Int.J.Numer.Methods Eng., Vol.23, pp.1807-1829, 1986.

On the determination of the unknown coefficients through phase change problems with temperature-dependent thermal conductivity

D.A. Tarzia

Departamento de Matemática, FCE, Universidad Austral, Paraguay 1950, 2000, Rosario, Argentina

ABSTRACT

We study the determination of unknown thermal coefficient of a semi-infinite material through a phase-change process with an overspecified condition on the fixed face with temperature-dependent thermal conductivity. We determine necessary and sufficient conditions on data in order to obtain the existence of the solution. We also give formulae for the unknown coefficients.

INTRODUCTION

Heat transfer problems with phase-change such as melting and freezing have been studied in the last century because of their wide scientific and technological applications. For example, a review of a long bibliography on moving and free boundary problems for the heat equation, particularly concerning the Stefan problem, is presented in [3] with a large bibliography.

We consider the following solidification problem for a semi-infinite material with an overspecified condition on the fixed face :

$$\begin{vmatrix} \rho \, c \, T_t = (\, k(T) \, T_x \,)_x \, , & 0 < x < s(t) \, , t > 0, \\ s(0) = 0 \, , \\ T(0,t) = T_o < T_f \, , t > 0 \, , \end{vmatrix} \qquad (1)$$

$$T(s(t),t) = T_f \ , t > 0 \ ,$$
$$k(T_f) \, T_x(s(t),t) = \rho \, h \, \dot{s}(t) \ , t > 0 \ , \tag{1}$$
$$k(T_o) \, T_x(0,t) = \frac{q_o}{\sqrt{t}} \ , t > 0 \ ,$$

where $T = T(x,t)$ is the temperature of the solid phase, $\rho > 0$ is the density of mass, $h > 0$ is the latent heat of fusion by unity of mass, $c > 0$ is the specific heat, $x = s(t)$ is the phase-change interface, T_f is the phase-change temperature (T_o is a reference temperature), $k = k(T) = k_o \, [1 + \beta \, (T - T_o)/(T_f - T_o)]$ [1,2] is the thermal conductivity, $\alpha_o = k_o/\rho c$ is the diffusion coefficient to the reference temperature $T = T_o$, and coefficients $\beta > 0, q_o > 0$.

In [4,5] one or two thermal coefficients for the case $k = k_o$ (i.e. $\beta \equiv 0$) were determined, and formulae for the unknown coefficients were given.

The goal of the present paper is to consider the general case $\beta \neq 0$. The problem consists of finding β and two other unknown elements among k_o, c, ρ, h and $s(t)$. Moreover, the coefficients $q_o > 0$ (which characterizes the heat flux at the fixed face $x = 0$) and $T_o > 0$ (which is the temperature at the fixed face $x = 0$) must be found through the experimental phase-change process.

The solution is given by :

$$T(x,t) = T_o + (T_f - T_o) \, \Phi_\delta(\eta) \ , \quad \eta = \frac{x}{2\sqrt{\alpha_o t}} \quad (\text{with } \delta > -1) \ ,$$
$$s(t) = 2 \, \sigma \, \sqrt{t} = 2 \, \lambda \, \sqrt{\alpha_o t} \ , \quad \sigma = \lambda \, \sqrt{\alpha_o} = \lambda \, \sqrt{\frac{k_o}{\rho c}} \ , \tag{2}$$

where the unknown coefficients must satisfy the following system of equations :

$$\beta = \delta \, \Phi_\delta(\lambda) \ ,$$
$$[1 + \delta \, \Phi_\delta(\lambda)] \, \frac{\Phi_\delta'(\lambda)}{\lambda \, \Phi_\delta(\lambda)} = \frac{2}{\text{Ste}} \ , \tag{3}$$
$$\frac{\Phi_\delta'(0)}{\Phi_\delta(\lambda)} = \frac{2 \, q_o}{(T_f - T_o) \, \sqrt{k_o \rho c}} \ ,$$

where $\text{Ste} = \dfrac{c(T_f - T_o)}{h} > 0$ is the Stefan number and $\Phi = \Phi_\delta = \Phi_\delta(x)$ is the error modified function which is the unique solution of the following value boundary problem :

$$[(1 + \delta \, y(x)) \, y'(x)]' + 2 \, x \, y'(x) = 0$$
$$y(0^+) = 0 \ , \quad y(+\infty) = 1 \ . \tag{4}$$

We suppose that $\delta > -1$ is a known real number. Function Φ verifies the following conditions

$$\Phi(0^+) = 0 \;,\;\; \Phi(+\infty) = 1 \;,\;\; \Phi' > 0 \;\text{ and }\; \Phi'' < 0 \;. \tag{5}$$

For $\delta = 0$, function $\Phi = \Phi_0$ is the classical error function given by

$$\Phi_0(x) = \mathrm{erf}(x) = \frac{2}{\sqrt{\pi}} \int_0^x \exp(-u^2)\, du \;, \tag{6}$$

which is utilized in [4, 5] for the determination of unknown thermal coefficients.

The experimental determination of the coefficients $q_0 > 0$ and $\sigma > 0$ (when necessary) can be obtained respectively through the least squares in the following expressions :

$$q_0 = t^{1/2} k(T_0) T_X(0,t) \; (\; t^{1/2} \text{ times heat flux in } x = 0 \text{ at time } t) \text{ for all } t > 0 \;,$$

$$\sigma = \frac{s(t)}{2\, t^{1/2}} \;\;,\;\; \text{ for all } t > 0 \;,$$

through a discrete number of measurement at time $t_1, t_2, \ldots, t_n$ of the corresponding quantities.

We shall give necessary and sufficient conditions to obtain a solution of the above type and we also give formulae for the unknown thermal coefficients in ten different cases :

Case 1 : Determination of the unknown coefficients β, λ, k_0 ;

Case 2 : Determination of the unknown coefficients β, λ, ρ ;

Case 3 : Determination of the unknown coefficients β, λ, h ;

Case 4 : Determination of the unknown coefficients β, λ, c ;

Case 5 : Determination of the unknown coefficients β, ρ, k_0 ;

Case 6 : Determination of the unknown coefficients β, c, k_0 ;

Case 7 : Determination of the unknown coefficients β, h, k_0 ;

Case 8 : Determination of the unknown coefficients β, ρ, c ;

Case 9 : Determination of the unknown coefficients β, ρ, h ;

Case 10 : Determination of the unknown coefficients β, c, h .

In the Table 1 (see below) we give, case by case, the formulae for the unknown thermal coefficients and the restriction for the data to obtain the solution of the corresponding problem.

In order to simplify the building of the Table 1, let us consider the following restrictions (which is the necessary and sufficient condition for the existence and unicity of the solution) :

$$\frac{(T_f - T_0)}{2 q_0} \, \Phi'(0) \, \sqrt{\rho c k_0} \; < \; 1 , \tag{R_1}$$

$$\frac{\rho h k_0 (T_f - T_0)}{2 q_0^2} \; < \; 1 , \tag{R_2}$$

$$\frac{\rho h \sigma}{q_0} \; < \; 1 , \tag{R_3}$$

$$\frac{k_0 (T_f - T_0)}{2 \sigma q_0} \; < \; 1 . \tag{R_4}$$

We also consider the following six functions, defined by $x > 0$:

$$F_1(x) = 1 + \delta \, \Phi(x) , \qquad\qquad F_2(x) = \frac{x \, \Phi(x)}{\Phi'(x)} ,$$

$$F_3(x) = [1 + \delta \, \Phi(x)] \, \Phi'(x) , \qquad F_4(x) = x \, \Phi(x) , \tag{7}$$

$$F_5(x) = \frac{\Phi(x)}{x} , \qquad\qquad F_6(x) = \frac{x}{\Phi(x)} = \frac{1}{F_5(x)} ,$$

which satisfy the following conditions :

$$F_1(0^+) = 1 \; , \;\; F_1(+\infty) = 1 + \delta \; ,$$

$$F_1' > 0 \;\text{ for }\; \delta > 0 \;\text{ and }\; F_1' < 0 \;\text{ for }\; -1 < \delta < 0,$$

$$F_2(0^+) = 0 \; , \;\; F_2(+\infty) = +\infty \; , \;\; F_2' > 0 ,$$

$$F_3(0^+) = \Phi'(0) > 0 \; , \;\; F_3(+\infty) = 0 \; , \;\; F_3' < 0 , \tag{8}$$

$$F_4(0^+) = 0 \; , \;\; F_4(+\infty) = +\infty \; , \;\; F_4' > 0 ,$$

$$F_5(0^+) = \Phi'(0) > 0 \; , \;\; F_5(+\infty) = 0 \; , \;\; F_5' < 0 ,$$

$$F_6(0) = \frac{1}{\Phi'(0)} > 0 \; , \;\; F_6(+\infty) = +\infty \; , \;\; F_6' > 0 ,$$

Case No.	Unknown coefficients	Restriction	Solution $\left(\text{In all cases } \beta \text{ is given by } \beta = \delta\,\Phi_\delta(\lambda)\right)$
1	β, λ, k_o	—	$k_o = \dfrac{4\,q_o^2}{\rho\,c\,(T_f - T_o)^2}\,\dfrac{\Phi^2(\lambda)}{\left(\Phi'(0)\right)^2}$ where λ is the unique solution of the equation $F_1(x) = \dfrac{2}{Ste}\,F_2(x)\ ,\ \ x > 0\ .$
2	β, λ, ρ	—	$\rho = \dfrac{4\,q_o^2}{c\,k_o(T_f - T_o)^2}\,\dfrac{\Phi^2(\lambda)}{\left(\Phi'(0)\right)^2}$ where λ is given as in Case 1 .
3	β, λ, h	R_1	$h = \dfrac{c\,(T_f - T_o)}{2}\,\dfrac{\Phi'(\lambda)}{\lambda\,\Phi(\lambda)}\,[1 + \delta\,\Phi(\lambda)]$ where λ is the unique solution of the equation $\Phi(x) = \dfrac{(T_f - T_o)}{2\,q_o}\,\Phi'(0)\,\sqrt{\rho\,c\,k_o}\ ,\ \ x > 0\ .$
4	β, λ, c	R_2	$c = \dfrac{4\,q_o^2}{\rho\,k_o(T_f - T_o)^2}\,\dfrac{\Phi^2(\lambda)}{\left(\Phi'(0)\right)^2}$ where λ is the unique solution of the equation $F_3(x) = \dfrac{\rho h k_o\,(T_f - T_o)}{2\,q_o^2}\left(\Phi'(0)\right)^2 F_6(x),\ x > 0.$
5	β, ρ, k_o	—	$\rho = \dfrac{2\,q_o}{\sigma\,c\,(T_f - T_o)}\,\dfrac{\lambda\,\Phi(\lambda)}{\Phi'(0)}$ $k_o = \dfrac{2\,\sigma\,q_o}{T_f - T_o}\,\dfrac{\Phi(\lambda)}{\lambda\,\Phi'(0)}$ where λ is given as in Case 1 .
6	β, c, k_o	R_3	k_o is given as in Case 5 $c = \dfrac{2\,q_o}{\rho\,\sigma\,(T_f - T_o)}\,\dfrac{\lambda\,\Phi(\lambda)}{\Phi'(0)}$ where λ is the unique solution of the equation $F_3(x) = \dfrac{\rho\,h\,\sigma}{q_o}\,\Phi'(0)\ ,\ \ x > 0\ .$

Case No.	Unknown coefficients	Restriction	Solution $\left(\text{In all cases } \beta \text{ is given by } \beta = \delta\,\Phi_\delta(\lambda)\right)$
7	β, h, k_o	—	h is given as in Case 3 $$k_o = \frac{\rho\,c\,\sigma^2}{\lambda^2}$$ where λ is the unique solution of the equation $$F_4(x) = \frac{\rho\,c\,\sigma\,(T_f - T_o)}{2\,q_0}\,\Phi'(0) \ , \quad x > 0 \ .$$
8	β, ρ, c	R_4	$$c = \frac{2h}{T_f - T_o}\,\frac{\lambda\,\Phi(\lambda)}{\Phi'(\lambda)}\,\frac{1}{1 + \delta\,\Phi(\lambda)}$$ $$\rho = \frac{\lambda k_o\,(T_f - T_o)}{2h\,\sigma^2}\,\frac{\Phi'(\lambda)\,[1 + \delta\Phi(\lambda)]}{\Phi(\lambda)}$$ where λ is the unique solution of the equation $$F_5(x) = \frac{k_o\,(T_f - T_o)}{2\,\sigma\,q_0}\,\Phi'(0) \ , \quad x > 0 \ .$$
9	β, ρ, h	R_4	h is given as in Case 3 $$\rho = \frac{k_o\lambda^2}{c\,\sigma^2}$$ where λ is given as in Case 8 .
10	β, c, h	R_4	$$h = \frac{k_o\,(T_f - T_o)}{2\,\rho\,\sigma^2}\,[1 + \delta\Phi(\lambda)]\,\frac{\lambda\,\Phi'(\lambda)}{\Phi(\lambda)}$$ $$c = \frac{k_o\lambda^2}{\rho\,\sigma^2}$$ where λ is given as in Case 8 .

Table 1.   Restrictions and formulae for the unknown thermal coefficients.

SOLUTION

Now we shall only prove the following properties for case 4 (determination of coefficients β, λ, c) and case 6 (determination of coefficients β, k_o, c).

Property 1.— The necessary and sufficient condition with β, λ and c unknown to obtain a unique solution is that data $q_o > 0$, $T_f > T_o$, $\delta > -1$ and coefficients $k_o > 0$, $h > 0$, $\rho > 0$ of the phase-change material verify condition (R_2). In such a case, the solution is given by (2) and

$$\beta = \delta \, \Phi(\lambda) , \tag{9}$$

$$c = \frac{4 \, q_o^2}{\rho \, k_o \, (T_f - T_o)^2} \, \frac{\Phi^2(\lambda)}{\left(\Phi'(0)\right)^2} , \tag{10}$$

and $\lambda > 0$ is the unique solution of the equation :

$$F_3(x) = \frac{\rho \, h \, k_o \, (T_f - T_o)}{2 \, q_o^2} \left(\Phi'(0)\right)^2 F_6(x) , \quad x > 0. \tag{11}$$

Proof.— The first and third equations in (3) give us the expression (9) for β and (10) for c respectively. From (10), the properties of functions F_3 and F_6 , and the second equation in (3) we obtain the equation (11) which has a unique solution $\lambda > 0$ if and only if

$$F_3(0^+) = \Phi'(0) \; > \; \frac{\rho \, h \, k_o \, (T_f - T_o)}{2 \, q_o^2} \, F_6(0^+) , \tag{12}$$

i.e. (R_2) .

Property 2.— The necessary and sufficient condition with β, k_o and c unknown to obtain a unique solution is that data $q_o > 0$, $T_f > T_o$, $\sigma > 0$, $\delta > -1$ and coefficients $h > 0$, $\rho > 0$ of the phase-change material verify condition (R_3). In such a case, the solution is given by (2), β is given by (9) and

$$k_o = \frac{2 \, \sigma \, q_o}{T_f - T_o} \, \frac{\Phi(\lambda)}{\lambda \, \Phi'(0)} , \tag{13}$$

$$c = \frac{2 \, q_o}{\rho \sigma \, (T_f - T_o)} \, \frac{\lambda \, \Phi(\lambda)}{\Phi'(0)} , \tag{14}$$

where $\lambda > 0$ is the unique solution of the equation :

$$F_3(x) = \frac{\rho h \sigma}{q_0} \Phi'(0) \quad , \quad x > 0 . \tag{15}$$

Proof.— The expression for β is given by the first equation in (3). Owing to σ is known we get

$$\lambda = \sigma \sqrt{\frac{\rho c}{k_0}} \quad , \tag{16}$$

i.e.

$$c = \frac{\lambda^2 k_0}{\rho \sigma^2} . \tag{17}$$

From (17) and the third equation in (3) we obtain the expression (12) for k_0. Then, by using (13) and (17) we have (14). Now, the second equation in (3) gives us the equation (15) for λ, which has a unique solution $\lambda > 0$ if and only if

$$F_3(0^+) = \Phi'(0) > \frac{\rho h \sigma}{q_0} \Phi'(0) , \tag{18}$$

i.e. (R_3).

REFERENCES

1. Cho, S.H. and Sunderland, J.E. "Phase change problems with temperature-dependent thermal conductivity", *J. Heat Transfer*, Vol. 96C, pp. 214 − 217, 1974.

2. Lunardini, V.J. *Heat transfer with freezing and thawing*, Elsevier, Amsterdam, 1991.

3. Tarzia, D.A. "Una revisión sobre problemas de frontera móvil y libre para la ecuación del calor. El problema de Stefan", *Mathematicae Notae*, Vol. 29, 147 − 241, 1981. See also "*A bibliography on moving−free boundary problems for the heat diffusion equation. The Stefan problem*" (with 2528 titles), Progetto Nazionale M.P.I. : "Equazioni di Evoluzione e Applicazioni Fisico− Matematiche", Firenze, 1988.

4. Tarzia, D.A. "Determination of the unknown coefficients in the Lamé-Clapeyron problem (or one-phase Stefan problem)", *Advances in Applied Mathematics*, Vol 3, pp. 74 − 82, 1982.

5. Tarzia, D.A. "Simultaneous determination of two unknown thermal coeficients through an inverse one-phase Lamé-Clapeyron (Stefan) problem with an overspecified condition on the fixed face", *Int. J. Heat Mass Transfer*, Vol. 26, pp. 1151 − 1157, 1983.

Analysis of columnar crystals growth during the solidification in magnetic field

J. Szajnar

Foundry Institute, Silesian Technical University, 44-100 Gliwice, Towarowa 7, Poland

ABSTRACT

Interaction of rotational magnetic field on molten metal solidifying in a mould causes an intensive motion of liquid material. In these conditions a crystallization process and primary structure of casting is generated. In this paper the investigations concerning experimental and numerical analysis of Al 99.7 primary structure formation are presented. First of all conditions of columnar crystals formation have been taken into account. The crystals come into existence in molten metal being in rotational constrained motion and the direction of their growth is a result of asymmetrical heat flux distribution on the surface of crystal front. The numerical computations confirmed that a changeable heat transfer coefficient on the crystal front surface causes the aberration of crystal growth direction in comparison with typical conditions of crystallization.

INTRODUCTION

In the area of casting solidifying in typical conditions it means withoutless the forced convection of molten metal the columnar crystals growth comes into being from heterogenous nuclei formed on the mould internal surface. The columnar crystals zone is a result of continuous competitive growth of individual crystals and the structure character is determined by these crystals grains whose main direction of crystallographic axis is the most close to heat flux direction − Figure 1a.

One of the methods of casting structure improvement is the realization of crystallization process in conditions of changeable magnetic field action. The typical feature of this technology is a fact that solidification process proceeds in forced motion of molten metal [1, 2, 3, 4].

Up to now the results of investigations concerning the influence of molten metal motion on its crystallization allow to distinguish three basic phenomena associated with the process
− dynamic activation of nuclei generation,
− thermal processes changing temperature field and kinetics of casting solidification,
− mechanical phenomena forming in a certain way the solidification front.
Theoretical investigations associated with discussed problem first of all concern the final effect of refinement of structure [5, 6, 7] and in this paper these problems are not taken into account.
The experiments realized by the author show that the direction of columnar crystal growth does not coincide with normal vector at considered point of casting − mould surface. It can be noticed that columnar crystals growth in rotating magnetic field changes according to direction of its motion and the axis of crystals are oppositely directed in relation to molten metal movement
− Figure 1b.

a)   b)

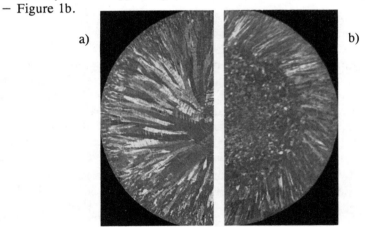

Fig. 1. Macrostructure of unstirred casting (a), stirred (b), pure Al

GROWTH OF COLUMNAR CRYSTALS SOLIDIFYING IN FLOWING MELT

A crystal growth can be considered as a process in atomic scale or microscopic one [9]. The first process depends on the addition of liquid atoms to crystal lattice of solid phase (nucleus). Crystal growth is determined at least by two phenomena it means atoms diffusion to crystallization front and their addition to the lattice. Intensity of this process depends on the kind of crystallization front. Metals and alloys solidified with atomic-coarse crystallization front which has a very big number of convenient positions of liquid atoms addition. A crystal growth as a process of atoms addition (in typical conditions) is presented schematically in Figure 2a.

If the atoms flux j_v shifts in parallel to crystallization front forced by magnetic field then on the surface of growing crystal from the side of this flux appear conditions assuring the bigger intensity of addition process (Figure 2b).

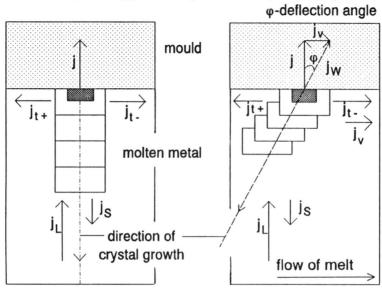

Fig. 2. Atoms addition

Additional atoms flux j_v changes direction of columnar crystal growth ($\varphi \in [0, \pi]$) according to the growth rate u and molten metal velocity v [8].

Microscopic growth can be treated as an increment of solid phase being a result of casting cooling in particular the Stefan condition should be taken into account. The natural trend of the process is a crystal growth in the direction corresponding to resultant heat flux neglecting the certain aberrations caused by agent of crystallographic nature.

In static conditions of crystallization the heat flux is oriented perpendicular to casting surface and the same is columnar crystals direction (Figure 1a). Forced by magnetic field the motion of molten metal caused the essential asymmetry in heat transfer process in the region of growing crystals. Above phenomena is a result of better intensity of heat exchange on this part of crystal surface which is under the direct influence of molten metal flux.

In theoretical part of investigations it was assumed that columnar crystals in pure Al can be approximated by superposition of cylinder and hemisphere (Kurz−Fisher model [9]). In conditions of working magnetic field the motion of melt caused the equalization of temperature field in liquid sub-domain [5]. On the basis of above considerations deflected crystals growth can be presented schematically as in Figure 3.

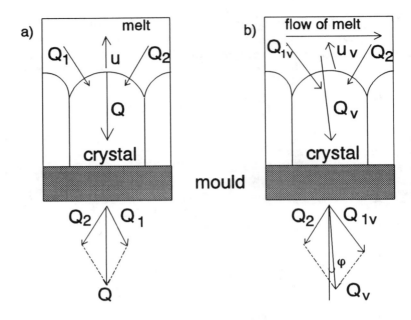

Fig. 3. Heat transfer on the crystal end face
a) typical conditions b) forced motion of melt

MATHEMATICAL MODEL OF COLUMNAR CRYSTALS SOLIDIFICATION IN MAGNETIC FIELD

A characteristic feature of crystallization in rotating magnetic field is waving structure of columnar crystals. The crystals generating from molten metal are deflected in this way that a crystal axis are oriented upstream of liquid metal shifting in mould domain and the direction of growth do not coincide with normal vector to contact surface casting − mould. After a change of magnetic field direction the repeated axis deflection takes place and as a result of this process the waving structure can be observed. The aim of presented fragment of above paper was a numerical verification of proposition concerning the thermal mechanism of this phenomena.

The following mathematical model of columnar crystal growth has been proposed.

At the initial moment of time ($t=0$) on the mould surface (the real shape of sample casting was cylindrical one) semicircular nuclei with radius 0.1 mm are generated. A temperature in nuclei domain corresponds to solidification point T^* whereas temperature of internal mould surface results from formulae

$$T_c = \frac{T^* - T_{0m}}{\dfrac{b_m}{b_2} \operatorname{erf}\left(K/2\sqrt{a_2}\right) + 1} \quad , \qquad K = \frac{2b_m\left(T^* - T_{0m}\right)}{\sqrt{\pi}\,\rho_2 L} \tag{1}$$

where T_c is a contact temperature, T_{0m} — initial temperature of mould domain, b_m, b_2 — coefficients of mould and casting materials accumulation, $a_2 = \lambda_2/\rho_2 c_2$, λ_2, ρ_2, c_2 — thermal conductivity, mass density and specific heat of solid metal, K — solidification constant, L — latent heat. Equations (1) result from Schwarz solution (e.g. [10]) and for interval of time directly after pouring they are a good approximation of real heat transfer processes.

The numerical computations concern the area of nine nuclei (comp. Figure 4).

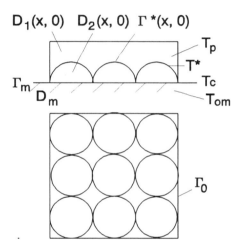

Figure 4. Nuclei domain

They are in thermal contact with molten metal domain which temperature for $t=0$ $T_1(x, 0)=T_p$ (pouring temperature). So the following initial condition has been assumed

$$
\begin{aligned}
x \in D_2(x, 0) \cup \Gamma^*(x, 0) : \quad & T(x, 0) = T^* , \\
x \in D_1(x, 0) \qquad\quad : \quad & T(x, 0) = T_p , \\
x \in D_m(x) \qquad\quad\;\; : \quad & T(x, 0) = T_{0m} , \\
x \in \Gamma_m(x) \qquad\quad\;\; : \quad & T(x, 0) = T_c .
\end{aligned}
\tag{2}
$$

During the solidification and cooling process the crystallization front $T^*(x, t)$ displaces and after a certain time t^f achieves the position shown in Figure 5.

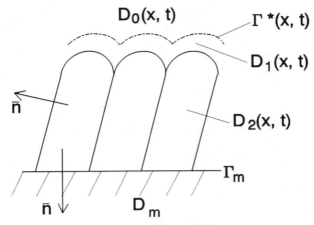

Fig. 5. The shifting of solidification front

Now the boundary conditions of considered boundary—initial problem will be formulated.

Along the surface $\Gamma_m(x)$ the condition of continuity of the form

$$x \in \Gamma_m(x) : \quad \begin{cases} -\lambda_2 \bar{n} \cdot \operatorname{grad} T_2(x, t) = -\lambda_m \bar{n} \cdot \operatorname{grad} T_m(x, t) , \\[2mm] T_2(x, t) = T_m(x, t) \end{cases} \quad (4)$$

can be assumed, at the same time $\bar{n} \cdot \operatorname{grad} T$ denotes a normal derivative.

Condition (4) assuring the continuity of temperature on Γ_m is as a rule accepted in the case of computations concerning the problem of type "casting — sand mould" or "casting — shell mould" [11].

Along surface Γ_0 conventionally limiting the analyzed area it was assumed that for $t=0+\delta t$ (δt — a certain interval of time after pouring into mould)

$$-\lambda_k \bar{n} \cdot \operatorname{grad} T_k(x, t) = 0 , \quad k=1 \cup 2 \cup m \quad (5)$$

and next for $t > \delta t$ the boundary condition (heat flux) corresponds to adequate heat fluxes calculated in numerical way for the surfaces limiting a central crystal of considered domain. This approach allows "to extend" the area of columnar crystals whose have been taken into account.

For $x \in \Gamma^*(t)$ a generalized Stefan condition has been introduced

$$x \in \Gamma^*(t) : \quad \begin{cases} -\lambda_1 \bar{n} \cdot \operatorname{grad} T_1(x, t) + \alpha(x, t)\big(T_\infty - T^*\big) = \\[2mm] = -\lambda_2 \bar{n} \cdot \operatorname{grad} T_2(x, t) + \rho_2 L v_n , \\[2mm] T_1(x, t) = T_2(x, t) = T^* \end{cases} \quad (6)$$

In last equation v_n is a crystallization rate, $\alpha(x, t)$ — heat transfer coefficient, T_∞ — temperature of molten metal in domain of forced convection.

Coefficient $\alpha(x, t)$ is a function of position of considered point on the nucleus end face and the value of $\alpha(x, t)$ has been changed in wide limits. The problem of α determining was treated as an inverse one, but the method of proper choice of function describing the course $\alpha(x, t) \approx \alpha(x)$ based on a traditional trial-and-error method. A temperature T_∞ results from energy balance for molten metal domain and it was assumed that $T_\infty = $const for $x \in D_0(t)$ at the same time $D_0(t)$ correspond to the area of forced convection resulting from "work" of magnetic field. Close to surface $\Gamma^*(t)$ the area of boundary layer $D_1(x\ t)$ has been assumed. The temperature field from the range $< T^*, T_\infty >$ in this domain results from Fourier equation.

Non-steady temperature field in domains $D_m(x)$, $D_1(x, t)$, $D_2(x, t)$ describes a system of equations

$$c_k \rho_k \frac{\partial T(x, t)}{\partial t} = \text{div}\left[\lambda_k \,\text{grad}\, T(x, t)\right], \quad k = 1, 2, m \qquad (7)$$

supplemented by above presented boundary-initial conditions.

Numerical model of columnar crystal growth has been constructed on the basis of control volume method (e.g. [11, 12]). The area has been divided into cylindrical elementary volumes (the end face of nuclei was approximated by "stepped figure").

Elementary balances for distinguished volumes allowed to determine a temperature field for successive levels of time (explicit differential scheme) and additionally to find the predominant direction of heat flux in the region of nuclei end face it means the direction of crystals growth. It turned out that during the time which was taken into account the predominant direction was practically the same. It should be pointed that the results of numerical computations were close to experimental data. In Figure 6 a temporary temperature field in parallel direction to molten metal motion in a section of columnar crystal is shown.

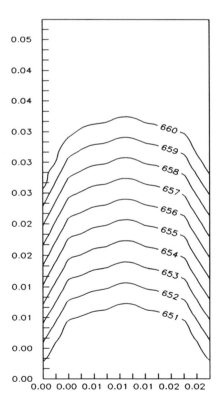

Fig. 6. Temperature field after 0.0002s

ACKNOWLEDGMENT

This paper was prepared in the range of research work realized in project No 3 0862 91 01 sponsored by KBN

REFERENCES

1. Lesoult, G., Neu, P. and Birat,J.P. *Modeling of Equiaxed Solidification Induced by Electromagnetic Stirring on a Steel Continuous Caster*, Pro. IUTAM Symposium on Metallurgical Applications of Magnetohydrodynamics, Cambridge, 1982.
2. Szajnar, J. *Doctor's thesis*. Publ. of the Silesian Technical University, Gliwice, Poland, 1986.
3. Sakwa, W., Gawroński, J. and Szajnar, J.'Effect of Rotating Reversing Magnetic Field on the Solidification of Aluminium Castings' *Giessreiforschung*, Vol.40, No.1, pp. 17 - 22, 1988
4. Etienne, A.'Columnar and Equiaxed Dendrite Growth in Continuosly Cast Products' *Steel Research*, T.61, No.10, pp. 472 - 477, 1990
5. Fredriksson, H. et al.'The Effect of Stirring on the Solidification Process in Metals' *Scandinavian Journal of Metallurgy*, Vol.15, pp. 127 - 137, 1986
6. Miksch, E.S. 'Solidification of Ice Dendrites in Flowing Supercooled Water' *Transactions of the Metallurgical Society of AIME*, Vol.245, pp. 2069 - 2072, 1969
7. Quenisset, J.M. and Naslain, R.'Effect of Forced Convection on Eutectic Growth' *Journal of Crystal Growth*, Vol.54, pp. 465 - 474, 1981
8. Szajnar, J.'Hypothesis of Columnar Crystals Growth in Electromagnetic Field' *Solidification of Metals and Alloys*, No.16, pp. 191 - 201, 1992
9. Kurz, W. and Fischer, D.J. *Fundamentals of Solidification* Trans Tech Publications, Switzerland-Germany-UK-USA, 1984.
10. Longa, W. *Solidification of Castings in Sand Molds*, Śląsk, Katowice 1977.
11. Mochnacki, B. and Suchy, J. *Modeling and Simulation of Casting Solidification*, PWN, Warsaw 1993.
12. Szargut, J. *Thermal Calculations of Industrial Furnaces*, Śląsk, Katowice 1977.

Numerical approaches to melting/solidification problems

J. Caldwell, C.K. Chiu

Department of Mathematics, City Polytechnic of Hong Kong, 83 Tai Chee Avenue, Kowloon, Hong Kong

MELTING/SOLIDIFICATION PROBLEMS

Melting and solidification problems occur in numerous important areas of science, engineering and industry. For example, freezing and thawing of foods, production of ice, ice formation on pipe surface, solidification of steel and chemical reaction all involve either a melting or solidification process. Mathematically, melting/solidification problems are special cases of moving boundary problems.

There are only very limited exact solutions to melting/solidification problems, and existing closed form solutions to these significant problems are highly restrictive as to allowable initial conditions and boundary conditions. So numerical solution becomes the main tool in the study of moving boundary problems. In this paper, we consider the solution of melting/solidification problems using one simple front-fixing method, namely the Heat Balance Integral Method (HBIM).

PROBLEM FORMULATION

In this section we consider the classical one phase, one-dimensional Stefan problems. These problems constitute the simplest non-trivial problems which display all the mathematical difficulties inherent in more complicated problems.

Consider the idealised problem of solidification of a liquid, initially at its freezing temperature T_f, in contact with a surface maintained at a constant, lower temperature T_s. The liquid solidifies on the surface and the process may be described by

$$\frac{\partial T}{\partial t} = \frac{\kappa}{r^\beta} \frac{\partial}{\partial r} \left[r^\beta \frac{\partial T}{\partial r} \right], \qquad a < r < R(t), \qquad t > 0 \tag{1}$$

where $\beta = 0$, 1 or 2 depending on the geometry of the problem, and represents solidification processes in planes, infinite cylinders and spheres, respectively. Suitable initial and boundary conditions for this problem are

$$T = T_f, \quad r \geq R(t), \quad t > 0 \quad \text{and} \quad T = T_s, \quad r = a, \quad t \geq 0$$

and for the solid-liquid interface

$$K\left(\frac{\partial T}{\partial r}\right)_{R(t)} = L\rho \frac{dR(t)}{dt} \tag{2}$$

where $T(r,t)$ is temperature and $R(t)$ is the position of the solid-liquid interface. It is assumed that the physical properties of the material remain constant throughtout the process and there is no change of volume on solidification. The constants κ, K, ρ and L are thermal diffusivity, conductivity, density and latent heat of freezing, respectively.

It is further assumed that the material is initially cooled sufficiently rapidly that a discontinuous change in the temperature takes place at $r = a$ when $t = 0$. This provides the initial condition for the solid-liquid interface, that is $R(0) = a$. Sometimes it is more convenient to work with non-dimensional variables. We can simplify the above equations by introducing the variables

$$z = r/a, \quad \tau = \kappa t/a^2$$
$$U = (T - T_s)/(T_f - T_s), \quad \alpha = L/c(T_f - T_s)$$

The equations (1) and (2) then become

$$\frac{\partial U}{\partial \tau} = \frac{1}{z^\beta} \frac{\partial}{\partial z}\left[z^\beta \frac{\partial U}{\partial z}\right], \quad 1 < z < Z(\tau), \quad \tau > 0 \tag{3}$$

with $U = 1, z \geq Z(\tau), \tau > 0$ and $U = 0, z = 1, \tau \geq 0$ and for the solid-liquid interface, we have

$$\left(\frac{\partial U}{\partial z}\right)_{Z(\tau)} = \alpha \frac{dZ(\tau)}{d\tau}, \quad Z(0) = 1 \tag{4}$$

where α is a dimensionless latent heat parameter, and is sometimes called the Stefan number.

HEAT BALANCE INTEGRAL METHOD

The Heat Balance Integral Method (HBIM) was first propounded by Goodman [5, 6]. It has many pleasing features and can be applied to a wide range of problems and the accuracy obtained is usually sufficient for most practical situations.

The choice of a satistfactory approximation to the temperature profile is acknowledged to be a major difficulty in the heat balance approach. This sensitivity to the choice of profile is demonstrated in the results presented by Langford [8] for the simple case of heat flow in a semi-infinite plane. The result obtained from a cubic profile is less accurate than that produced by a quadratic one.

Noble [10] suggested that the best way of improving the accuracy of the heat balance integral method was by repeated spacial sub-division, using quadratic profiles in each sub-region. Bell [1, 2] modified Noble's method, so that instead of sub-division of the independent variable—space, in the usual way, the equal sub-division of the dependent variable—temperature, is considered.

Using a suitable form of the heat balance integral, a system of first order, non-linear differential equations is produced for a set of penetration variables. Each penetration variable is associated with an isotherm created by the sub-division. Therefore, the solution of the system of equations provides the position of each isotherm which automatically includes the location of the moving boundary.

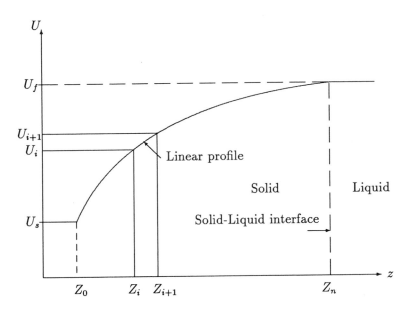

Figure 1: Sub-division of the region for HBIM

Consider the classical one-dimensional Stefan problem in non-dimensional form. We first divide the temperature range into n equal intervals as illustrated in Figure [1], that is, $U_i = i/n$, $i = 0, 1, 2, \ldots, n$ and assume a linear profile for the temperature at each sub-range, so that

$$U = \frac{i}{n} + \frac{z - Z_i}{n(Z_{i+1} - Z_i)} \tag{5}$$

Multiplying the heat equation by z^β and integrating over each sub-range $[Z_i, Z_{i+1}]$, gives

$$\int_{Z_i}^{Z_{i+1}} z^\beta \frac{\partial U}{\partial \tau} dz = \int_{Z_i}^{Z_{i+1}} \frac{\partial}{\partial z}\left[z^\beta \frac{\partial U}{\partial z}\right] dz \tag{6}$$

$$\frac{d}{d\tau}\left[\int_{Z_i}^{Z_{i+1}} z^\beta U dz - \frac{z_{i+1}^{\beta+1} U_{i+1}}{\beta + 1} + \frac{z_i^{\beta+1} U_i}{\beta + 1}\right] = \left(z^\beta \frac{\partial U}{\partial z}\right)_{Z_{i+1}} - \left(z^\beta \frac{\partial U}{\partial z}\right)_{Z_i} \tag{7}$$

Replacing U by the appropriate profile in each heat balance equation and ensuring that expressions representing change in flux are approximated by the discontinuous change in adjacent profile gradients, the following system of equations is obtained,

$$\frac{d}{d\tau}\left[\frac{Z_{i+1}^{\beta+2} - Z_i^{\beta+2}}{Z_{i+1} - Z_i}\right] = (\beta + 1)(\beta + 2)\left[\frac{Z_i^\beta}{Z_{i+1} - Z_i} - \frac{Z_{i+1}^\beta}{Z_{i+2} - Z_{i+1}}\right], \quad i = 0, 1, \ldots, n-2$$

$$\frac{d}{d\tau}\left[\frac{Z_n^{\beta+2} - Z_{n-1}^{\beta+2}}{Z_n - Z_{n-1}} + \alpha n(\beta + 2)Z_n^{\beta+1}\right] = (\beta + 1)(\beta + 2)\frac{Z_{n-1}^\beta}{Z_n - Z_{n-1}} \tag{8}$$

INITIAL TIME APPROXIMATION

To start the heat balance integral method, a special starting solution is needed for small times as there is a singularity at $\tau = 0$. The appropriate small time solution is given by Poots [11] and the initial motion of each isotherm Z_i is assumed to have the form

$$Z_i(\tau) = 1 + \mu_{i,0}\tau^{1/2} + \mu_{i,1}\tau + \mu_{i,2}\tau^{3/2} + \cdots \tag{9}$$

Note that we have $Z_0(\tau) = 1$ and $Z_n(\tau) = Z(\tau)$ for the solidifcation front.

The process of finding $\mu_{i,j}$ by Poots's method is extremely laborious. In the heat balance integral method, the coefficients $\mu_{i,j}$ can also be found by substituting the small time series into the system of ordinary differential equations. This is one of the advantages of the heat balance integral method over other methods, as in many practical cases the exact behaviour of the approximation is either unknown or difficult to determine.

CYLINDRICAL SOLIDIFICATION

Consider the case of the solidification of a liquid about a cylindrical pipe (see Figure [2]), that is the case when $\beta = 1$ in the heat equation (3).

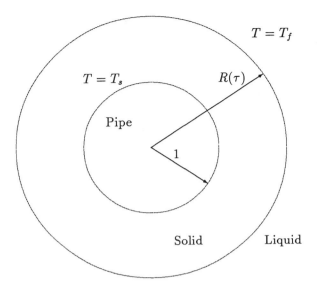

Figure 2: Cylindrical solidification

Following the method described above, we can reduce the heat equation into n heat balance equations,

$$\frac{d}{d\tau}\left[\frac{Z_{i+1}^3 - Z_i^3}{Z_{i+1} - Z_i}\right] = 6\left[\frac{Z_i}{Z_{i+1} - Z_i} - \frac{Z_{i+1}}{Z_{i+2} - Z_{i+1}}\right], \qquad i = 0, 1, \ldots, n-2$$

and

$$\frac{d}{d\tau}\left[\frac{Z_n^3 - Z_{n-1}^3}{Z_n - Z_{n-1}} + 3\alpha n Z_n^2\right] = \frac{6Z_{n-1}}{Z_n - Z_{n-1}} \qquad (10)$$

with $Z_0(\tau) = 1$ for all τ. We rearrange to get a system of first order ordinary differential equations for the penetration depth Z_i, namely

$$(2Z_1 + 1)\dot{Z}_1 = \frac{6}{Z_1 - 1} - \frac{6Z_1}{Z_2 - Z_1}$$

$$(2Z_{i+1} + Z_i)\dot{Z}_{i+1} + (Z_{i+1} + 2Z_i)\dot{Z}_i = \frac{6Z_i}{Z_{i+1} - Z_i} - \frac{6Z_{i+1}}{Z_{i+2} - Z_{i+1}}, \qquad i = 1, 2, \ldots, n-2$$

$$[2(1 + 3\alpha n)Z_n + Z_{n-1}]\dot{Z}_n + (Z_n + 2Z_{n-1})\dot{Z}_{n-1} = \frac{6Z_{n-1}}{Z_n - Z_{n-1}} \qquad (11)$$

The above equations can be solved by standard numerical methods for systems of ordinary differential equations (for example, Runge-Kutta method) or in cases of large n by a simple numerical iteration algorithm in order to improve the performance of the method.

SPHERICAL SOLIDIFICATION

In the heat equation, $\beta = 2$ corresponds to the case of solidification of a sphere. Following exactly the same method described in the cylindrical case, we get n heat balance equations for each penetration depth Z_i,

$$\frac{d}{d\tau}\left[\frac{Z_{i+1}^4 - Z_i^4}{Z_{i+1} - Z_i}\right] = 12\left[\frac{Z_i^2}{Z_{i+1} - Z_i} - \frac{Z_{i+1}^2}{Z_{i+2} - Z_{i+1}}\right], \qquad i = 0, 1, \ldots, n - 2$$

and

$$\frac{d}{d\tau}\left[\frac{Z_n^4 - Z_{n-1}^4}{Z_n - Z_{n-1}} + 4\alpha n Z_n^3\right] = \frac{12 Z_{n-1}^2}{Z_n - Z_{n-1}} \tag{12}$$

with $Z_0(\tau) = 1$ for all τ. We rearrange to get a system of first order ordinary differential equations for the penetration depth Z_i,

$$(3Z_1^2 + 2Z_1 + 1)\dot{Z}_1 = \frac{12}{Z_1 - 1} - \frac{12 Z_1^2}{Z_2 - Z_1}$$

$$(3Z_{i+1}^2 + 2Z_{i+1}Z_i + Z_i^2)\dot{Z}_{i+1} + (3Z_i^2 + 2Z_i Z_{i+1} + Z_{i+1}^2)\dot{Z}_i = \frac{12 Z_i^2}{Z_{i+1} - Z_i} - \frac{12 Z_{i+1}^2}{Z_{i+2} - Z_{i+1}}$$

$$i = 1, 2, \ldots, n - 2$$

$$[3(1+4\alpha n)Z_n^2 + 2Z_n Z_{n-1} + Z_{n-1}^2]\dot{Z}_n + (3Z_{n-1}^2 + 2Z_{n-1}Z_n + Z_n^2)\dot{Z}_{n-1} = \frac{12 Z_{n-1}^2}{Z_n - Z_{n-1}} \tag{13}$$

NUMERICAL RESULTS

The motion of the solidification front $Z(\tau)$ is obtained from the solution of the heat balance integral method. Other useful and important information, e.g. the emerging flux F can also be estimated from the solution of the system of differential equations, namely

$$F = K\left(\frac{\partial T}{\partial r}\right)_{r=a} = \frac{K(T_f - T_s)}{a}\left(\frac{\partial U}{\partial z}\right)_{z=1} \approx \frac{K(T_f - T_s)}{an(Z_1 - 1)} \tag{14}$$

The cylindrical and spherical problems were solved for various numbers of sub-divisions and the results are presented in Tables [1] and [2].

Table 1: Position of $Z(\tau)$ and emerging flux F^* for HBIM.
$\alpha = 1$, $\beta = 1$, $\tau = 0.01$, $h = 1 \times 10^{-6}$

τ	n		$Z_{n/2}$		Z_n	F^*
0.05	1				1.2415	4.1406
	2		1.1151		1.2524	4.3441
	4	1.0558	1.1156	1.1820	1.2597	4.4793
	8	1.0557	1.1158	1.1833	1.2639	4.5590
	16	1.0556	1.1159	1.1840	1.2662	4.6024
	32	1.0556	1.1159	1.1843	1.2673	4.6253
Isotherm Mirgration Method			1.1160		1.2695	
Lardner & Pohle					1.2526	
Churchill & Gupta						4.5561

τ	n		$Z_{n/2}$		Z_n	F^*
0.10	1				1.3337	2.9971
	2		1.1573		1.3510	3.1795
	4	1.0758	1.1584	1.2515	1.3622	3.2987
	8	1.0757	1.1588	1.2536	1.3685	3.3684
	16	1.0756	1.1590	1.2546	1.3719	3.4063
	32	1.0756	1.1591	1.2551	1.3736	3.4261
Isotherm Mirgration Method			1.1590		1.3769	
Lardner & Pohle					1.3543	
Churchill & Gupta						3.3561

Table 2: Position of $Z(\tau)$ and emerging flux F^* for HBIM.

$\alpha = 1$, $\beta = 2$, $\tau = 0.01$, $h = 1 \times 10^{-6}$

τ	n	$Z_{n/2}$			Z_n	F^*
0.05	1				1.2273	4.3992
	2		1.1053		1.2411	4.7493
	4	1.0502	1.1062	1.1709	1.2498	4.9784
	8	1.0501	1.1065	1.1724	1.2547	5.1125
	16	1.0501	1.1066	1.1731	1.2587	5.1856
	32	1.0501	1.1067	1.1734	1.2587	5.2238

τ	n	$Z_{n/2}$			Z_n	F^*
0.10	1				1.3081	3.2454
	2		1.1398		1.3302	3.5771
	4	1.0659	1.1414	1.2310	1.3438	3.7944
	8	1.0659	1.1419	1.2333	1.3514	3.9218
	16	1.0658	1.1421	1.2344	1.3554	3.9913
	32	1.0658	1.1421	1.2349	1.3575	4.0277

SUMMARY AND COMMENTS

The results from Figures [3] and [4] show that the heat balance integral method can be applied to many melting/solidification problems. We can get good accuracy by increasing the number of sub-divisions, and the computational time is not unreasonable. In addition, the heat balance method can be considered as self-starting for problems where small time expansions are not available. Other methods for melting/solidification problems usually require special small time starting procedures.

The main drawback of this method is that the resulting system of ordinary differential equations tends to be unstable, especially when n is large and τ is small. This is mainly because in these cases two adjacent isotherms $[Z_i, Z_{i+1}]$ are very close together, which means that some accuracy is lost during the calculation. Further improvment on the heat balance integral method is possible by modifying the temperature profile to avoid this problem.

REFERENCES

1. Bell, G.E. 'A refinement of the heat balance integral method applied to a melting problem' *Int. J. Heat Mass Transfer* **21**, pp1357–1362, 1978.

2. ———, 'Solodification of a liquid about a cylindrical pipe' *Int. J. Heat Mass Transfer* **22**, pp1681–1686, 1979.

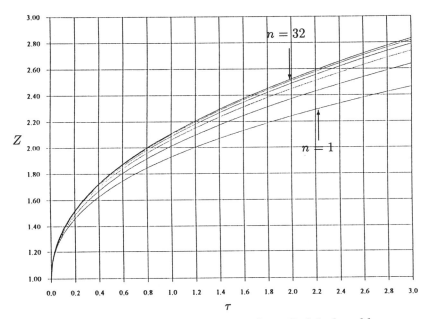

Figure 3: Depth of solidification for cylindrical problem

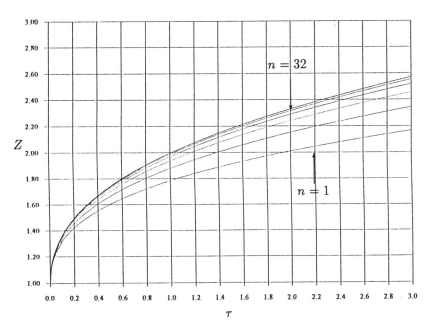

Figure 4: Depth of solidification for spherical problem

3. Churchill, S.W. and Gupta, J.P. 'Approximations for Conduction with Freezing or Melting' *Int. J. Heat Mass Transfer* **20**, pp1251–1253, 1977.

4. Crank, J. *Free and Moving Boundary Problems*, Clarendon Press, Oxford, 1984.

5. Goodman, T.R. 'The heat-balance integral and its application to problems involving a change of phase' *Transactions of the ASME* **80**, pp335–342, 1958.

6.   Goodman, 'The heat-balance integral—further considerations and refinements' *Journel of Heat Transfer* **83**, pp83–86, 1961.

7. Hill, J.M. *One-dimensional Stefan Problems: an introduction*, Longman Scientific and Technical, London, 1987.

8. Langford, D. 'The heat balance integral method' *Int. J. Heat Mass Transfer* **16**, pp2424–2428, 1973.

9. Lardner, T.J. and Pohle, F.V., 'Application of the heat balance integral to problems of cylindrical geometry' *Journal of Applied Mechanics* **28**, pp310–312, 1961.

10.   Noble, B. 'Heat balance methods in melting problems' in *Moving Boundary Problems in Heat Flow and Diffusion*, (Ed. Ockendon, J.R. and Hodgkins, W.R.), pp208–209, Clarendon Press, Oxford, 1975.

11.   Poots, G. 'On the application of integral methods to the solution of problems involving the solidification of liquids initially at fusion temperature' *Int. J. Heat Mass Transfer* **5**, pp525–531, 1962.

Interfacial kinetics and pressure-transition temperature effects and several planar solidification problems

Ch. Charach, B. Zaltzman

Center for Energy and Environmental Physics, J. Blaustein Institute for Desert Research, Ben-Gurion University of the Negev, Sede-Boger Campus 84993, Israel

ABSTRACT

Continuum models, that generalize the classical Stefan setup for a pure substance by incorporating interfacial kinetics and pressure-transition temperature effects, are considered. Several planar solidification problems, classical solutions of which are either singular, or do not exist within the Stefan formulation, are addressed within the above continuum models. Asymptotic and numerical solutions for these problems are developed. The dynamics of these solidification processes is discussed.

INTRODUCTION

The classical Stefan problem, as stated in Carslaw & Jaeger [1], is the simplest continuum model of solidification in a pure substance. It treats the solid-liquid interface as a sharp moving boundary of negligible mass and energy. A local thermodynamic equilibrium at the interface is assumed, while the phase transition temperature and the latent heat are considered as given constants. Particular modifications of the classical Stefan setup, incorporating thermomechanical effects both in the bulk and at the interface, have been proposed in the last decades. A comprehensive framework for continuum models with sharp fronts has been developed by Caroli et al.[2] It is based on the fundamental laws of irreversible thermodynamics and enables one to control systematically the underlying physical assumptions. This scheme has been utilized in Charach and Rubinstein [3] and Charach and Zemel [4] in order to develop rather general boundary conditions at the freezing front. They account for kinetic undercooling, the Gibbs-Thompson effect [5], and unequal densities of solid and liquid. The latter effect induces a fluid flow in the liquid. The pressure, developed by such a flow, is of the order of fracture strength. It might significantly affect the interface temperature. These boundary conditions yield a hierarchy of continuum models for solidification in a pure substance. Several planar models of this sort have been recently addressed by Charach and Rubinstein [3], Charach and Zaltzman [6] and Charach, Götz and Zaltzman [7], focusing on the asymptotic solutions for short and long times. This paper summarizes the main accomplishments of the latter works and presents new numerical results concerning the initial, the intermediate, and the final stages of these processes.

STATEMENT OF THE PROBLEMS

Let us now formulate the planar solidification problems incorporating the interfacial kinetics, the unequal densities of solid and liquid, and the resulting flow in the liquid. Following Charach and Rubinstein [3] and Charach, Götz, and Zaltzman [7] the liquid is treated as incompressible inviscid fluid. The governing equations and the interfacial boundary conditions are stated as follows:

$$T_{s,t} = \alpha_s T_{s,xx} \qquad x<R, \tag{1}$$

$$T_{L,t} + v_L T_{L,x} = \alpha_L T_{L,xx} \ , \quad R<x \tag{2}$$

$$T_c = T_* - aR_{,t} + b(p-p_*) \tag{3}$$

$$\rho L R_{,t} = k_s T_{s,x} - k_L T_{L,x}, \quad x=R \tag{4}$$

$$L = L_* + \rho'(p-p_*)/\rho_L + (T_c-T_*)(c_L-c_s) \tag{5}$$

$$v = -\rho' R_{,t} \tag{6}$$

$$\rho L v_{,t} = - p_{,x} \tag{7}$$

Here x is the spatial coordinate, t is the time, T is the temperature, p is the pressure, R(t) is the interface location, ρ is the density, v is the velocity of the fluid, L is the latent heat, c is the specific heat, k is the thermal conductivity, $\alpha=k/\rho c$ is the thermal diffusivity. The subscripts L and s denote the liquid and the solid, respectively. The relative density difference is denoted by $\rho' = (\rho_s - \rho_L)/\rho_s$, and we assume $\rho'>0$. The equilibrium values of pressure, freezing temperature and the latent heat are denoted by p_*, T_* and L_*, respectively. The actual interface temperature is denoted by T_c.

Equations (3) and (5) represent the major modifications of boundary conditions at the phase-change front, as compared with the classical Stefan setup. They follow as a particular case of interface conditions derived by Charach and Rubinstein [4]. The undercooling at the interface, T_*-T_c is a sum of the kinetic term aR, and the pressure-induced contribution, which is due to the fluid flow towards interface. The kinetic coefficient a is of the order 10^{-2} -1 Ksec/m, whereas the coefficient of the pressure undercooling, $b=T_*\rho'/L_*\rho_L$, is typically of the order 10^{-7} Km^2/n. Although b is rather small, flow pressure of the order of fracture strength might affect the interface temperature at the onset of freezing.

FREEZING IN A SLAB, INITIALLY AT $T=T_*$, WITH $\rho_L=\rho_S$.

We consider now freezing in a semi-infinite slab $(0<x<\infty)$, initially liquid at $T_i=T_*$, the fixed boundary of which is maintained at a constant temperature T_w $(T_w<T_*)$ for $t>0$:

$$T_S(0,t)=T_w, \quad T_L(x,0)=T(\infty,t)=T_*; \quad R(t=0)=0 \qquad (8)$$

For $a=0$ (classical Stefan setup) the above problem admits an exact solution, given in Carslaw and Jaeger [1], and refered to as the Neumann solution:

$$T_S=T_w+(T_*-T_w)\{erf(x/2\sqrt{\alpha_S t})\}/erf\ \Omega_1, \quad T_L=T_*, \qquad (9)$$

$$R = 2\Omega_1\sqrt{\alpha_S t}, \qquad (10)$$

where the constant Ω_1 is a solution of the equation

$$\sqrt{\pi}\ \Omega_1[exp(\Omega_1)^2]erf\ \Omega_1 = Ste \qquad (11)$$

As $t\to 0$ the interface velocity blows up, indicating the failure of underlying assumptions. This singularity can be eliminated by accounting for the kinetic undercooling $(a>0)$. In order to show this let us define the natural scales of the problem $t_0= \alpha_S[a/(T_*-T_w)^2]$, $x_0 = \sqrt{\alpha_S t_0}$. For a typical value of α_S of the order 10^{-7}m^2/s, t_0 is in the range 10^{-5}-10^{-8}s and and x_0 is of the order of 10^{-9}- 10^{-7}m. The analysis simplifies by using the dimensionless quantities

$$t'= t/t_0, \quad r = R/x_0, \quad \alpha = \alpha_L/\alpha_S, \quad k = k_L/k_S, \qquad (12)$$

$$c = c_L/c_S, \quad r'= dr/dt', \quad x'=x/x_0, \quad \xi=x/R, \qquad (13)$$

$$\Theta=(T-T_*)/(T_*-T_w), \quad Ste=c_S(T_*-T_w)/L_*. \qquad (14)$$

The approximate analytic solution of this problem, developed by Charach, Götz and Zaltzman [6], reads:

$$\Theta_s = -1 + (1-r') \frac{erf(\xi\sqrt{Urr'}/2)}{erf(\sqrt{Urr'}/2)} \quad , \quad U=1-(rr''/r') , \qquad (15)$$

$$\Theta_L = -r' \frac{erfc(\xi\sqrt{Urr'}/2)}{erfc(\sqrt{Urr'}/2)} \qquad (16)$$

$$1-r'\{1-(k/\sqrt{\pi\alpha})\sqrt{Urr'}\} = [1-r'Ste(c-1)]rr'/Ste \qquad (17)$$

For short times Equations (15)-(17) yield

$$r \approx t'-(2kt'/3)\sqrt{t'/\pi\alpha} , \qquad \Theta_c \approx - r' \qquad (18)$$

whereas as t⇒∞ this solution tends to the classical
solution, given by Equations (9)-(11). For Ste≪1
Equation (15) can be simplified, and in the lowest
order it yields

$$r \approx -Ste + Ste\sqrt{1 + 2t'/Ste} \qquad (19)$$

As follows from the above solution the interfacial
kinetics regularizes the initial singularity of the
interface velocity: R is a linear function of time
at the onset of freezing. In order to verify the

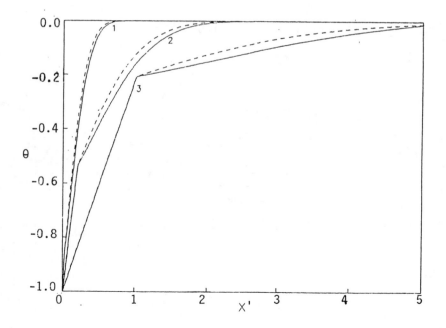

Figure 1. Temperature profiles for Ste=0.1. Solid
lines-numerical results, dashed lines-Equations (15)
and (16). Lines: 1- t'=0.01; 2- t'=0.1; 3- t'=1.

above analytic solution and to study the transition
from the kinetics-dominated initial stage to the
diffusion-controlled freezing at long times we developed a numerical solution of this problem. Figures
1 and 2 demonstrate the temperature profiles and the
advance of the freezing fronts, respectively. For
small values of the Stefan number (Ste=0.1) the
accuracy of the analytic solution is about 5%.

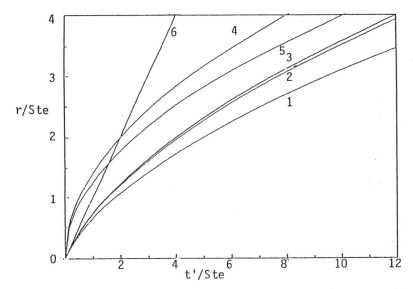

Figure2. Interface position as a function of time.
1-numerical solution for Ste=0.1; 2-numerical solution for Ste=1.0; 3-Equation (19); 4- Neumann solution for Ste=0.1; 5-Neumann solution for Ste=1.0;
6-initial asymptotics, r=t′.

FREEZING IN A SLAB, INITIALLY AT $T=T_*$, WITH $\rho_s > \rho_L$.

Let us consider now freezing in a finite slab,
accounting for solid-liquid density difference ($\rho' >$
0). We assume that that the x=0 boundary is fixed
and the end of the slab, x=A(t), is a free boundary,
maintained at $T=T_*$, and a constant pressure p_*. Initially the slab is at rest at $T=T_*$. At t=0 the temperature at x=0 drops to $T_w < T_*$ and remains at this
value during the entire process. We address here
only the onset of freezing, accounting both for the
kinetics and for the pressure-induced undercooling
at x=R. Denoting by $A_0 = A(0)$, the function A(t) is
given by

$$A(t) = A_0 - \rho' R(t) \qquad (20)$$

For $R \ll A_0$, Equation (7) yields

$$p(x=R) - p_* \approx -\rho' \rho L A_0 R_{,tt} \tag{21}$$

and the interface undercooling reads

$$T_* - T_c = aR_{,t} + b\rho' \rho L A_0 R_{,tt} \tag{22}$$

For $t \to 0$, $T_c \to T_w$. Since for $t=0$, $v=0$, it follows that as long as $T_c \approx T_w$,

$$R(t) = \{t + t_*[\exp(-t/t_*) - 1]\}/q \tag{23}$$

Here $q = a/(T_c - T_*)$, $t_* = b\rho\rho' A_0/a = t_1\sqrt{t_1/t_0}$, and $t_1 = \alpha_s^{1/3}[b\rho' \rho_L A_0/(T_*-T_0)]\}/3$ is a characteristic time scale of pressure-transition temperature effects. For $t \ll t_*$, Equation (23) yields $R \approx t^2/2q$, which is the result first found in Charach & Rubinstein [4]. Again, the initial singularity of the Neumann solution is regularized, but this time by the pressure-induced undercooling at $x=R$. The flow characteristics are also regular as $t \to 0$. Relaxation of T_c from T_w to T_* depends on the ratio t_1/t_0. Here we restrict the discussion to the case $t_1/t_0 \ll 1$. Then $t_* \ll t_0$, so that for $t_* \ll t < t_0$, $R(t)$ advances as $R \approx t/q$. At this stage the problem reduces to that studied in the previous section.

PLANAR GROWTH OF A SOLID GERM FROM AN UNDERCOOLED MELT.

Let us consider a uniformly undercooled melt at $T_L(0,x) = T_i = T_\infty < T_*$, occupying an infinite space. At $t=0$ a planar solid germ of infinitesimal thickness has nucleated at $x=0$. Its initial temperature, is assumed to be equal to T_*. We assume planar growth of this germ, symmetric relative to the $x=0$ plane and neglect the density difference, assuming $\rho'=0$. It is also assumed that as $x \infty$ T_L tends to a constant value T_∞. Owing to the symmetry of the problem we restrict the analysis to a domain $0 < x < \infty$. The initial-boundary data are stated now as follows:

$$T_L(0,x) = T_i = T(t,\infty) = T_\infty, \quad T_{S',x}|_{x=0} = T_{L',x}|_{x=0} = 0, \tag{24}$$

with $R(0)=0$. The scales of time and length are now $t_0 = \alpha_s a^2/(T_* - T_\infty)\}$, $x_0 = \sqrt{\alpha_s t_0}$. The dimensional temperature and the Stefan number, are defined in this section as $\Theta = (T-T_*)/(T_*-T_\infty)$, $Ste = c_L(T_*-T_\infty)/L_*$. All other dimensionless variables are defined by Equations (12) and (13). For $a=0$ (instantaneous kinetics) this problem admits an exact solution given in Carslaw and Jaeger [1]:

$$\Theta_L =-1 + erfc(\Omega_2 x'/r)/erfc \ \Omega_2, \quad \Theta_S = 0, \tag{25}$$

$$R(t)=2\Omega_2\sqrt{\alpha_S t}, \quad \sqrt{\pi}\Omega_2 \exp(\Omega_2) erfc \ \Omega_2 = Ste \tag{26}$$

It exists only for Ste<1. Following Charach and Zaltzman [7] we now show how the kinetic effect modifies this result for Ste<1, and yields solutions also for Ste≥1. For t'→0 we obtain

$$r(t') \approx t'-2Bt'\sqrt{t'}/3, \tag{27}$$

$$B = 2/Ste'\sqrt{\pi\alpha}, \quad Ste'=1/[(1/c)-1+(1/Ste)] \tag{28}$$

$$\Theta_L \approx -1+B\sqrt{\pi t'} \ ierfc[(\xi-1)\sqrt{t'/4\alpha}], \quad \Theta_S \approx -r'=-1+B\sqrt{t'} \tag{29}$$

The long-time regime depends on the initial su-
percooling. For Ste<1 the solution tends to that, defined by Equations (25)-(26). The Ste>1 solution tends at t→∞ to the travelling wave-type solution derived first by Glicksman and Shaefer [8]:

$$R=c(Ste-1)(L_*/ac_L)t, \quad \Theta_S=-r'=-c(1-Ste^{-1}) \tag{30}$$

$$\Theta_L =-1+(1-c+cSte^{-1})]exp[-(x'- r't')r'/\alpha] \tag{31}$$

In the case Ste=1, the long time solution reads

$$R(t)=(9\alpha_L cL_*/8ac_L)^{1/3}t^{2/3} \tag{32}$$

$$\Theta_S \approx -(2/3)\gamma t^{-1/3}\{1+ 3[(x'^2/\gamma t'^{4/3})-1]/2\} \tag{33}$$

$$\Theta_L \approx -1+exp[-(r'/\alpha)(x'-r(t')] \tag{34}$$

Here $\gamma=(9c\alpha/8)^{1/3}$, $r'=(2/3)\gamma t'^{-1/3}$. The Θ_L profile is a pulse, propagating with a velocity $\dot{r}'$, and as t→∞ the interface temperature tends to T_*.

Recently we developed a numerical solution of this problem. It supports the asymptotic solutions and enables one to study also the transient stage. In Figure 3 we demonstrate the time dependence of the interface temperature for various levels of initial undercooling, obtained numerically. The numerical studies show that for the diffusion-controlled growth with Ste=0.1 the long time asymptotic solution is approached at t'≈1. For Ste=1 transiti-
on to the long regime occurs on time scales t'≈10^3. For the kinetics-dominated process, with Ste=10, the relaxation towards the long-time travelling wave regime takes place at time-scales t'≈10.

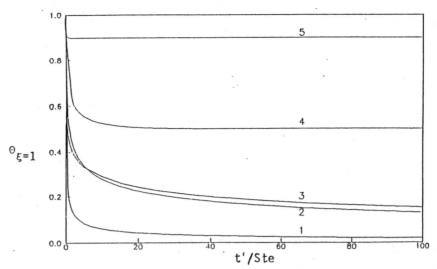

Figure 3. Dimensionless Temperature at the interface $\Theta(\xi=1,t')$ as a function of t'/Ste (numerical
solution). 1: Ste=0.1; 2: Ste=0.9; 3: Ste=1.0, 4:
Ste=2.0; 5: Ste=10.0

REFERENCES

1. Carslaw,H.S. and Jaeger,J.C. *Conduction of Heat
in Solids*, Claredon Press, Oxford, 1959.
2. Caroli,B., Caroli,C., and Roulet,B. 'Nonequilibrium Thermodynamics of Solidification Problem',
J. Crystal Growth, Vol.66, pp.575-585, 1984.
3. Charach,Ch. and Rubinstein,I.L., 'Pressure-
Transition Temperature Effect in Planar Stefan
Problems With Density Change', *J. Appl. Physics*,
Vol.71 pp. 1128-1137, 1982.
4. Charach,Ch. and Zemel,A. 'Nonequilibrium Thermodynamics of Phase Change Heat Transfer: Basic Principles and Applications to Latent Heat Storage',*Open
Systems and Information Dynamics* (in press).
5. Schaefer,R.J. and Glicksman,M.E., 'Fully Time-
Dependent Theory of the Growth of Spherical Crystal
Nuclei', *J. Crystal Growth*, Vol.5, pp.44-58, 1969.
6. Charach,Ch., Götz,I.G., and Zaltzman,B., 'Interfacial Kinetics and Pressure-Transition Temperature
Effects in Planar Solidification Problems Without
Initial Undercooling', *CEEP preprint*, 1993.
7. Charach,Ch. and Zaltzman,B.,'Planar Solidification From an Undercooled Melt: Asymptotic Solutions
to Continuum Model with Interfacial Kinetics',
Physical Review E (in press).
8. Glicksman,M.E. and Schaefer,R.J.,'Investigation
of Solid/Liquid Interface Temperatures Via Isoen-
thalpic Solidification', *J. Crystal Growth*, Vol.1,
pp. 297-310 (1967).

SECTION 9: METAL CASTING AND WELDING

A coherence between a castings shape and its total solidification time

J. Hloušek, F. Kavička

Department of Mechanical Engineering, Technical University of Brno, Technická 2, 616 69 Brno, Czech Republic

ABSTRACT

The solidification coefficient and it 's dependence on the geometrical shape of a casting solidifying within the sand mould was analysed. It has been proved that an experimental measurement can be approximated by numerical solution of solidification of the casting. The program for PC was applicated for 1D, 2D and 3D systems composed of the steel casting and of a sand mould. The results of numerical solution of this problem show that Chvorinov 's formula for calculation of the total solidification time must be corrected. The paper consists of the mathematical formulation of the problem, transforming the basic theoretical equations into numerical ones. It is explained how generation of latent heat is numerically formulated. It was applicated to the change of basic parameters with temperatures.

INTRODUCTION

A presented study is based on numerical solution of casting 's temperature field and it concerns the solidification of the iron casting in the sand mould. Numerous previous solutions had confirmed a justification for using the set up mathematical model of given problem. In the mathematical model which has been laied out upon the Technical University of Brno (Czech Republic) [1] the problem of latent heat liberation by an introduction of an enthalpy has been solved . The results of numerical solution were verified with the temperature measurements on castings during past eight years. A very good correspondence of results had been proved. It had been demonstrated that when using the sand mould it is not necessary to take into account the heat resistance between the mould and the casting. From the thermomechanical point of view it is called the ideal heat contact. We can say that the numerical solution of a solidification process substitues for experiment. That is the reason why the computational results presented in next chapters have not been verified experimentally.

ANALYTICAL SOLUTION OF ONE DIMENSIONAL SOLIDIFICATION

A temperature field (Fig.1) of a system consisted of the pure liquid metal-solid metal-sand mould is described by the system of partial differential equations

$$\rho.c.\frac{\partial T}{\partial t} = \frac{\partial}{\partial x}\left(k.\frac{\partial T}{\partial x}\right) \qquad \text{for } x \in\; < 0,\xi\;) \tag{1}$$

$$\rho'.c'.\frac{\partial T'}{\partial t} = \frac{\partial}{\partial x}\left(k'.\frac{\partial T'}{\partial x}\right)+q \qquad \text{for } x\; < \xi,\infty\;) \tag{2}$$

$$\rho_m.c_m.\frac{\partial T_m}{\partial t} = \frac{\partial}{\partial x}\left(k_m.\frac{\partial T_m}{\partial x}\right) \qquad \text{for } x \in (-\infty\;,\; 0\;) \tag{3}$$

where ρ [kg.m^{-3}] is a density,
$\quad$ c [J.kg^{-1}.K^{-1}] is a specific heat,
$\quad$ k [W.m^{-1}.K-1] is a conductivity heat transfer coefficient,
$\quad$ T [°C] is a temperature,
$\quad$ t [s] is time,
$\quad$ q [J.m^{-3}] is a heat source (latent heat of solidification)
Upper index ′ denotes liquid metal and lower one m the sand mould. The initial conditions for the solution are

$$T'(x,0) = T_0 \tag{4}$$

$$T_m(x,0) = T_{mo} \tag{5}$$

The boundary conditions are

$$\lim_{x \to\; +\infty} T'(x,t\;) = T_0 = const \tag{6}$$

$$T'(\xi,t\;) = T(\xi,t\;) = T_{cry} = const \tag{7}$$

$$-k.\frac{\partial T(\xi,t)}{\partial x} = -k'.\frac{\partial T'(\xi,t)}{\partial x} +\rho'.\Delta l_{cry}.\frac{d\xi}{dt} \tag{8}$$

$$T(0,t) = T_m(0,t) = T_s = const \tag{9}$$

$$-k \cdot \frac{\partial T(0,t)}{\partial x} = -k_m \cdot \frac{\partial T_m'(0,t)}{\partial x} \tag{10}$$

$$\lim_{\substack{m \\ \text{for } x \to -\infty}} T_m(x,t) = T_{mo} = const \tag{11}$$

The temperature of a liquid phase is defined by the relation

$$T' = T_o - \frac{T_o - T_{cry}}{erfc\left(\dfrac{\xi}{2 \cdot \sqrt{a' \cdot t}}\right)} \cdot \left[1 - erf\left(\dfrac{x}{2 \cdot \sqrt{a' \cdot t}}\right)\right] \tag{12}$$

The temperature of a solid phase is defined by the relation

$$T = T_s + \frac{T_{cry} - T_s}{erfc\left(\dfrac{\xi}{2 \cdot \sqrt{a \cdot t}}\right)} \cdot erf\left(\dfrac{x}{2 \cdot \sqrt{a \cdot t}}\right) \tag{13}$$

The temperature of the sand mould is defined by the relation

$$T_m = T_s + \left(T_s - T_{mo}\right) \cdot erf\left(\dfrac{x}{2 \cdot \sqrt{a_m \cdot t}}\right) \tag{14}$$

The temperature at the contact between the solid phase of the casting and the mould is defined by the relation

$$T_s = \frac{T_{cry} + \dfrac{b_m}{b} \cdot T_{mo} \cdot erf\left(\dfrac{CS}{2\sqrt{a}}\right)}{1 + \dfrac{b_m}{b} \cdot erf\left(\dfrac{CS}{2 \cdot \sqrt{a}}\right)} \tag{15}$$

The constant of solidification (CS) is defined by the relation

$$\frac{b.exp\left(\dfrac{-CS^2}{4.a}\right)}{\dfrac{b}{b_m}+erf\left(\dfrac{CS}{2.\sqrt{a}}\right)}\cdot\left(T_{cry}-T_{mo}\right)-b'\cdot\left(T_o-T_{cry}\right)\cdot\frac{exp\left(-\dfrac{CS^2}{4.a'}\right)}{1-erf\left(\dfrac{CS}{2.\sqrt{a}}\right)} \tag{16}$$

$$-\rho.\Delta l_{cry}\cdot\frac{\sqrt{\Pi}}{2}.CS=0$$

where a $=$ k/(ρ.c) and similarly a', a_m,
     b $=$ $\sqrt{k.\rho.c}$ and similarly b', b_m,
     Δl_{cry} is latent heat of solidification,
     T_{cry} is a temperature of solidification of pure metal.

A BRIEF INTERPRETATION OF THE NUMERICAL METHOD

The system consisted of the casting and the mould is divided into volume elements of a prism shape. Each volume element is represented by a nodal point usually placed in the body centre of the the volume element. When the nodal point i,j,k is in the mould the next computational formula[2] is used

$$T_{i,j,k}^{(t+\Delta t)}=T_{i,j,k}^{(t)}+\frac{\Delta t}{C.V_{i,j,k}}\sum Q_{i,j,k}^{(t)} \tag{17}$$

where upper index denotes time,
     C $=$ ρ.c [J.m^{-3}.°C^{-1}] is a capacitance of the element,
     $V_{i,j,k}$ [m^3] is it's volume,
     $\Sigma Q^{(t)}$ [W] is a sum of heat fluxes from neighbouring elements in time t.
When the nodal point is in the casting then

$$e_{i,j,k}^{(t+\Delta t)}=e_{i,j,k}^{(t)}+\frac{\Delta t}{V_{i,j,k}}\cdot\sum Q^{(t)} \tag{18}$$

where $e_{i,j,k}$ [J.m^{-3}] is enthalpy of the element, defined as

$$e_{i,j,k}=\rho.c_{sol}.T_{i,j,k} \qquad for\ T_{i,j,k}\leq T_{sol}$$

$$e_{i,j,k}=e_{sol}+\rho'.\Delta l_{cry}+\rho'.c'.\left(T-T_{lik}\right) \qquad for\ T_{i,j,k}\geq T_{lik}$$

Between the temperatures T_{sol}(solidus) and T_{lik}(likvidus) the enthalpy relationship e and is linear. The temperature field and heat fluxes calculated numerically according to previous equations for one case are at fig.2.

EXPERIMENTAL RESULTS OF SOLIDIFICATION ACCORDING TO CHVORINOV

The system of equations (12 to 16) is the exact solution of the given task. From the analytical solution of the problem it is evident that the most important parameter which occurs in equation (12) up to (14) is

$$\frac{x}{2.\sqrt{a.t}}$$

According to Chvorinov this parameter must be constant. Therefore solidification level progresses according to equation

$$\xi = CS.\sqrt{t} \tag{19}$$

where CS is called the solidification coefficient. The equation (17) is a well known parabolic relation for solidification progress. The experimental results collected by Chvorinov have been published in 1954 for 20 steel castings [3] of various geometrical shapes (see Fig.3). The solidification coefficient has the same value along the whole line $CS = 0,854.10^{-3} m.s^{-1/2}$. The dependence of solidification time upon the thickness equivalent is valid for steel castings casted in sand or ceramic moulds.

THE SOLIDIFICATION COEFFICIENT AND ITS DEPENDENCE ON GEOMETRY OF THE CASTING (2D PROBLEM)

The dependence of solidification time on the thickness equivalent can be verified using the results of numerical solution the temperatures fields of solidifying steel castings within the sand moulds. For verification had been elected the most simple shape of the casting i.e. a long bar of rectangular cross section with dimensions a×b. With respect to symmetry it had been solved numerically for only a quarter of cross section a/2×b/2. With the respect to simplicity of numerical solution it had not been taken into account the ingate and the riser. The number of solved variations was so big to be able to plot the dependence curve of the solidification constant CS on a ratio of h/c (i.e. a geometrical parameter) influencing the solidification time and the solification constant. From the thermokinetic point of view the problem described in this chapter is a purely twodimensional task (2D). From the results (see Fig.4) one can make several obvious conclusions:

i)At the point b/a = 0 the twodimensional task transfers into onedimensional one(1D).
  The numerical value of CS is the highest and the solidification time is the shortest.
ii)At the point b/a = 0,15 the numerical value of CS is the lowest and the solidification
  time is the longest.
iii)At the point b/a = 1 the rectangular shape transfers to square one.
iv)The same curve appears from the point b/a = 1 to b/a → ∞ but in a reflected image
  The minimum of the curve must appear at the point b/a = 1/0,15 = 6,66. At the point
  b/a → ∞ there is the same numerical value of CS as at the point b/a = 0.

v)The temperature distribution along the cross section is the same when a/b = constant it is not dependent on the magnitude of edges of the bar.

THE SOLIDIFICATION COEFFICIENT FOR THE PLATE CASTING (3D PROBLEM)

Similarly as in the previous chapter here is described the threedimensional plate (3D). The base of the plate is the square with dimensions c×c and the hight is h. Also in this case it had been solved only the quarter of the plate. The casting hed been solved without the riser and the ingate. The results of solution are plotted at Fig.3 and the curve relating to the plate is labelled as 3D. The conclusions of this case are as follows:

i)The original point h/c = 0 must correspond to 2D problem, because in both cases there is solved the infinite plate with the thickness h.

ii)The minimum value of CS is at point h/c = 0,15, but the numerical value of CS is lower in comparison with 2D problem.

iii)The point h/c = 1 corresponds to the cube.

iv)For h/c → ∞ the shape of the casting approaches to the bar and CS must approach to that value obtained for b/a = 1 in 2D problem.

THE SOLIDIFICATION COEFFICIENT FOR THE CYLINDRICAL CASTING

The cylindrical casting is a special case of 2D problem. Coordinates are a radius (r) and a hight (h) of the cylinder.With the respect to symmetry it had been solved the pie with the angle of 1 rad. The results are at Fig.3 where the values of CS depend on the ratio h/d.

CONCLUSION

It has been proved that the parameter CS is not constant but it is dependent on the geometrical shape of the casting. The influence of risers and ingates must be analysed in detail in future time.

REFERENCES

[1] Chvorinov N.,Krystalizace a nestejnorodost oceli, nakl.ČSAV, Praha 1954.
[2] Hloušek J.,Příspěvek k řešení přenosových jevů v metalurgických procesech, VUT v Brně, 1981.
[3] Hloušek J.,Kavička F.,Havelka L.,Teplotní pole odlitku ve tvaru klínu, zpráva VUT v Brně, 1986.

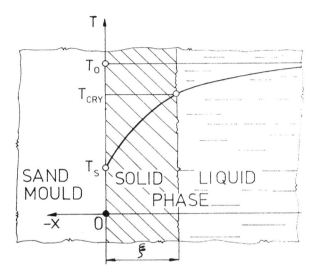

Fig.1. The solidification process within the infinite space.

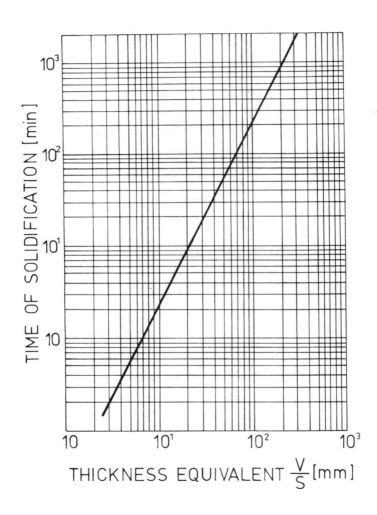

Fig.2. Solidification time for the plate castings according to Chvorinov.

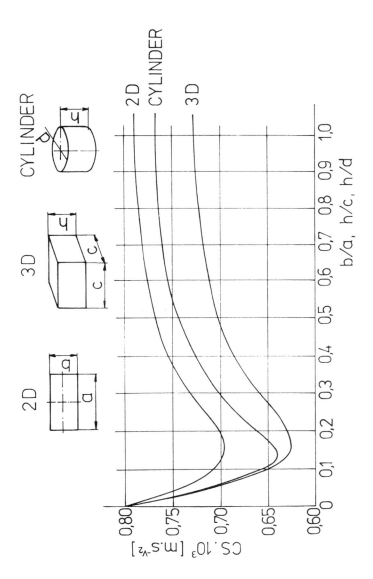

Fig.3. The relationship of CS parameter and geometrical shape ratio.

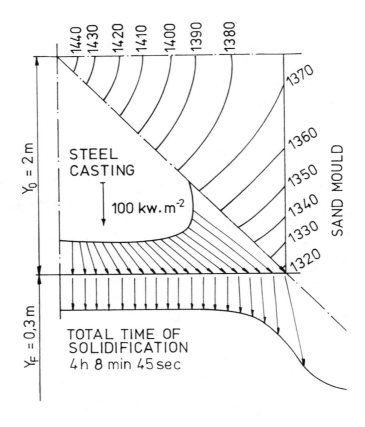

Fig.4. The temperature field and heat fluxes calculated numerically for one
case.

A boundary collocation heat flow model for arc welding

E. Mahajerin

Mechanical Engineering Department, Saginaw Valley State University, University Center, Michigan, 48710 USA

ABSTRACT

Heat flow during welding may strongly affect phase transformation in the workpiece material. Therefore, there will be possible changes in physical as well as in mechanical properties of the material. For these reasons, the welding process requires a suitable computational method for estimating peak temperature and also the cooling rate during welding. Analytical models may be found for idealized models involving infinitely large regions, simple boundary conditions and constant material properties. Consequently, general cases involving finite geometries, temperature-dependent material properties and arbitrary boundary conditions may require a suitable numerical method. In this paper different governing differential equations of welding are investigated. In general, the resulting governing differential equations are nonlinear and their numerical solution may require an iterative approach. A boundary-oriented formulation based on the fundamental collocation [1] is presented which is suitable for use on personal computers. The method is illustrated using an example involving temperature distribution in a thin plate during arc welding.

INTRODUCTION

Welding is a commonly used fabrication process which has gained attention in recent years because of its heat transfer phenomena. An analytical model based on idealized assumptions is available [2] which may be used to estimate temperature distribution as well as cooling rates. Modifications including a Gaussian distribution of the heat source are given in [3,4]. However, since material properties change at higher temperatures, a numerical procedure such as the finite element method [5] becomes necessary. Unfortunately, the finite element method for time-dependent problems and/or temperature-dependent properties becomes tedious and may not be suitable on personal computers. In this paper, an alternate approach based on the boundary element method is presented which does not require extensive computation or computer memory. The method can be used to find temperature distributions as well as cooling rates in the workpiece.

GOVERNING DIFFERENTIAL EQUATIONS OF ARC WELDING

The governing differential equation of heat flow in an arbitrary region R during welding may be obtained from the energy equation. In the absence of radiation, Joule heating, heat generation (or consumption), and viscous dissipation, the energy equation for a volume element fixed in the body (i.e., material element) inside workpiece R, (**Figure 1**) becomes:

$$\nabla \cdot K \nabla T = \rho C_p \partial T / \partial \tau \quad \text{inside R} \tag{1}$$

where T is temperature, K is the thermal conductivity of the workpiece material, ρ is density, C_p is specific heat, τ is time and ∇ is the gradient operator in the fixed coordinates (X,Y,Z). On the boundary of the region, ∂R, a Rubin-type boundary condition is considered, i.e.,

$$aT + b \, \partial T/\partial n = c \qquad \text{on } \partial R \qquad (2)$$

where n is the outward normal to the boundary and c is the prescribed boundary condition on ∂R. Parameters a and b are selected as follows:

For the Dirichlet condition   : $a=1$, $b=0$
For the Neumann condition   : $a=0$, $b=1$ (3)
For Rubin's-type condition   : $a\neq0$, $b\neq0$

The governing equation (1) corresponds to the stationary (fixed) coordinate system (X,Y,Z) in which differentiations are performed in the (X,Y,Z) coordinates and $T=T(X,Y,Z;\tau)$. With respect to the moving coordinate system (x,y,z), which is attached to the electrode (heat source), the solution is expressed as $T=T(x,y,z;t)$. In this case the energy equation applies to a volume of a material at a particular (x,y,z) location which is not a volume fixed in the body. If the coordinate system moves past the volume element at a speed u along the x-axis we can find, from the energy equation,

$$\nabla.K\nabla T = \rho C_p \Delta T/\Delta\tau \qquad \text{inside } R \qquad (4)$$

Where ∇ is the gradient operator in the moving coordinates (x,y,z) coordinates and $\Delta T/\Delta\tau$ means change in temperature over time Δt for a fixed material element. Now, since the fixed element lies at $X=x+u\tau$, then since $X=$constant, $dX=0=dx+ud\tau$. This means that in order to be at a fixed location in the material, if one changes time by $d\tau$, then one must move back along the x-axis by an amount $dx=-ud\tau$ in order to stay at one spot in space. means

$$\Delta T/\Delta\tau =[T(x-u\Delta t,y,z;t+\Delta t)-T(x,y,z;t)]/\Delta t = -u\partial T/\partial x + \partial T/\partial t \qquad (5)$$

Therefore, with respect to the moving coordinate system (x,y,z) the governing differential equation will be:

$$\nabla.K\nabla T = \rho C_p(-u\partial T/\partial x + \partial T/\partial t) \qquad \text{inside } R \qquad (6)$$

Derivation of (6) by mathematical transformation of (1) is as follows: $\partial T/\partial X$ means $\Delta T/\Delta X$ at a fixed time. But at a fixed time, form $X=x+ut$ we obtain $\Delta X=\Delta x$. Therefore, $\partial T/\partial X=\partial T/\partial x$. Likewise for y and z. Therefore, the gradient operators in coordinate systems (X,Y,Z) and (x,y,z) are the same. However, $\partial T/\partial\tau$ means $\Delta T/\Delta\tau$ at a fixed (X,Y,Z). But since the solution is now expressed in terms of $(x,y,z;t)$, fixing X and changing time requires that x changes. As in (5),

$$\Delta T =[T(x-u\Delta t,y,z;t+\Delta t)-T(x,y,z;t)]=(-u\Delta t)\partial T/\partial x +(\Delta t)\partial T/\partial t \qquad (7)$$

we find that $\partial T/\partial\tau$ transforms to $-u\partial T/\partial x + \partial T/\partial t$.

Note that above results are easily obtained using the following mathematical chain rule:

$$\partial T/\partial\tau=(\partial T/\partial x)(\partial x/\partial\tau) + (\partial T/\partial t)(\partial t/\partial\tau) \qquad (8)$$

Sincere $\partial x/\partial\tau=-u$ and $\partial t/\partial\tau=1$ we obtain

$$\partial T/\partial \tau = -u(\partial T/\partial x) + (\partial T/\partial t) \tag{9}$$

However, this method does not provide any physical interpretation.

COMPARISON OF (1) AND (6)

The governing differential equation (1) involves both time (τ) and space coordinates (X,Y,Z). The corresponding boundary condition(s) may become complicated because it involves a surface point heat source which moves from point to point on the surface. The governing equation (6), on the other hand, is complicated (in form) but its boundary condition is relatively simple; it involves a fixed point heat source. Furthermore, using the "*quasistationary*" assumption, $\partial T/\partial t = 0$, we can write

$$v.K \nabla T = -\rho C_p u \partial T/\partial x \tag{10}$$

This assumption indicates that if the electrode moves at a constant speed and the thermal disturbance does not move faster than the electrode, then the temperature field appears to be stationary. The situation is similar to what happens in a boat: if the boat (electrode) moves faster than the speed of the waves (thermal disturbances) in the water, then the wake behind the boat at a certain distance behind always looks the same to an observer on the coordinates (x,y,z) on the boat. But if the boat moves slower than the waves, the disturbance (wake) propagate past the boat and the wake does not appear stationary.

EFFECTS OF MATERIAL PROPERTIES

Table 1 shows corresponding governing differential equations for three possible cases. In the isotropic case, material properties are considered to be independent of direction. In the orthotropic case, it is assumed that x-y are the axes of material symmetry. The temperature-dependent conductivity case is a more realistic model because of variation of K, C_p and α with temperature.

Table 1. Effects of the Material Behavior on the Governing Equation

Material	Properties	Governing Differential Equation
Isotropic	K = constant	$\nabla^2 T = -2u(\partial T/\partial x)/\alpha$
Orthotopic	K = (K_x,K_y,K_z)	$K_x(\partial^2 T/\partial x^2) + K_y(\partial^2 T/\partial y^2) + K_z(\partial^2 T/\partial z^2) = -2\rho C_p u(\partial T/\partial x)$
Temperature-Dependent Conductivity	K = K(T)	$\nabla^2 T = -\{(\partial K/\partial T)[(\partial T/\partial x)^2 + (\partial T/\partial y)^2 + (\partial T/\partial z)^2 + 2\rho C_p u(\partial T/\partial x)\}/K$

where $\alpha = \rho C_p/K$ is the thermal diffusivity of the workpiece material and $\nabla^2 T = (\partial^2 T/\partial x^2) + (\partial^2 T/\partial y^2) + (\partial^2 T/\partial z^2)$ (11)

The governing differential equation of the isotropic case and the K = K(T) case are special cases of the following equation:

$$\nabla^2 T = f(x,y,z,T,\partial T/\partial x,\partial T/\partial y,\partial T/\partial z) \tag{12}$$

The orthotopic governing differential equation may be converted to the form in Equation (12) by means of the following transformations:

$$x_1 = x/\sqrt{K_x} \ , \ x_2 = y/\sqrt{K_y} \ \text{and} \ z_2 = z/\sqrt{K_z} \tag{13}$$

In the $K = K(T)$ case the resulting governing differential equation is nonlinear. As in many nonlinear cases, its numerical treatment may require an iterative approach.

TWO DIMENSIONAL MODELS

Although a three-dimensional model may be required for most welding processes, it is possible to study the problem by means of appropriate two dimensional models. If the plate thickness is small compared to other dimensions (**Figure 2**), then $\partial T/\partial z$ is negligible. and we can write (12) as

$$\nabla^2 T = f(x,y,T,\partial T/\partial x,\partial T/\partial y) \tag{14}$$

Consequently, the upper half of the top plane may be used for numerical purposes. A different two-dimensional model (suitable for thick plates) is a section in the y-z plane. However, since the heat source moves in the x-direction, the resulting governing differential equation for this case is (1) in the y-z plane. Clearly, in this case discretization of time becomes necessary. Discussion of this case and extension of the fundamental collocation approach to three dimensional case are subjects of future investigations.

NUMERICAL SOLUTION OF (14)

If T^* is a fundamental solution of $\nabla^2 T(x,y) = 0$, then temperature T at any internal point $F(xF,yF)$ may be expressed as

$$T(F) = \int_{\partial R} W(S)T^*(F;S)d\Gamma \ + \ \int_R f(x,y,T,\partial T/\partial x,\partial T/\partial y)T^*(F;P)dR \tag{15}$$

where $d\Gamma$ is the element along the boundary ∂R, dR is the surface element in R, $S(xS,yS)$ and $P(xP,yP)$ are integration points along ∂R and in R respectively. The basic fundamental solution of the Laplace equation in two dimensions is $T^* = \ln r^2$ where $r^2 = x^2 + y^2$ which satisfies $\nabla^2 T(x,y) = 0$ for all (x,y) except $(0,0)$. Consequently, a finite series of translated fundamental solutions in the form

$$\sum_{j=1}^{N} W_j \ln r^2(x;S_j) \tag{16}$$

where $r^2(x;S_j) = (x - xS_j)^2 + (y - yS_j)^2 \tag{17}$

also satisfies $\nabla^2 T(x,y) = 0$ for any combination of N coefficients (weights), W_j, except at the "source" points $S_j = (xS,yS)_j$. Therefore, if it is required to satisfy $\nabla^2 T(x,y) = 0$ inside the region, the source points need to be located outside R. For simplicity, the N sources are applied at source points $S_j = (xS,yS)_j$ located on a similar boundary at distance DS away from ∂R (**Figure 4**). The overall solution of Equation (15) which is the sum of the homogeneous part Equation (16) and the particular part (due to f), will be constructed by approximating the area integral using M cells of elemental area ΔA_k, $k = 1,2,3,...,M$ (**Figure 5**). If center points of these cells are represented by $P_k = (xP,yP)_k$ we can write

$$T(F) = \sum_{j=1}^{N} W_j \ln r^2(F;S_j) + (1/4\pi) \sum_{k=1}^{M} f_k \Delta A_k \ln r^2(F;P_k)$$
(18)

where $r^2(F;S_j) = (xF-xS_j)^2 + (yF-yS_j)^2$
(19)

and $r^2(F;P_k) = (xF-xP_k)^2 + (yF-yP_k)^2$
(20)

When F and P_k coincide, the integration over a rectangular 2ax2b cell of area $\Delta A = 4ab$ is performed analytically. It can be shown that in this case

$$\int \ln(x^2+y^2)dA = [\ln(a^2+b^2)+(a^2+b^2)\pi/\Delta A\text{-qarctanq-3}]\Delta A$$
(21)

where $q = .5(a/b - b/a)$
(22)

In a square cell, $a=b$, Equation (21) becomes $[\ln(\Delta A/2)+\pi/2-3]\Delta A$.

Since $\partial T/\partial n = 2(x\cos\theta + y\sin\theta)/r^2$ where θ is the angle that the normal to the boundary makes with the positive x-axis, we can simply obtain corresponding expressions for the Neumann and the Rubin-type boundary conditions. However, in the resulting expressions, as in Equation (14), the dependent variable T and its derivatives appear on both sides of the equation. Satisfying boundary conditions at boundary points $B_i(xB,yB)_i$ leads to an implicit solution to Equation (12). As with many implicit forms, the solution may be obtained in an iterative manner. The matrix representation for a general case will be

$$D \, w + G \, f = c$$
(23)

where $D(d_{ij})$ $i=1,2,..,N$; $j=1,2,..,N$ is the influence matrix,
$w(w_i)$ $i=1,2,..,N$ is a vector containing the source strengths
$G(g_{ij})$ $i,j=1,2,...,N$; $j=1,2,..,M$ is the body force matrix
$f(fj)$ $j=1,..,M$ is a vector containing $\Delta A_k/(4\pi)$ times values of the forcing function f at field points F_j
$c(c_i)$ $i=1,2,..,N$ is a vector containing prescribed boundary conditions at points B_i.
For the Dirichlet condition   : $d_{ij} = \ln r_{ij}2$ where $r_{ij} = r(B_i;S_j)$
For the Neumann condition   : $d_{ij} = 2[(xB_i-xS_j)\cos\theta + (yB_i-yS_j)\sin\theta]/r_{ij}^2$
For the Rubin-type boundary condition a suitable combination of these (see Equation 2) is used.

THE ITERATION SCHEME

Multiplying Equation (23) by D^{-1} gives

$$w = p - E.f$$
(23)

where $p = D^{-1}c$ and $E = D^{-1}G$

The unknowns are w_i and the f_j's are functions of w_i. Iteration starts with a guess $f^{(0)}$ for f which is substituted in Equation (24) to compute $w^{(1)} = p-E.f^{(0)}$. Then $w^{(1)}$ is used to compute $f^{(1)}$ from which we compute $w^{(2)}$ and repeat the process in the hope that it converges. Once the w_i's are evaluated, temperature, T, and the temperature gradients, $\partial T/\partial x$ and $\partial T/\partial y$ are obtained from (18).

EXAMPLE

Consider the case where the corners of the upper half of the plate are symmetrically situated with respect to the electrode (i.e., the electrode is at $x=y=0$). Consequently, the first quadrant oABC would be appropriate for numerical solutions.

Workpiece material   : Steel AISI 1018
Melting point   : 1530 °C
Thermal Diffusivity   : $\alpha = .091$ cm^2/sec
Welding velocity   : $u = 5$ mm/sec
Plate dimensions   : Length $= 32$ cm, width$=8$ cm, thickness$=6$ mm
Numerical Data   : $N=30$, $M=80$ (**Figures 4 & 5**)

Boundary Conditions: On oA: At the heat source $T=1530$ °C; otherwise $\partial T/\partial y = 0$.
    On oB & AC: $\partial T/\partial x = 0$ On BC: $T=$ Ambient temperature.

Using an initial guess of $f^{(0)}=0$ and DS$=4$ cm, the iterative scheme in this paper converged in about four iterations. The results are graphically shown in **Figures 6 and 7**. These results may be combined with the iron-carbon phase diagram to study phase transformation in the material. The cooling curve, $\partial T/\partial \tau$ versus x, may be constructed from temperature gradients according to

$$\partial T/\partial \tau = (\partial T/\partial X)(\partial X/\partial \tau) = u\partial T/\partial x \tag{24}$$

CONCLUSIONS

Various heat flow models for arc welding have been studied. A simple procedure based on the fundamental collocation method has been presented. The method utilizes an iterative process to handle a resulting nonlinear governing differential equation for arc welding.

REFERENCES

1. Burgess, G. and Mahajerin, E. 'On the Numerical Solution of Laplace's Equation Using Personal Computers' Int. J. Mech. Engrg Education, Vol. 13, pp 45-54, 1984.

2. Rosenthal, D.'Mathematical Theory of Heat Distribution During Welding and Cutting' Welding Journal, Vol 20, pp220-234, 1941.

3. Goldak, J., Chakravarti, A. and Bibby, M. 'A New Finite Element Model for Welding Heat Sources' Metallurgical Trans. B, Vol. 15B, pp299-305, 1984.

4. Kuo, S. Welding Metallurgy, J. Wiley & Sons, 1987.

5. Krutz, G. W. and Segerlind, L. J. 'Finite Element Analysis of Welded Structures' Welding Journal Research Supplement (AWS), Vol. 57, pp211s-216s, July 1978.

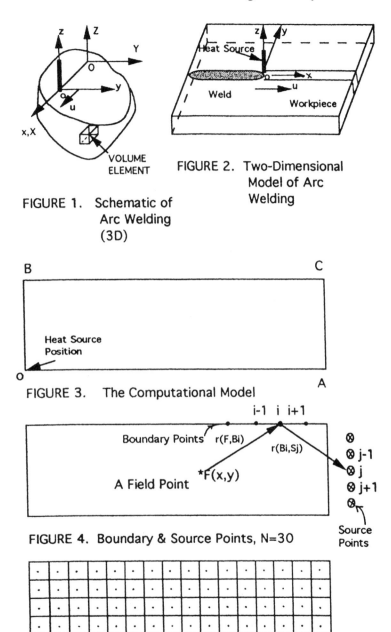

FIGURE 1.   Schematic of
             Arc Welding
             (3D)

FIGURE 2. Two-Dimensional
            Model of Arc
            Welding

FIGURE 3.   The Computational Model

FIGURE 4. Boundary & Source Points, N=30

FIGURE 5.   Internal Cells, M=80

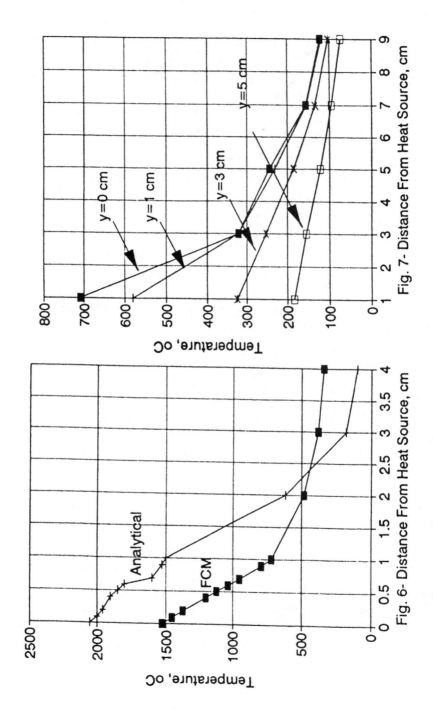

Fig. 7- Distance From Heat Source, cm

Fig. 6- Distance From Heat Source, cm

SECTION 10: INVERSE PROBLEMS

Determination of seepage flow under given free surface as an inverse problem

K. Kosorin, P. Kučerák

Institute of Hydrology and Hydraulics, Trnavská 32, 826 51 Bratislava, Slovak Republic

ABSTRACT

In following a theoretical basis and some practical results of solution of the problems of free boundary in seepage dynamics are presented. This solution originates from the hydrodynamic theory of boundaries, see [2],[3],[4]. Main product of the theory is the method for transformation of N-dimensional hydrodynamic task into N-1 dimensional one. It allows to formulate and solve an inverse task, where the seepage velocity field has to be determined in the domain below the given free water surface.

INTRODUCTION

Free surface of flow in correctly put boundary task is unknown and has to be found out simultaneously with solution of hydrodynamic task on the whole. But estimating the groundwater flow $q = - k$ grad P, on the basis of information from "in situ" observations one has to proceed in another way.

In case of general three-dimensional flow in non-homogeneous medium without Dupuit or Boussinesq simplifying assumptions it is necessary to determine (by means of measurement in discrete points) the field of the pressure function $P (x,y,z,t)$. Since in situ water surface monitoring is much easier than monitoring of the variable pressure function P in an aquifer, it is to be decided, whether the knowledge of the free water surface is sufficient for the determination of 3-D velocity field also in a general case, when the assumptions of the shallow water theory are not satisfied. Positive decision follows from the consequences of the hydrodynamic theory of boundaries [4].

ON THE FORMALISM OF HYDRODYNAMIC THEORY OF BOUNDARIES

In order to get up formalism for the theory we have to define and explain some terms. Let the N-1 dimensional relation

$$y = h(x,z,t) \tag{1}$$

define the moving surface ∂G which is a part of and belongs to N dimensional domain G of independent variables $x=(x,y,z,t)$; $i=1,2,3,4$ (N=4). One has to seek the function $f(x,y,z,t)$ as the solution of mixed hydrodynamic task in domain G. Let us mark by a strip those parts of the function f and their partial derivatives which are evaluated in points of surface. For f it means the formal notation, see Fig. 2.

$$\overline{f} = f(x,h(x,z,t),z,t) \tag{2}$$

which transforms $\overline{f}$ into N-1 dimensional "boundary function" $f(x,z,t)$ because on the surface ∂G (originally) independent variable y becomes a dependent one, due to relation (1).Differentiating the equation (2) with respect to N-1 vriables x_i one obtains

$$\overline{f}_{x_i} = \overline{f}_{x_i} + \overline{f}_y h_x \tag{3}$$

where two kinds of partial derivatives relating to surface ∂G have been incurred. The "inner $\overline{f}_{x_i} = \partial \overline{f}/\partial x_i$ as the partial derivatives of the boundary function and the "outer" $\overline{f}_{x_i} = \overline{\partial f/\partial x_i}$, $\overline{f}_y = \overline{\partial f/\partial y}$.

3-DIMENSIONAL SEEPAGE TASK TRANSFORMED INTO 2-DIMENSIONAL ONE ON MATERIAL BOUNDARY OF FLOW

Let a seepage flow in G (Fig.1) with lower boundary MB1 $(y=h_0(x,z))$, upper boundary MB2 $(y=h(x,z,t))$ or MB4 $(y=h(x,z))$ and geometrical boundaries GB be ruled by continuity equation $divq=0$ and dynamic equation $gradP+q/k=0$ for the seepage velocity vector $q=(u,v,w)$ and the pressure function

$$P = p/g\rho + y + const. \tag{4}$$

where p is pressure, y-vertical coordinate, u,v,w are velocity components in (x,y,z) space and $k=(k_u,k_v,k_w)$ is vector of hydraulic conductivity. Let us suppose that $k_u=k_w \equiv k$ with vertical anisotropy $a=k/k_v$. It is suitable to introduce dimensionless velocity (U,V,W) by

$$U = u/k; \qquad V = v/k_v; \qquad W = w/k \tag{5}$$

allowing to write the continuity equation as

$$U_x + \frac{1}{a}V_y + W_z = -R \qquad (6)$$

with $R = (Uk_x + Vk_{vy} + Wk_z)/k$ and dynamic equations in the simple form

$$P_x + U = 0; \qquad P_y + V = 0; \qquad P_z + W = 0. \qquad (7)$$

The velocity field in G in the form of Taylor series up to the N-th order with respect to vertical variable y is

$$U = \bar{U} + \sum_{n=1}^{N} U_n (y-h)^n / n!$$

$$V = \bar{V} + \sum_{n=1}^{N} V_n (y-h)^n / n! \qquad (8)$$

$$W = \bar{W} + \sum_{n=1}^{N} W_n (y-h)^n / n!$$

The expansion coefficients in (8) are the outer y-derivatives for $n=1,2,..,N$

$$U_n = \overline{\partial^n U / \partial y^n} \; ; \qquad V_n = \overline{\partial^n V / \partial y^n}; \qquad W_n = \overline{\partial^n W / \partial y^n} \qquad (9)$$

and $\bar{U}, \bar{V}, \bar{W}$ are boundary values of the velocity field on $y=h$ (or $y=h_o$).

This transformation process can be successfully completed by :
- finding out the outer y-derivatives (9) for expansion (8) as functions of inner derivatives on boundary;
- integration of the continuity equation along vertical independent variable y between h_o and h using the velocity field (8);
- use of dynamic boundary conditions (see Fig.1)

$$\bar{P} = h + const \quad \text{on MB2 (free surface)}$$
$$\qquad (10)$$
$$P = const \quad \text{on MB4 (river bed)}$$

and the kinematic conditions $h_t + \bar{u}h_x + \bar{w}h_z = \bar{v}$ on MB2 and $\bar{u}h_{ox} + \bar{w}h_{oz} = \bar{v}$ on MB1
- use of jump conditions on MB3, if such boundaries exist in G.

Crucial step is the first one. Nevertheless, it can be performed by solving the (algebraic) system (3) with (6) and (7) written for free surface.

ASSUMPTIONS ON FLOW DIRECTIONS

When the assumption is met that the groundwater flow direction does not vary along the vertical, the three-dimensional task may be favourably transformed into two-dimensional one in vertical plane, normal to the water surface contour line. The searched variables would be the vertical velocity component v and the horizontal one u_r, both occuring in the vertical plane, normal to the surface contour line in the given point of the space. Component u_r is consequently perpendicular to water surface contour line. If the assumption on constant flow direction along the vertical is fulfilled, then the velocity vector is normal to water surface contour line along the vertical over the whole water depth. This hypothesis is based on the circumstance that the surface velocity vector is normal to the water surface contour line, if the horizontal component of the filtration coefficient is uniform in all directions. This could be verified as follows:

Equations for flow velocity on free water surface show that the relationship of horizontal velocity components on the surface is equal to the relationship of surface gradients in respective directions, i.e.

$$w/u = h_z/h_x, \tag{11}$$

where u and w are the horizontal components of the velocity vector on the surface.

Flow direction in the horizontal plane is given by the relationship

$$k_p = dz/dx = w/u. \tag{12}$$

On the other hand it is supposed, that along the surface contour line, the surface $h(x,z,t)$ is constant i.e. $dh = h_x dx + h_z dz = 0$. Thus, the line tangent to surface contour line has the slope

$$k = dz/dx = - h_x/h_z \tag{13}$$

Comparison of equations (11), (12) and (13) results in

$$k_p = -1/k, \tag{14}$$

confirming the perpendicularity of surface velocity direction towards the surface contour line.

Thus, if the flow direction along the vertical does not vary, the velocity vector would be normal to surface contour lines over the whole water depth.

It is considered that this assumption is met with sufficient precision there, where the variability of the horizontal component of filtration coefficient in the horizontal direction is low, especially when compared with its variability in vertical direction.

DETERMINATION OF 3-D VELOCITY FIRLD APPLYING THE HYDRODYNAMICS THEORY OF BOUNDARIES

Significant condition, resulting from this theory is that the velocity field of the groundwater seepage flow is characterized by the shape and time variation of its free surface.

If the rectangular coordinates system (x,y,z) · is located and turned in such a way, that the axis y remains vertical, and axis x is perpendicular to one of the free surface contour lines, the axis z would become the tangent line to the contour line. If the basic equations of seepage motion are written for the origin of coordinates it can be realized that the horizontal component of velocity w on the surface would be zero. Values of this component along the vertical y would differ from zero only proportionally to higher derivatives of surface h in point P and proportionally to filtration coefficient variations in horizontal direction z.

For relative velocities $U = u/k_h$ and $V = v/k_v$ on water surface in a stationary case we would obtain from equations (10) in [2] (water surface values are marked with a strip)

$$\bar{U} = - h_r /a; \qquad \bar{V} = h_r^2 /a, \qquad (15)$$

where $a = k_v/k_h$ is the anisotropy coefficient (in the vertical), r is the radius of curvature of the surface contour line, u is the velocity component (radial), perpendicular to the contour line a, v is the vertical velocity component, $h_r = \partial h/\partial r$ is the surface gradient (slope) of h in the direction normal to contour lines. Its square h_r^z was neglected in equations (15) against the value a.

As to define the velocity course along the vertical y also the continuity equation is to be used, which in this case will be

$$U_r + aV_y = - Vk_{vy}/k_h - Uk_h/r, \qquad (16)$$

where $k_{vy} = \partial k_v/\partial y$, while gradients of quantities in the direction tangential to contour lines were neglected. The non-vorticity condition, ensuing for dimensionless velocities U and V from dynamic equations (2) in [2] may be written as follows

$$U_y = V_r \tag{17}$$

corresponding to the defining U. as the gradient of pressure function in radial direction (perpendicular to contour lines), i.e. $U = -\partial P/\partial r$.

If boundary relationships (used in the hydrodynamic theory of boundaries) are added to equations (6) and (7), one obtains

$$\overline{U}_r + \overline{U}_y h_r = \overline{U}_r \qquad a \qquad \overline{V}_r + \overline{V}_y h_r = \overline{V}_r \tag{18}$$

After providing equations (6) and (7) with strips we obtain the first (external) derivatives of velocities U and V of the vertical y on water surface

$$\overline{U}_y = - \frac{h_r}{a} \; (1/r + h_r^2 \; \overline{k_{vy}} / k_v) \tag{19}$$

$$\overline{V}_y = h_r^2 \, k_{vy} / ak_v . \tag{20}$$

As to define the velocity distribution along the vertical y by means of expansion into the Taylor series of at least the second degree, the y-derivatives of the second order are required (on water surface). They may be obtained from two equations provided by the formalism of the hydrodynamic theory of boundaries, see ([2] and [3]),

$$(\overline{U}_y)_r = \overline{U}_{ry} + \overline{U}_{yy} h_r$$

$$(\overline{V}_y)_r = \overline{V}_{ry} + \overline{V}_{yy} h_r , \tag{21}$$

in which left hand sides are given by equations (19) and (20) and from two equations

$$\overline{U}_{ry} + a\overline{V}_{yy} = - \overline{V(k_{vy}/k_h)_y} - \overline{U(k_h)_y}/r$$

$$\overline{U}_{yy} - \overline{V}_{ry} = 0 \tag{22}$$

obtained by means of derivating (16) and (17) according to y. In the first of equations (22) the members with y-gradient of a, U,

V were neglected against members with y-gradient of filtration coefficient.

Coefficients and right hand sides in equations (15), (19), (20), (21) and (22), if input quantities are correcty posed, can be expressed numerically and then required values of expansion coefficients for U(r,y) may be determined. From those the relation

$$U(r,y) = \overline{U} + \overline{U_y}(y-h) + \overline{U_{yy}}(y-h)^2/2 + \ldots \tag{23}$$

provides the vector of horizontal velocity, perpendicular to contour lines of free water surface, by means of the relationship

$$u_n(r,y) = k_h U. \tag{24}$$

By means of its integration along the vertical y from the boundary of unpermeable subsoil h_0 up to the free water surface h, the value of the horizontal flow through the water-bearing layer $H = h - h_0$ is obtained as

$$q = \int_{h_0}^{h} k_h U dy, \tag{25}$$

signifying the unit water discharge (m^2/s), normal to free surface isolines.

An example of the described proceedure is presented in Fig.3, showing the velocity field in Žitný ostrov (South Slovakia) aquifer, computed for prognosis of water surface regime in the variant 5, see [2] and [5]. The computation was carried out within the scope of works connected with the monitoring of the effect of the Danube river power scheme Gabčíkovo on the environment.

CONCLUSIONS

By means of before-mentioned relationships it is possible to approximately determine the three-dimensional velocity field and relevant horizontal streams over the whole region of seepage flow, where the free surface is given Fitness of such computation is given by mentioned simplifications. Among them especially the magnitude and distribution of filtration coefficients and the location of unpermeable subsoil, often known only as rough estimates, are decisive for a sufficient precision of all computations.

REFERENCES

1.   Books:
[1]   Hálek, V. and Švec. J.:Groundwater Hydraulics; Academia, Prague 1979

2. **Papers in a journal:**
[2]   Kosorin,K.: Motion   on   Boundary   of   non   –   Viscous   Fluid;   (in Slovak   with   English   summary);   Vodohos.   čas.   Vol.   3,   pp. 154–163, 1978
[3]   Kosorin,K.:   2-D   Modelling   of   Groundwater   Surface   Water Interaction   by   Means   of   Hydrodynamic   Theory   of   Boundaries; Vodohospodársky časopis, prepared for No. 2, 1993

3. **Paper in Congress Proceedings:**
[4]   Kosorin,K.:   On   Solution   of   Unknown   Boundary   Problem   in   Free Surface   Flow   Hydrodynamics;   Proceedings   of   the   2-nd   World Congress on Computational Mechanics; Stuttgart, FRG, 1990

4. **Research report:**
[5]   Influence   of   Surface   Streams   on   Groundwater   Regimen   of   Žitný Ostrov; Research report ÚHH SAV, Bratislava, 1992

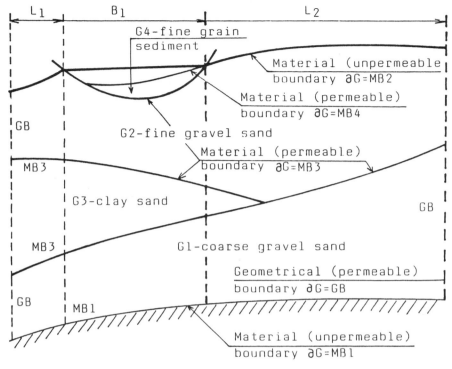

Fig. 1 Various kinds of hydrodynamic bondaries in
       seepage domain   G=G1+G2+G3+G4

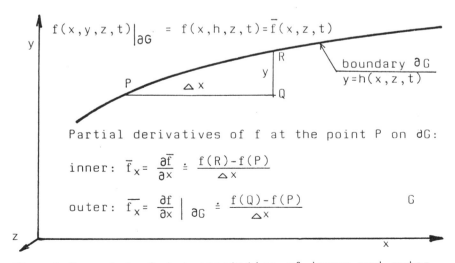

Fig. 2 Geometrical interpretation of inner and outer
       derivatives of f(x,y,z,t) on ∂G

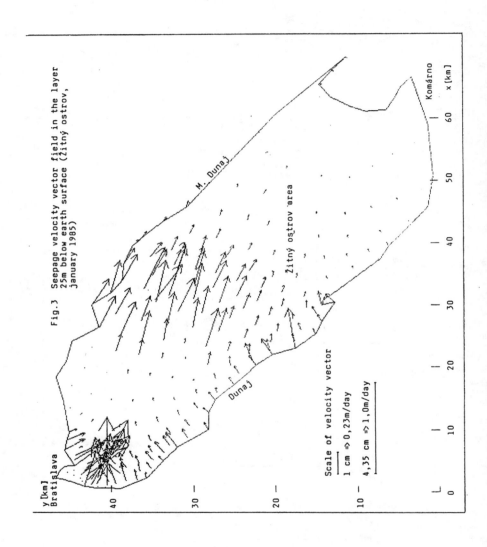

Fig.3 Seepage velocity vector field in the layer 25m below earth surface (Žitný ostrov, january 1985)

Invited Paper

An inverse problem related to the three-dimensional modelling of aluminium electrolytic cells

A. Bermúdez[a], L. Carpintero[a], M.C. Muñiz[b], P. Quintela[a]

[a]*Department of Applied Mathematics, University of Santiago de Compostela, 15706 Santiago, Spain*
[b]*Department of Applied Mathematics, University of Vigo, Campus Marcosende, 36200 Vigo, Spain*

In this paper we study an inverse problem for a system of partial differential equations modelling the thermoelectric behaviour of an aluminium electrolytic cell. In a first part, we consider the direct three-dimensional thermoelectric problem which is a free boundary problem. We solve it by a fixed domain method for a given heat flux through the surface of the ledge, which is the interface between the solid and the liquid phases. We use pentahedral finite elements of six degrees of freedom to discretize both temperature and electric potential fields. In a second part, we consider an inverse problem, which is very important in industrial applications: to compute the heat flux through the free boundary departing from a known ledge profile. To validate the proposed methodology it has been applied to a test example having a known analytical solution. Numerical results are shown.

INTRODUCTION

In the Hall-Héroult process, aluminium is produced by electrolytic reduction of alumina (Al_2O_3) dissolved in a bath based on molten cryolite (Na_3AlF_6) (see Grjotheim and Kvande [9], Grjotheim, Krohn, Malinovsky, Matiasovsky and Thonstad [8]).

An aluminium electrolytic cell consists of a rectangular steel shell, usually lined with thermally insulating refractory materials. Inside of this there is an inner lining of prebaked carbon cathode blocks with embedded steel current collector bars. A frozen bath layer, the so-called ledge, protects the side wall of the cathode from corrosive electrolyte. This ledge also reduces heat loss from the cathode, and works as a heat sink when the extra power is supplied to the cell.

On the other hand magnetic effects produce the liquid metal and bath to move. The profile of the ledge strongly influences the horizontal current components thus playing a major role on the hydrodynamic behaviour of the cell. Both the thickness of the ledge and the extension under the anode affect the current components. The electro-magnetic force due to this current causes strong convection of the metal, which may induce its surface oscillation. Thus, the ledge profile influences the cell voltage stability and current efficiency in commercial cells. This is why one of the objectives of cell sidewall design is to promote the formation of a good ledge profile to give stable, efficient cell operation and long sidewall life.

Numerical simulation of the behaviour of the cell has been studied in several papers (see Bruggemen and Danka [5], Arita, Urata and Ikeuchi [1], Utne [13], Sulmont and Hudault [11]). In these papers the form of the ledge is fitted along an iterative procedure. Alternatively, a fixed domain method has been introduced in Bermúdez, Muñiz and Quintela [2], [3].

The thickness of the frozen ledge is controlled by the rate of convective heat transfer from the superheated electrolyte. To know this parameter as a function of the superheat of the electrolyte above its liquidus temperature is essential to predict the thermoelectrical behaviour of the cell and the ledge thickness by using mathematical models.

Calculation of the heat transfer coefficient between the molten and frozen electrolyte phases is complicated. Some experimental work has been done (see Taylor and Welch [12]) but results are difficult to extrapolate to real electrolytic cells. On the other hand in Bruggemen and Danka [5] this coefficient is obtained from theoretical considerations by introducing an enhanced conductivity of the liquid phase.

In the present paper we propose a method based on measurements of the ledge profile. It leads to an inverse problem for the thermoelectrical model of the cell when the ledge profile is given together with its temperature (Dirichlet boundary condition) and the heat flux has to be computed (Neumann boundary condition). The technique is described for a three-dimensional finite element method and it has been applied to a test example. Numerical results are in good agreement with the analytical solution.

STATEMENT OF THE THERMOELECTRICAL PROBLEM

In this section we introduce a mathematical model for the thermoelectrical behaviour of an aluminium electrolytic cell. For simplicity we consider a piece of the cell corresponding to one of the cathodic blocks. Moreover, taking the symmetry into account it is enough to consider only a half of this domain. We refer to figure 1 for notations. (See Bermúdez, Muñiz and Quintela [2], [3] for further details).

Let Ω_T be the open set occupied by the part of the cell under consideration. We denote by Γ_T the boundary of Ω_T. We consider the following decomposition of Γ_T (see figure 1):

$$\Gamma_T = \Gamma_d \cup \Gamma_{cr} \cup \Gamma_b \cup \Gamma_s \cup S. \tag{1}$$

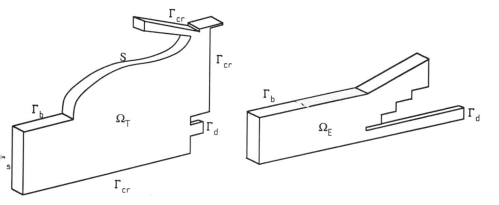

Figure 1: The thermal and electric domains.

The set S represents the surface of the ledge which is a free boundary; determining this surface is a part of our problem.

Let us denote by Ω_E the subset of Ω_T occupied by the electric conductors of the cell (see figure 1).

If $V = V(x)$ is the electric potential in Ω_E and $T = T(x)$ the temperature in Ω_T, the following equations express respectively the conservation of current and energy

$$- \nabla.(\sigma(x,T)\nabla V(x)) = 0 \text{ in } \Omega_E, \qquad (2)$$

$$- \nabla.(k(x,T)\nabla T(x)) = \sigma(x,T) \mid \nabla V(x) \mid^2 \text{ in } \Omega_E. \qquad (3)$$

The Joule effect is considered in the energy equation (3). The same equation holds in the rest of Ω_T by replacing its right hand side by zero. We denote electric and thermal conductivities by σ and k, respectively, which depend not only on temperature but on position x as well. Let J be the current density vector given by $J = -\sigma\nabla V$.

To complete the model, boundary conditions are given both for electric

$$\begin{aligned}
J(x).n &= -j(x) \text{ on } \Gamma_d & (4) \\
V(x) &= 0 \text{ on } \Gamma_b & (5) \\
J(x).n &= 0 \text{ on } \partial\Omega_E \setminus (\Gamma_d \cup \Gamma_b) & (6)
\end{aligned}$$

and thermal equations

$$\begin{aligned}
k(x,T)\frac{\partial T(x)}{\partial n} &= \alpha(x,T)(T_c(x) - T(x)) \\
&+ \beta(x,T)((T_r(x) + 273)^4 - (T(x) + 273)^4) \text{ on } \Gamma_{cr} \ (7)
\end{aligned}$$

$$k(x,T)\frac{\partial T(x)}{\partial n} = 0 \text{ on } \Gamma_s \tag{8}$$

$$T(x) = T_d \text{ on } \Gamma_d \tag{9}$$

$$T(x) = T_o \text{ on } \Gamma_b \tag{10}$$

Equation (7) establishes that the heat flux through the exterior boundary Γ_{cr} is due to the losses by convection and radiation. The homogeneous Neumann boundary condition (8) holds by symmetry. Notice that Γ_d represents the part of the boundary where temperature and current density are given; similarly we assume that temperature and electric potential are known on Γ_b.

Functions α, β, T_c and T_r appearing in equation (7) represent physical parameters related to convective and radiative heat transfer. Furthermore

- $j(x)$: electric current density at point x of the boundary Γ_d.

- T_d: temperature of the cathodic bar 11 cm away from the shell of the cell.

- T_o: operation temperature of the cell.

We assume the following conditions on the free boundary S

$$T(x) = T_o \tag{11}$$

$$k(x,T(x))\frac{\partial T(x)}{\partial n} = h(x_2)\triangle T n_1(x), \tag{12}$$

where n_1 represents the first component of the outward unit normal vector to S at point x, $\triangle T$ is the superheating, i.e. the difference between the operation temperature T_o and the liquidus temperature, and $h(x_2)$ is a function to be given. In practice, h has to be identified from experimental measurements and this identification is the main objective of this paper. Equation (12) expresses the heat flux through S. It is related to the ones given in Taylor and Welch [12] and in Arita, Urata and Ikeuchi [1], unless we include n_1 because it is convenient from both mathematical and physical points of view. Indeed, experimental measures show the greater the slope of the free boundary, the greater the heat transfer.

In order to solve this free boundary problem, we use a fixed domain method. The idea is to embed the problem into another one defined in a extended domain which widely contains the unknown boundary. This new problem has been introduced in Bermúdez, Muñiz and Quintela [2].

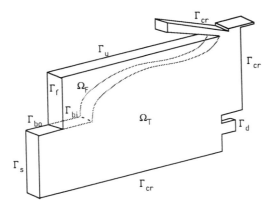

Figure 2: The physical and fictitious domain.

WEAK FORMULATION AND FINITE ELEMENT DISCRETIZATION

Let us denote by Ω the domain defined by $\Omega = \Omega_T \cup \Omega_F \cup S \cup \Gamma_{bi}$ (see figure 2). As it can be seen in the previous reference, introducing this new problem allows us to obtain a weak formulation of (2)-(12) which consists of finding three functions T and q defined in Ω and V defined in Ω_E such that

$$\int_{\Omega_E} \sigma(x, T) \nabla V(x) . \nabla z(x) dx = \int_{\Gamma_d} j(x) z(x) d\Gamma,$$

$$\forall z \in H^1(\Omega_E); \ z/\Gamma_b = 0, \qquad (13)$$

$$\int_{\Omega} k(x, T) \nabla T(x) . \nabla z(x) dx + \int_{\Omega} f(x_2) q(x) \frac{\partial z(x)}{\partial x_1} dx =$$

$$\int_{\Gamma_{cr}} g(x, T) z(x) d\Gamma + \int_{\Omega_E} \sigma(x, T) \mid \nabla V(x) \mid^2 z(x) dx + \qquad (14)$$

$$\int_{\Gamma_f} f(x_2) z(x) d\Gamma, \qquad \forall z \in H^1(\Omega); \ z/(\Gamma_d \cup \Gamma_{bo}) = 0.$$

$$q \in H(T - T_o), \qquad (15)$$

and Dirichlet boundary conditions given by (5), (9) and (10) on Γ_{bo}, where H denotes the Heaviside multivalued function defined by

$$H(s) = \begin{cases} 0 & \text{si} \quad s < 0 \\ [0,1] & \text{si} \quad s = 0 \\ 1 & \text{si} \quad s > 0 \end{cases} \qquad (16)$$

and $f(x_2) = h(x_2) \Delta T$. For a theoretical analysis we refer to Bermúdez, Muñiz and Quintela [2] where a proof of existence of solution of a simplified thermal submodel is given.

For numerical solution we discretize this weak formulation by a finite element approximation:

Associated with Ω, we consider the following spaces W_h and W_{Eh}

$$W_h = \{T_h \in C^0(\Omega) : T_{h|K} \in W_K, \forall K \in \tau_h\} \tag{17}$$

$$W_{Eh} = \{V_h \in C^0(\Omega_E) : V_{h|K} \in W_K, \forall K \in \tau_h\} \tag{18}$$

where τ_h is a pentahedral mesh and the space W_K is defined by

$$W_K = \{z \in C^0(K) : z \circ F_K \in \hat{W}\}. \tag{19}$$

In (19) F_K denotes the map transforming the reference finite element into the element K, and $\hat{W}$ is the linear space given by

$$\hat{W} = P_1(\mathbb{R}^2) \otimes P_1(\mathbb{R}). \tag{20}$$

This finite element has six degrees of freedom which are the values at vertices of pentahedrons (see figure 3).

Figure 3: Pentahedral finite element.

Then we introduce the discretized problem by replacing $H^1(\Omega)$ and $H^1(\Omega_E)$ by W_h and W_{Eh} in (13) and (14) respectively. Equation (15) is replaced by

$$q_h(p) \in H(T_h(p) - T_o) \text{ for all vertex } p. \tag{21}$$

Numerical solution of this discretized problem by using iterative algorithms has been done in Bermúdez, Muñiz and Quintela [3].

AN INVERSE PROBLEM: IDENTIFICATION OF THE HEAT FLUX THROUGH THE FREE BOUNDARY

Let us consider an inverse problem to the one given in the previous paragraph. For this we suppose that we can determine the profile of the ledge from experimental measurements, as a surface S . Then we want to compute a function $f(x_2)$ such that the solution of the problem (13)-(15) has S as free boundary.

Let S_h be an approximation of S relative to the mesh τ_h, i.e. S_h is a union of faces of pentahedrons. Then the domain Ω is decomposed as $\Omega = \Omega_{Th} \cup S_h \cup \Omega_{Fh} \cup \Gamma_{bih}$. We suppose that the pentahedral mesh τ_h satisfies the following requirements:

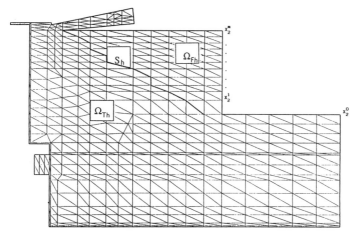

Figure 4: Mesh of a cross section of domain Ω

i) There exists a finite collection $\{x_2^0, x_2^1, ..., x_2^m\}$ of heights for which the corresponding x_1x_3-section of Ω_{Fh} can be covered by a union of faces of pentahedrons.

ii) If $x_2 \neq x_2^i, i = 0, ..., m$ the corresponding x_1x_3-section of Ω_{Fh} does not contain any face (see figure 4).

Let us consider the following discretized problem:
Find $\mathcal{V}_h$ defined in Ω_E and $\mathcal{T}_h$ defined in Ω_{Th} such that:

$$\int_{\Omega_E} \sigma(x, \mathcal{T}_h) \nabla \mathcal{V}_h(x) . \nabla z_h(x) dx = \int_{\Gamma_d} j(x) z_h(x) d\Gamma,$$
$$\forall z_h \in W_{Eh}; \; z_h/\Gamma_b = 0, \qquad (22)$$

$$\int_{\Omega_{Th}} k(x, \mathcal{T}_h) \nabla \mathcal{T}_h(x) . \nabla z_h(x) dx = \int_{\Gamma_{cr}} g(x, \mathcal{T}_h) z_h(x) d\Gamma$$
$$+ \int_{\Omega_E} \sigma(x, \mathcal{T}_h) \mid \nabla \mathcal{V}_h(x) \mid^2 z_h(x) dx,$$

$$\forall z_h \in W_{Th}; \; z_h \mid (\Gamma_d \cup \Gamma_{bh} \cup S_h) = 0, \; (23)$$
$$\mathcal{T}_h = T_o \text{ on } \Gamma_{bh} \cup S_h \text{ and } \mathcal{T}_h = T_d \text{ on } \Gamma_d \qquad (24)$$

Notice that the difference between problems (22)-(24) and the discrete version of (13)-(15) is that the former is defined in the domain Ω_{Th}, which is a priori known because now S_h is given and we take Dirichlet boundary condition on S_h (temperature is equal to the operation temperature), while the latter is defined in the domain Ω and S_h is unknown.

Let extend $\mathcal{T}_h$ to the domain Ω_{Fh} by T_o. We remark that if $z_h \in W_h$ is such that $z_h \mid \overline{\Omega}_{Fh} \neq 0$ then the expression

$$\int_{\Omega} k(x, \mathcal{T}_h) \nabla \mathcal{T}_h(x) . \nabla z_h(x) dx - \int_{\Gamma_{cr}} g(x, \mathcal{T}_h) z_h(x) d\Gamma$$
$$- \int_{\Omega_E} \sigma(x, \mathcal{T}_h) \mid \nabla \mathcal{V}_h(x) \mid^2 z_h(x) dx \qquad (25)$$

needs not to be zero. In particular, let w_p be the basis element associated with the vertex p i.e. $w_p \in W_h$ and it takes the value 1 at the corresponding node p and vanishes at all others nodes. Since the domain Ω_{Fh} is not an electric conductor, the residual

$$Res(p) = \int_\Omega k(x, T_h) \nabla T_h(x). \nabla w_p(x) dx - \int_{\Gamma_{cr}} g(x, T_h) w_p(x) d\Gamma \qquad (26)$$

is, in general, non null for vertices p in $\overline{\Omega}_{Fh}$.

On the other hand, recall that our objective is to compute an approximated function $f_h(x_2)$ such that (V_h, T_h) verifies (13)-(15) in the discrete sense. This implies, in particular

$$Res(p) = \int_{\Gamma_f} f_h(x_2) w_p(x) d\Gamma - \int_\Omega f_h(x_2) q_h(x) \frac{\partial w_p(x)}{\partial x_1} dx \qquad (27)$$

where $q_h(p) \in H(T_h(p) - T_o)$ for each vertex p.

The fact that f_h depends only on x_2 suggests to consider for each $x_2^i, 0 \le i \le m$ the set J_i of all vertex p in $\overline{\Omega}_{Fh}$ such that its second coordinate is equal to x_2^i. Then, we have for each i

$$\sum_{p \in J_i} Res(p) = \sum_{p \in J_i} \left(\int_{\Gamma_f} f_h(x_2) w_p(x) d\Gamma - \int_\Omega f_h(x_2) q_h(x) \frac{\partial w_p(x)}{\partial x_1} dx \right)$$

$$= \int_{\Gamma_f} f_h(x_2) (\sum_{p \in J_i} w_p(x)) d\Gamma - \int_\Omega f_h(x_2) q_h(x) \frac{\partial}{\partial x_1} (\sum_{p \in J_i} w_p(x)) dx. \qquad (28)$$

Notice that $\sum_{p \in J_i} w_p$ only depends on x_2 and furthermore

$$\sum_{p \in J_i} w_p(x) = \begin{cases} 1 & \text{if} & x_2 = x_2^i, \\ 0 & \text{if} & x_2 = x_2^{i-1} (\text{for } i > 1) \text{ or } x_2 = x_2^{i+1} (\text{for } i < m). \end{cases} \qquad (29)$$

Therefore $\frac{\partial}{\partial x_1} (\sum_{p \in J_i} w_p(x)) = 0$. By considering an approximated integration we have,

$$\sum_{p \in J_i} Res(p) = \int_{\Gamma_f} f_h(x_2) (\sum_{p \in J_i} w_p(x)) d\Gamma =$$

$$\int_0^{x_3^0} \left(\int_{x_2^{i-1}}^{x_2^i} f_h(x_2) (\sum_{p \in J_i} w_p)(x_2) dx_2 + \int_{x_2^i}^{x_2^{i+1}} f_h(x_2) (\sum_{p \in J_i} w_p)(x_2) dx_2 \right) dx_3$$

$$\cong \int_0^{x_3^0} \left(\frac{f_h(x_2^i)}{2} (x_2^i - x_2^{i-1}) + \frac{f_h(x_2^i)}{2} (x_2^{i+1} - x_2^i) \right) dx_3$$

$$= \frac{f_h(x_2^i)}{2} (x_2^{i+1} - x_2^{i-1}) x_3^0, \qquad \text{for } 1 < i < m, \qquad (30)$$

where x_3^0 is the thickness of the domain in the x_3 direction. Hence we can compute the value of function f_h at point x_2^i by

$$f_h(x_2^i) = \sum_{p \in J_i} Res(p) \frac{2}{((x_2^{i+1} - x_2^{i-1}) x_3^0)}, \qquad \text{for } 1 < i < m, \qquad (31)$$

Similarly, for $i = 1$ and $i = m$ it is easy to see that

$$f_h(x_2^1) = \sum_{p \in J_1} Res(p) \frac{2}{((x_2^2 - x_2^1)x_3^0)}, \tag{32}$$

$$f_h(x_2^m) = \sum_{p \in J_m} Res(p) \frac{2}{((x_2^m - x_2^{m-1})x_3^0)}. \tag{33}$$

NUMERICAL RESULTS

In order to validate the proposed methodology we have solved a test problem which has a known analytical solution. First of all in order to construct this test problem at ease we add source terms ψ_T and ψ_E to the thermal and electric equations (3) and (2), respectively.

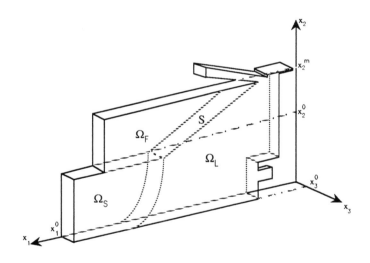

Figure 5: The numerical test domain.

Let Ω be the domain of the figure 5 with $x_1^0 = 2.292$, $x_2^0 = 0.824$ and $\Omega_E = \Omega$.
Let T_L and T_S be the functions defined by

$$T_L(x) = 2x_1 + 3x_2 + 20 \tag{34}$$
$$T_S(x) = -(x_2 - x_2^0)^2 + T_o \tag{35}$$

where $T_o = 24.877$ and $x = (x_1, x_2, x_3)$. Let us denote by Ω_S and Ω_F the subsets of Ω given by

$$\Omega_S = \left\{x \in \Omega : x_2 < x_2^0,\ T_L(x) - T_S(x) > 0\right\} \tag{36}$$

$$\Omega_F = \left\{x \in \Omega : x_2^0 < x_2 < x_2^m,\ T_L(x) > T_o\right\} \tag{37}$$

and $\Omega_L = \Omega \setminus (\Omega_S \cup \Omega_F)$.

Then we have taken data for problem (2)-(10) in such a way that its solution is given by:

$$V(x) = (2x_1 + 3x_2 + 20)^2 \quad \forall x \in \Omega \tag{38}$$

$$T(x) = \begin{cases} T_L & \text{if} \quad x \in \Omega_L \\ T_S & \text{if} \quad x \in \Omega_S \\ T_o & \text{if} \quad x \in \Omega_F \end{cases} \tag{39}$$

and the free boundary by $S = \partial\Omega_L \cap \partial\Omega_F$.

In order for this solution to hold, the thermal conductivity in $\Omega_L \cup \Omega_F$ has been taken as

$$k(x, T) = -2T + 100 \tag{40}$$

and in order to get the right transmission conditions on $\partial\Omega_L \cap \partial\Omega_S$, k_S has been defined in Ω_S by

$$k_S(x, T) = (T - 50)(8.056 + 6x_2)/[(x_2 - x_2^0)(1.352 + 2x_2)]. \tag{41}$$

The electrical conductivity σ has been given as

$$\sigma(x, T) = \frac{1}{2T^2}, \tag{42}$$

and the source terms ψ_E and ψ_T as

$$\psi_E(x) = \begin{cases} 13T_L^{-2} & \text{if} \quad x \in \Omega_L \\ -13T_o^{-2} & \text{if} \quad x \in \Omega_F \\ (-13T_S - 12T_L(x_2 - x_2^0))T_S^{-3} & \text{if} \quad x \in \Omega_S \end{cases} \tag{43}$$

and

$$\psi_T(x) = \begin{cases} 0 & \text{if} \quad x \in \Omega_L \\ -\sigma(x, T_o) \mid \nabla T_L^2 \mid^2 & \text{if} \quad x \in \Omega_F \\ -\nabla.(k_S(x, T_S)\nabla T_S) - \sigma(x, T_S) \mid \nabla T_L^2 \mid^2 & \text{if} \quad x \in \Omega_S. \end{cases} \tag{44}$$

We have considered Neumann boundary conditions on Γ_s and Γ_d for the electrical problem and on $(\Gamma_{cr} \cup \Gamma_s) \cap \partial\Omega_s$ and $\Gamma_{cr} \cap \partial\Omega_L \cap [x_2' = 0]$ for the thermal one and usual symmetry conditions of null flux on the planes $x_3 = 0$ and $x_3 = x_3^0$. Dirichlet boundary conditions have been taken elsewhere.

The heat transfer coefficient through the free boundary S has been defined by

$$f(x_2) = 13(-T_o + 50) = 326.469 \tag{45}$$

Mesh 1		Mesh 2	
x_2	$f_h(x_2)$	x_2	$f_h(x_2)$
$x_2^0 = 0.824$	312.82	$x_2^0 = 0.824$	312.06
$x_2^1 = 0.880$	312.82	$x_2^1 = 0.852$	312.06
$x_2^2 = 0.936$	319.25	$x_2^2 = 0.880$	316.58
$x_2^3 = 0.969$	319.76	$x_2^3 = 0.908$	319.22
$x_2^4 = 1.002$	320.82	$x_2^4 = 0.936$	321.02
$x_2^5 = 1.049$	322.28	$x_2^5 = 0.969$	320.97
$x_2^6 = 1.081$	322.93	$x_2^6 = 1.002$	321.75
$x_2^7 = 1.113$	325.13	$x_2^7 = 1.049$	322.92
$x_2^8 = 1.169$	326.01	$x_2^8 = 1.081$	323.48
$x_2^9 = 1.241$	326.25	$x_2^9 = 1.113$	325.26
$x_2^{10} = 1.314$	326.52	$x_2^{10} = 1.141$	325.55
$x_2^{11} = 1.376$	326.63	$x_2^{11} = 1.169$	325.82
		$x_2^{12} = 1.241$	326.21
		$x_2^{13} = 1.314$	326.46
		$x_2^{14} = 1.376$	326.57

Table 1: Computed f

In a first step we have solved the direct problem by using two three dimensional meshes, the first one with 5320 elements and 3842 vertices and the second one with 7187 pentahedrons and 5136 vertices. The maximun relative errors for temperature were 0.504×10^{-2} and 0.474×10^{-2}, respectively. Finally, we have solved the inverse problem by using the method described in the previous section. We have obtained the values for the function f at points x_2^i shown in table 1. The maximum relative errors for temperature were 0.852×10^{-2} and 0.680×10^{-2}, respectively.

ACKNOWLEDGEMENTS

Authors would like to thank Mr. J.L. López Sangil, G. Tirapu, A. López Alba, C. Palacios and L.M. Díaz from INESPAL (La Coruña, Spain) for many fruitful discussions and suggestions.

REFERENCES

[1] Y. Arita, N. Urata and H. Ikeuchi, Estimation of frozen bath shape in aluminium reduction cell by computer simulation, Light Metals (1978) 59-72.

[2] A. Bermúdez, M.C. Muñiz and P. Quintela, Numerical solution of a Stefan problem arising in the thermoelectrical modelling of aluminium

electrolytic cells, in: L.C. Wrobel and C.A. Brebbia, eds. Computational Modelling of Free and Moving Boundary Problems, vol. 2 (Computational Mechanics Publications/de Gruyter, Southampton, 1991) 39-58.

[3] A. Bermúdez, M.C. Muñiz and P. Quintela, Numerical solution of a three-dimensional thermoelectric problem taking place in an aluminium electrolytic cell, Comput. Methods Appl. Mech. Engrg. (To appear).

[4] A. Bossavit, A. Damlamian and M. Frémond, Free Boundary Problems: Applications and Theory, (Pitman, London, 1985).

[5] N.J. Bruggemen and D.J. Danka, Two-dimensional thermal modelling of the Hall-Héroult cell, Light Metals (1990) 203-209.

[6] C. Elliot and J.R. Ockendon, Weak and Variational Methods for Free Boundary Problems, (Pitman, London,1985).

[7] A. Fasano and M. Primicerio, Free Boundary Problems: Theory and Applications,(Pitman, London, 1983).

[8] K. Grjotheim, C. Krohn, M. Malianovsky, K. Matiasovsky and J. Thonstad, Aluminium Electrolysys (Aluminium Verlag, Dusseldorf, 1982).

[9] K. Grjotheim and H. Kvande, Understanding the Hall-Héroult Process for Production of Aluminium (Aluminium Verlag, Dusseldorf, 1986).

[10] K.H. Hoffman and J. Sprekels, Free Boundary Problems: Applications and Theory, (Pitman, London, 1990).

[11] B. Sulmont and G. Hudault, Application of thermoelectric model to the investigation of reduction cell thermal equilibrium, Light Metals (1978) 73-86.

[12] M.P. Taylor and B.J. Welch, Melt/freeze heat transfer measurements in cryolite-based electrolytes, Metallurgical Transactions B 18 (1987) 391-398.

[13] P. Utne, Freeze profile in side-break cells: calculations and measurements, Light Metals (1982) 359-371.

[14] L.C. Wrobel and C.A. Brebbia, Computational Modelling of Free and Moving Boundary Problems, (Computational Mechanics Publications/de Gruyter, Southampton, 1991).

The inverse Stefan design problem

N. Zabaras

Sibley School of Mechanical and Aerospace Engineering, 188 Engineering and Theory Center Bldg., Cornell University, Ithaca, NY 14853, USA

ABSTRACT

The major goal of this work is to develop and experimentally verify computational models that provide direct information for the optimum thermomechanical design and control of casting processes and utilize experimental data to accurately evaluate the thermo-mechanical material state during solidification.

In particular, this paper addresses an ill-posed inverse design Stefan problem where one calculates the fluxes on the fixed walls that produce a desired freezing front velocity and fluxes. To account for the mathematical incorrectness of the proposed models, this work explores several mathematical techniques, but particularly iterative regularization methods, filtering and the adjoint method. Front-tracking finite element implementations are considered. Other problems and techniques of interest are briefly being mentioned.

INTRODUCTION

For pure metals, the freezing front motion and heat flux on the solid side of the freezing front define the crystallographic growth morphology and the scale of microstructures during solidification. The grain size together with the grain morphology should be selected such that desired macroscopic mechanical properties and soundness of the final cast product are achieved. In unidirectional heat flow, the cooling rate, which is the product of the imposed temperature gradient and growth rate, controls the scale of the obtained microstructures. Thus, the grain refinement can be modified even without altering the grain morphology by changing the imposed cooling rate. The growth morphology is mainly defined by the ratio of the imposed thermal gradient and growth velocity. With a fixed cooling rate, one can gradually change the grain morphology, for example, from planar to cellular, then to oriented dendritic and finally to equiaxed dendritic by appropriately increasing the growth rate and decreasing the thermal gradient [1].

In multidimensional solidification processes *to independently control both the freezing front velocity and fluxes*, one, in addition to calculating the unknown heat flux on the fixed mold wall, must introduce and evaluate an extra variable that accounts for the otherwise "*over-specified inverse Stefan problem*". Such variables can be a heat generation source term in the melt related with the liquid feeding to the contracting freezing front or an electromagnetic field that is used to stir the melt. A forced melt convection analysis must then be performed.

Of interest here is a design Stefan problem where one calculates the history of boundary cooling conditions that results in a desired freezing front motion. A one dimensional design example is shown, where both freezing front fluxes and velocity are described.

MATHEMATICAL FORMULATION

The solid/liquid front is assumed to be isothermal. Let us consider the melt at initial temperature $T_{in}(\underset{\sim}{x})$ to occupy a two-dimensional region Ω_0 with boundary $\partial\Omega_0$ (Fig. 1). At time t>0, the boundary $\partial\Omega_0$ is cooled down to a temperature lower than the melting temperature. Solidification starts around $\partial\Omega_0$ and proceeds inwards. Let us denote the isothermal interface at time t as $\partial\Omega_I(t)$. The governing differential equations are:

$$\rho\, c_S \frac{\partial T_S(\underset{\sim}{x},t)}{\partial t} = \underset{\sim}{\nabla} \cdot (K_S \underset{\sim}{\nabla} T_S(\underset{\sim}{x},t)) \qquad \underset{\sim}{x} \in \Omega_S \qquad (1)$$

$$\rho\, c_L \frac{\partial T_L(\underset{\sim}{x},t)}{\partial t} = \underset{\sim}{\nabla} \cdot (K_L \underset{\sim}{\nabla} T_L(\underset{\sim}{x},t)) \qquad \underset{\sim}{x} \in \Omega_L \qquad (2)$$

The freezing interface conditions include the energy balance (Stefan condition)

$$K_S(T_S(\underset{\sim}{x},t)) \frac{\partial T_S(\underset{\sim}{x},t)}{\partial \underline{\mathbf{n}}} - K_L(T_L(\underset{\sim}{x},t)) \frac{\partial T_L(\underset{\sim}{x},t)}{\partial \underline{\mathbf{n}}} = \rho L \, \underline{V} \cdot \underline{\mathbf{n}} \, , \underset{\sim}{x} \in \partial \Omega_I(t) \tag{3}$$

and the isothermal condition:

$$T(\underset{\sim}{x},t)=T_m \qquad \underset{\sim}{x} \in \partial \Omega_I(t) \tag{4}$$

where $\underline{\mathbf{n}}$ is a unit normal vector to $\partial \Omega_I(t)$, at a point $\underset{\sim}{x} \in \partial \Omega_I(t)$ pointing away from the solid region, $\underline{V}$ is the velocity vector at the same point on the freezing interface, and L denotes the latent heat of fusion.

Finally, the initial and boundary conditions take the form:

$$T(\underset{\sim}{x}, 0) = T_{in}(\underset{\sim}{x}), \qquad\qquad \underset{\sim}{x} \in \Omega_0 \tag{5}$$

$$K_S(T(\underset{\sim}{x},t)) \frac{\partial}{\partial \underline{\mathbf{n}}_0} T(\underset{\sim}{x},t) = q(\underset{\sim}{x}, t), \qquad \underset{\sim}{x} \in \partial \Omega_0 \tag{6}$$

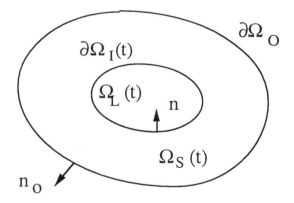

Fig. 1. Geometry of a Stefan process

A direct Stefan problem is defined as one of "*solving equations (1)-(4) for the temperature field, and the freezing interface location/motion, given the initial temperature and appropriate boundary conditions (equations (5)-(6))*".

The inverse Stefan design problem of concern here can be stated as follows: "*Given the material properties, initial temperature, melting temperature, and the motion/location of the freezing front at all times, calculate the boundary flux history on $\partial \Omega_0$*". For a solution of this problem to exist, the given data must satisfy certain *regularity conditions*.

This problem was analyzed previously by Zabaras and colleagues using sequential optimization methods together with spatial regularization and time smoothing [2-3]. They have treated the temperature field as a continuous function of the applied flux on $\partial\Omega_0$, taking the flux discontinuity (rather than T_m) as the boundary condition on $\partial\Omega_I$. In this way they obtained an algorithm that minimizes the square error of the calculated temperature at $\partial\Omega_I$ with the given melting point T_m.

In mathematical terms, we want to find the optimal boundary heat flux $q^*(\underset{\sim}{x},t)$, $\underset{\sim}{x} \in \partial\Omega_0$, such that:

$$S(q^*) \leq S(q), \quad q \in L_2([\partial\Omega_0]x[0, t_{max}]) \tag{7}$$

where

$$S(q) = \frac{1}{2} \int_0^{t_{max}} \int_{\Omega_I(t)} (T_m - T(\underset{\sim}{x},t; q))^2 d\Gamma dt \tag{8}$$

A gradient method of optimization, in general consists in constructing the minimizing sequence $q^0, q^1, \cdots, q^k, \cdots$ according to

$$q^{k+1} = q^k + \alpha^k p^k (q^k) \tag{9}$$

where here, p^k, is taken to be the conjugate search direction. It is assumed that the gradient $S'(q^k)$ depends continuously on q^k. However, inverse problems are usually ill-posed in nature and this ill-posedness produces a non-smooth cost functional, an unstable minimization algorithm and low rates of convergence [4]. To treat this behavior, it may be necessary to introduce smoothing to the optimization algorithm. This can be done implicitly via the regularization method [5] or explicitly by restricting $q(\underset{\sim}{x}, t)$ to be a member of a finite dimensional function space. In the regularization method, additional smoothing terms are added to the existing cost functional. Then, the modified cost functional is minimized in a new infinite dimensional function space. For minimization in finite dimensional function spaces, the cost functional is written in terms of finite number of unknown real parameters by using a finite dimensional approximation of the boundary flux.

In the conjugate gradient method(CGM), α^k is the minimizer of the functional $S(q^k + \alpha^k p^k(q^k))$. Here, the gradient of the cost functional, $S'(q^k)(\underset{\sim}{x},t)$, is obtained via the **adjoint method**.

Denoting $\theta(\underset{\sim}{x},t\,;\,q,\Delta q) \equiv T_q(\underset{\sim}{x},\,t\,;\,q)\,(\Delta q),\,(\underset{\sim}{x},t) \in ([\Omega_0]x[0,t_{max}])$, where $T_q(\underset{\sim}{x},t\,;\,q)$, is the gradient of T at $(\underset{\sim}{x},t\,;\,q)$, we arrive at the following **sensitivity equations:**

$$\frac{\partial}{\partial t}\,[c(T(\underset{\sim}{x},t;q))\theta(\underset{\sim}{x},t;q,\Delta q)] = \underline{\nabla}^2[K(T(\underset{\sim}{x},t\,;q))\theta(\underset{\sim}{x},t\,;q,\Delta q)] \tag{10a}$$

$$\theta\,(\underset{\sim}{x},\,0\,;\,q,\,\Delta q)\,=0, \quad \underset{\sim}{x}\,\in\,\Omega_L\,(0) \tag{10b}$$

$$\frac{\partial}{\partial \mathbf{n_o}}\,[K_S(T_S\,(\underset{\sim}{x},\,t;\,q\,))\,\theta_S\,(\underset{\sim}{x},\,t;\,q,\,\Delta q)]\,=\,\Delta q\,(\underset{\sim}{x},\,t), \qquad \underset{\sim}{x}\,\in\,\partial\Omega_0 \tag{10c}$$

$$\frac{\partial[K_S(T_S)\theta_S(\underset{\sim}{x},t;q,\Delta q)]}{\partial \mathbf{n}}\,-\,\frac{\partial[K_L(T_L)\theta_L(\underset{\sim}{x},t;q,\Delta q)]}{\partial \mathbf{n}}\,=\,0, \quad \underset{\sim}{x}\in\partial\Omega_I(t) \tag{10d}$$

where $c = c_S$, $K = K_S$ when $\underset{\sim}{x}\in\Omega_S$, while $c = c_L$ and $K = K_L$ when $\underset{\sim}{x}\in\Omega_L$.

The adjoint system for $\psi(\underset{\sim}{x},\,t;\,q)$, $(\underset{\sim}{x},t) \in ([\Omega_0]x[0,t_{max}])$ is defined as:

$$c(T(\underset{\sim}{x},\,t;\,q))\,\frac{\partial \psi}{\partial t}\,(\underset{\sim}{x},\,t;\,q)\,+\,K(T(\underset{\sim}{x},\,t;\,q\,))\,\underline{\nabla}^2\,\psi(\underset{\sim}{x},\,t\,;\,q)\,=\,0 \tag{11a}$$

$$\psi\,(\underset{\sim}{x},\,t)|_{t\,=\,t_{max}}\,=\,0 \quad \underset{\sim}{x}\in\Omega_0 \tag{11b}$$

$$K_S\,\frac{\partial \psi}{\partial \mathbf{n_o}}\,|_{\partial\Omega_0}\,=\,0, \qquad \underset{\sim}{x}\in\partial\Omega_0 \tag{11c}$$

$$-K_S\,\frac{\partial \psi_S}{\partial \mathbf{n}}\,+\,K_L\,\frac{\partial \psi_L}{\partial \mathbf{n}}\,|_{\partial\Omega_I(t)}\,=\,T_m\,-\,T(\underset{\sim}{x},\,t;\,q), \quad \underset{\sim}{x}\in\partial\Omega_I(t) \tag{11d}$$

where c and K are defined as before.

It can be shown that the adjoint system has been defined in such a way that:

$$S'\,(q)(\underset{\sim}{x},\,t)\,=\,\psi(\underset{\sim}{x},\,t;\,q)\,, \quad (\underset{\sim}{x},t) \in ([\Omega_0]x[0,t_{max}]) \tag{12}$$

<u>The conjugate gradient algorithm:</u>

<u>Step 1</u>: Pick an initial guess $q(\underset{\sim}{x},t)$ in $L_2([\partial\Omega_0]x[0,t_{max}]\,)$. Set k=0.

Step 2: Calculation of conjugate search direction $p^k(x,t)$

   a. Define the scalar γ^k.

   a1. Solve the direct Stefan problem forward in time for $T(x,t; q^k(x,t))$.

   a2. Compute the residual $T_m - T(x,t; q^k(x,t))$ in

   $(x,t) \in (\partial\Omega_I(t) \times [0,t_{max}])$

   a3. Solve the adjoint equations backward in time for $\Psi(x, t; q^k(x,t))$.

   Evaluate $S'(q^k(x,t))(x,t) = \Psi(x, t; q^k(x,t))$ for

   $(x,t) \in ([\Omega_0] \times [0,t_{max}])$.

   a4. Set $\gamma^k = 0$ if k=0, otherwise set

$$\gamma^k = \frac{(S'(q^k)(x,t),\ S'(q^k)(x,t) - S'(q^{k-1})(x,t))_{L_2([\partial\Omega_0]\times[0,t_{max}])}}{\|S'(q^{k-1})(x,t)\|^2_{L_2([\partial\Omega_0]\times[0,t_{max}])}}$$

   b. Define the direction $p^k(x,t)$.

   If k=0, set $p^0(x,t) = - S'(q^k)(x,t)$, otherwise set

   $p^k(x,t) = - S'(q^k)(x,t) + \gamma^k\ p^{k-1}(x,t)$

Step 3: Calculate the optimal step size α^k

   a. Solve the sensitivity equations to calculate $\theta(x,t; p^k(x,t))$

   b. Set $\alpha^k = \dfrac{-(S'(q^k)(x,t),\ p^k(x,t)\ )_{L_2([\partial\Omega_0]\times[0,t_{max}])}}{\|D_p kT(x,t;q^k)\|^2_{L_2([\partial\Omega_I(t)]\times[0,t_{max}])}}$

Step 4: Update $q^{k+1}(x, t) = q^k(x, t) + \alpha^k\ p^k(x, t)$

Step 5: If $\|q^{k+1}(x,t) - q^k(x,t)\|_{L_2([\partial\Omega_0]\times[0,t_{max}])}$ < specified tolerance, stop
Otherwise set k = k+1 and go to step 2.

THE STATE AND PARAMETER SPACES

For the adjoint method, as was just presented, the state space (the approximation space used to solve the direct, sensitivity and adjoint problems) and the parameter space (the space where the unknown flux belongs) coincide with L_2. However, for numerical (FEM) calculations a finite element based space was used for the direct/sensitivity/adjoint problems. The values of the boundary flux at the finite element space/time nodes defined on $[\partial\Omega_o]\times[0,t_{max}]$ are calculated and saved. Those values together with the FEM shape functions were used to calculate the appropriate norms that are needed in the optimization algorithm.

Separate approximations can also be used for the state and parameter spaces. In essence, one could first introduce a finite approximation of $q(x,t)$ and then perform *the optimization in this finite dimensional space*. An adequate discretization of the state space is still needed for accurate solution of the sensitivity, adjoint and direct problems. In addition, the discretization of the state space should be much higher than that of the parameter space. The number of parameters to be estimated should be kept as small as possible to stabilize the problem and reduce computation time. The class of functions should be relatively smooth, easy and economical to evaluate, and flexible enough to closely approximate arbitrary smooth functions. Over large intervals, polynomial approximations of higher order, tend to oscillate. Greater flexibility can be achieved with piecewise polynomials. Polynomial splines are a class of piecewise polynomials with various degrees of smoothness between the pieces. Unlike polynomials, lower order splines exhibit flexibility without oscillation. The B-spline basis is preferred with the added benefit that part of the B-spline can be modified without greatly affecting the rest. Once a parameter space has been selected, the optimization problem is performed in a finite dimensional space.

SPATIAL REGULARIZATION METHODS

The regularization method of Tikhonov [5] increases stability by ensuring that the minimum lies in a compact set and by imposing a penalty against excessive oscillations. It involves the minimization of a smoothing functional, M:

$$M = S(q) + \alpha R \tag{13}$$

where S is the error defined in equation (8), R is the stabilizing functional, and α is the regularization parameter with $\alpha > 0$. The stabilizing functional of order p is expressed in terms of $q(x,t)$ and its derivatives over the entire boundary $\partial\Omega_o$ as:

$$R = \sum_{m=0}^{p} \xi_m \int_{\partial\Omega_o} \left(\frac{\partial^m q^k (x,t)}{\partial s^m}\right)^2 ds \tag{14}$$

The weighting factors, $\xi_m \geq 0$, control the relative importance of each derivative in the stabilizing functional. When dimensionless variables are used instead of s, one could take the weighting factors as 1.

The regularization parameter, α, determines the weight given to smoothing relative to matching the given data. The choice of regularization parameter is an important factor in the solution obtained with the regularization method. Several criteria for determining α exist. The most well known of these are the discrepancy principle and the modified order of magnitude rule. These methods have mostly been used for inverse problems with experimental data, but they can be used for design problems as well.

When optimization in an infinite dimensional function space is performed, one must define a new adjoint problem (depending on the form of R) and perform the optimization in a space different than $L_2([\partial\Omega_0]\times[0,t_{max}])$.

An additional complication also arises from the way the present adjoint problem was defined. Indeed, equ. (11b) results in iterative fluxes such that, $q^k(\underset{\sim}{x},t_{max}) = q^0(\underset{\sim}{x},t_{max})$. This has a significant effect on the accuracy of the calculated fluxes near t_{max}. Several methods have been introduced to eliminate the effects on the solution of this end condition [6]. In addition to those, one could add to the functional S(q) a quadratic regularization term that penalizes any deviations of the temperature solution at $t=t_{max}$ and $\underset{\sim}{x} \in \Omega_0$ from *a prescribed reference temperature* [7].

For a finite dimensional approximation, the stability of the least squares minimization process primarily depends on the approximation and discretization of the parameter space. The larger the number of unknown parameters, the greater the chance of numerical instability. A finite dimensional approximation of the smoothing functional R is required and it can easily be calculated [3].

NUMERICAL EXAMPLES

This example problem refers to solidification of a liquid initially super cooled at $T_{in}=-1$ ($T_m = 0$) in a region of length H=1, with $K_L=1$, $\rho= 1$, $c_L =1$, L=2 , front velocity V =0.432756 / $\sqrt{t}$ and front location h(t) = 0.865512 $\sqrt{t}$. The interface fluxes are given as $q_{ms}(t)$ =0.(solid), while $q_{mL}(t)$ (melt) is calculated through the Stefan condition. The inverse problem is concentrated only in the liquid phase. This problem is examined using a minimization scheme in both a finite dimensional space of linear and cubic B-spline functions and with a scheme over the L_2 space using the CGM.

Twenty linear elements are used to discretize the state space, while using the finite dimensional approximation. With fixed discretization of the parameter space, the accuracy of the algorithm is increased as the time step is reduced. Figure 2, shows $q_{0L}(t)$ for $\Delta t=0.0125$, p=6 and p=11 and using both linear and cubic-B spline basis functions. As it expected, reducing p results in a regularized solution that is closer to the exact solution.

Let us now concentrate in the CGM approach. Ten linear elements are used to analyze the direct problem, the adjoint equations and the sensitivity equations. Figure 3, shows the CGM calculated q_{0L} flux at different iteration steps for $\Delta t=0.1$. The initial guess is the zero solution. As the time step goes to zero, the solutions of the direct, adjoint, and sensitivity problems converge to their exact solutions, and so the calculated flux will also converge to its exact values. This is shown in Figure 4, where the CGM solutions at three different time steps are shown for the 10th iteration. The smaller time step solution is more accurate.

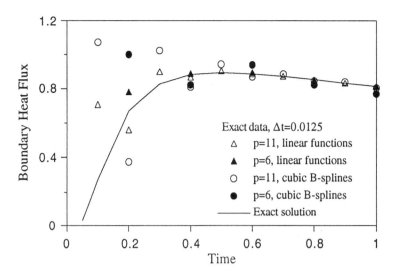

Fig. 2. Heat flux q_{oL} versus time for different approximations of $q(\underset{\sim}{x},t)$

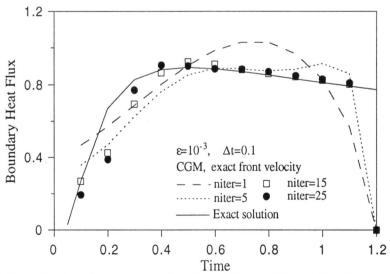

Fig. 3. Boundary heat flux q_{oL} as a function of time at different iterations.

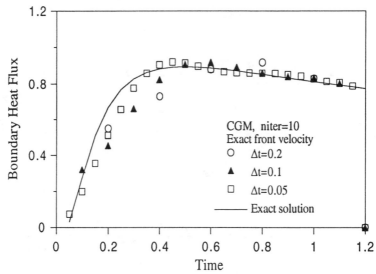

Fig. 4. Boundary flux q_{oL} versus time at the 10th iteration for various Δt.

ACKNOWLEDGEMENTS

This work was funded by NSF grants CTS-9115438 and DDM-9157189. The computing was supported by the Cornell National Supercomputer facility.

REFERENCES

1. Kurz, W. and Fisher, D. J., *Fundamentals of Solidification,* Tran Tech Publications, Switzerland, 1989.
2. Zabaras, N.,"Inverse FEM Techniques for the Analysis of Solidification Processes", *Int.J. Numer. Methods Eng.*, Vol. 29, pp. 1569-1587, 1990.
3. Zabaras, N., Ruan, Y., and Richmond, O., " On the Design of Two-Dimensional Stefan Processes with Desired Freezing Front Motion", *Numerical Heat Transfer*, Part B, Vol. 21, pp. 307-325, 1992.
4. Alifanov, O. M., *Identification of Heat Transfer Processes of Flying Vehicles*, Mashinestroenie Publishing Agency, Moskow, 1988.
5. Tikhonov, A. N. and Arsenin, V. Y., *Solution of Ill-Posed Problems*, V. H. Winston, Washington, D.C, 1977.
6. Zabaras, N. and Kang, S., " On the Solution of an Ill-Posed Inverse Design Solidification Problem Using Minimization Techniques in Finite and Infinite Dimensional Spaces", *Int.J. Numer. Methods Eng.*, submitted for publication.
7. Samai, M., Jarny, Y., and Delaunay, D., "An Optimization Method Using Adjoint Equation to Identify a Solidification Front Location", *Numerical Heat Transfer*, submitted for publication.

SECTION 11: ELASTICITY PROBLEMS

Unilateral contact with dry friction between a net and an obstacle

J.E. Souza de Cursi

Service de Mathématiques, Ecole Centrale de Nantes, 44072 Nantes Cedex 03, France

ABSTRACT

We consider a model for the contact between a homogeneous network of strings and an obstacle . The contact is unilateral with friction . The strings are submitted to gravity - like forces and have a stress - unilateral behaviour : all the internal efforts are traction efforts . In the general case of dry friction , there are situations where infinite solutions do exist . For the situation where friction follows the Coulomb's law , the uniqueness of the tensions and a numerical method are established (Finite Element Approximation of the solution) .

1. THE STRESS-UNILATERAL PROPERTY OF STRINGS

A string is a stress - unilateral structure , *i.e.* , a structure which is not capable of transmitting compression , *i.e.* , negative stress : **all its internal efforts are traction efforts** . Under compression , a string modifies its geometry in such a way that this condition is satisfied . Denoting by ε the unitary strain , by T the tension and by $K > 0$ the modulus of elasticity , the constitutive law of such a medium reads as : $\varepsilon = T/K$ and $T \geq 0$. The inequality in this law introduces functional and numerical difficulties in the analysis of strings even if contact with friction is not considered : non - existence of equilibrium configurations , convergence of the sequences of approximated solutions to functions which are not solutions . It can be treated by Pontryagyn's maximum principle or Non Convex Optimization methods , which leads to numerical methods (see Souza de Cursi [1] , [2] , [3]) .

2. THE EQUILIBRIUM OF A NETWORK OF STRINGS

The model considered is based on the following assumptions : the physical parameters are the same for each family of strings : the " horizontal " strings have the same constant of elasticity , the same density and the same lenght $h_1 \ll 1$. The " vertical " strings satisfy analogous properties : for example , their length is $h_2 \ll 1$. Moreover , the value of $\alpha = h_1/h_2$ is the same for all the meshes .

2.1 – Description of the network

The network is described by curvilinear coordinates $a = (a^1, a^2)$; $a \in \Omega$. Its configuration is a surface $\vec{x} : \Omega \longrightarrow R^3$, which associates the particle a to the vector $\vec{x}(a)$. We set

$$\partial_i \vec{x} = \partial \vec{x}/\partial a^i \quad , \quad \varepsilon_i = |\partial_i \vec{x}| - 1 \quad , \quad (i = 1,2) . \qquad (1)$$

2.2 – The constitutive law

Each line of coordinates $a^i = $ constant , $i \in \{1,2\}$ corresponds to stress unilateral strings : the internal efforts are characterized by the tension $T = (T_1, T_2)$ and given by $\vec{T} = (\vec{T}_1, \vec{T}_2)$:

$$\vec{T}_i = T_i \vec{t}_i \; , \; \vec{t}_i = \partial_i \vec{x}/|\partial_i \vec{x}| \quad , \quad (i = 1,2) \qquad (2)$$

$$T_i = K_i \varepsilon_i \quad , \quad T_i \geq 0 \quad , \quad (i = 1,2) \quad . \qquad (3)$$

In the sequel $\vec{T}$ defined by $(1) - (3)$ is referred to as the field of tensions generated by $\vec{x}$. The energy of elastic strain is

$$W(\vec{x}) = \int_\Omega \left[\frac{K_1}{2} \left(|\partial_1 \vec{x}(a)| - 1 \right)^2 + \frac{K_2}{2} \left(|\partial_2 \vec{x}(a)| - 1 \right)^2 \right] da \; .$$

2.3 – The equation describing the equilibrium

If the network is submitted to gravity forces and contact forces having lagrangian densities $\vec{g}$ and $\vec{r}$, respectively , we have :

$$\partial_1 \vec{T}_1 + \alpha \partial_2 \vec{T}_2 + \vec{g} + \vec{r} = \vec{0} \quad , \quad a \in \Omega . \qquad (4)$$

2.4 – The boundary conditions

We consider the situation where

$$\vec{x}(a) = \vec{x}_0(a) \quad , \quad a \in \Gamma_0 \subset \partial\Omega . \qquad (5)$$

and the forces applied to $\Gamma = \partial\Omega - \Gamma_0$ are known and defined by the lagrangian density $\vec{h} : \Gamma \longrightarrow R^3$. We denote by $\vec{\nu} = (\nu_1, \nu_2) \in R^2$ the unitary normal pointed outwards Ω . The boundary condition on Γ is :

$$\nu_1 \vec{T}_1 + \nu_2 \vec{T}_2 = \vec{h} \quad \text{on } \Gamma . \qquad (6)$$

2.5 A variational formulation (Principle of Virtual Works)
We set

$$V_0 = \{ \vec{y} : \Omega \longrightarrow R^3 \mid \vec{y} = \vec{0} \text{ on } \Gamma_0 \} \ , \tag{7}$$

$$\left(\vec{T} , [\vec{u}_1, \vec{u}_2] \right) = \int_\Omega (\vec{T}_1 \cdot \vec{u}_1 + \vec{T}_2 \cdot \vec{u}_2) da \ , \tag{8}$$

$$F\left([\vec{c} , \vec{h}] , \vec{y} \right) = \int_\Omega (\vec{c}) \cdot \vec{y} \, da + \int_\Gamma \vec{h} \cdot \vec{y} \, d\Gamma \ . \tag{9}$$

Then , a variational formulation for equations (4) - (6) is the following :

$$\left. \begin{array}{c} \vec{x} \in V = \vec{x}_0 + V_0 \ , \\ \left(\vec{T} , [\partial_1 \vec{y}, \partial_2 \vec{y}] \right) = F\left([\vec{g} + \vec{r} , \vec{h}] , \vec{y} \right), \forall \vec{y} \in V_0 . \end{array} \right\} \tag{10}$$

3. UNILATERAL CONTACT WITH DRY FRICTION

3.1 The difficulty of the general situation :
The obstacle is defined by the equation $\psi(\vec{\xi}) = 0$ ($\vec{\xi} \in R^3$) . It splits
the space in two unconnected regions where ψ has a constant sign and the
the network is restricted to the region $B = \{ \vec{\xi} \in R^3 \mid \psi(\vec{\xi}) \geq 0 \}$.
Thus ,

$$\vec{x} \in C = \{ \vec{y} \in V \mid \vec{y}(a) \in B , \forall a \in \Omega \} \ . \tag{11}$$

We assume that $x_0 \in C$. The part of cable laying on the bottom is

$$D(\vec{x}) = \{ a \in \Omega \mid \psi(\vec{x}(a)) = 0 \} \ . \tag{12}$$

It is unknown and must be determined . The efforts of contact $\vec{r} = R\vec{n} + \vec{\phi}$ are decomposed in a component $R\vec{n}$ ($\vec{n}$ is the unitary normal
to the obstacle , pointed inwards the admissible region) and a friction
effort $\vec{\phi}$, tangent to the obstacle . $\vec{\phi}$ follows the usual law of dry friction :

$$\vec{\phi} \cdot \vec{n} = 0 \ , \ | \vec{\phi} | \leq A = \mu R \ , \tag{13}$$

and R is equal to zero whenever the string is not in contact with the
bottom :

$$R(a) \geq 0 \text{ and } R(a) = 0 \ , \text{ if } \psi(\vec{x}(a)) > 0 \ , \text{ in } \Omega. \tag{14}$$

If the admissible region B is convex (see Souza de Cursi [1] for the typical
difficulties of a non convex B) , $(10) - (11)$ are equivalent to

$$\left. \begin{array}{c} \vec{x} \in C \ , \\ \left(\vec{T} , [\partial_1 \vec{y}, \partial_2 \vec{y}] \right) \geq F\left([\vec{g} + \vec{\phi} , \vec{h}] , \vec{y} \right), \forall \vec{y} \in C . \end{array} \right\} \tag{15}$$

The general problem of the equilibrium of the network is the following one :

Problem 3.1.1 - Find $(\overrightarrow{x}, \overrightarrow{T}, D(\overrightarrow{x}), \overrightarrow{\phi}, R)$ satisfying (1) - (3) , $(11) - (13)$ and (15) . $\Box$

We point to the fact that , in general , **both $D(\overrightarrow{x})$ and R are unknown and the values of $\overrightarrow{\phi}$ for a given R are multiple** : this is the main difficulty in problems with friction .

3.2 The problem of small perturbations

This situation arises in the numerical analysis of quasistatic problems with dry friction (Coulomb's law) : for example , if the forces $\overrightarrow{g}$ or $\overrightarrow{h}$ depend on time t , but we assume that the motion of the net is slow enough to be considered as being a sequence of configurations of equilibrium . In such a situation , a given initial configuration $\overrightarrow{x}_0$ and we are interested on the evolution for $0 \le t \le T$ ($T > 0$) . A discretization in time with step $\Delta t = T/N$ ($N > 0$) leads us to the problem of determining N configurations of equilibrium $\overrightarrow{x}_1, \ldots, \overrightarrow{x}_N$, where $\overrightarrow{x}_{i+1} = \overrightarrow{x}_i + \overrightarrow{u}_i$, $\overrightarrow{u}_i$ is "small" and $\overrightarrow{x}_{i+1}$ is the configuration of equilibrium under forces $\overrightarrow{g}(t_{i+1})$, $\overrightarrow{h}(t_{i+1})$, $t_{i+1} = (i+1)\Delta t$ ($i = 0, \ldots N - 1$) . So , we must solve N problems of the same type : at each time step a configuration of equilibrium $\overrightarrow{x}_R = \overrightarrow{x}_i$ is given , what determines the part of cable laying on the obstacle , $\overrightarrow{n}$ and A for this configuration : these values are denoted by $D(\overrightarrow{x}_R)$, the values of $\overrightarrow{n}_R$ and A_R , respectively . We must find the configurations of equilibrium $\overrightarrow{x}$ obtained from $\overrightarrow{x}_R$ by a "small" (infinitesimal) displacement $\overrightarrow{u} = \overrightarrow{x} - \overrightarrow{x}_R$. In such a situation , we approximate $D(\overrightarrow{x}) \approx D(\overrightarrow{x}_R)$ and

$$\overrightarrow{n}(a) \approx \overrightarrow{n}_R(a) , \quad A \approx A_R , \tag{16}$$

$$C \approx \{ \overrightarrow{y} \in V \mid (\overrightarrow{y} - \overrightarrow{x}_R) \cdot \overrightarrow{n} \ge 0, \text{ on } D(\overrightarrow{x}_R) \} . \tag{17}$$

We set $\overrightarrow{u}_T = \overrightarrow{u} - (\overrightarrow{u} \cdot \overrightarrow{n})\overrightarrow{n}$. A discretization of the Coulomb's law leads to

$$|\overrightarrow{\phi}| < A \Longrightarrow \overrightarrow{u}_T = \overrightarrow{0} , \tag{18}$$

$$|\overrightarrow{\phi}| = A \Longrightarrow \exists \lambda \ge 0 \text{ such that } \overrightarrow{u}_T = -\lambda \overrightarrow{\phi} . \tag{19}$$

The problem of the "small perturbations from a given state of reference " is the following one :

Problem 3.2.1 - Let the configuration $\overrightarrow{x}_R$ be given . We approximate $\overrightarrow{n}$, C , A as in $(16)-(17)$. Find $(\overrightarrow{x}, \overrightarrow{T}, D(\overrightarrow{x}), \overrightarrow{\phi}, R)$ satisfying $(1)-(3)$, $(11) - (12)$, (15) , $(18) - (19)$. $\Box$

We point out that these approximations do not concern the difficulties arising from the stress unilateral law but they eliminate those concerning the indetermination of A .

4. FUNCTIONAL RESOLUTION OF THE PROBLEM 3.2.1

In the following , this paper is restricted to the problem 3.2.1 . This problem can be studied by using a Principle analogous to the Principle of the Minimum of the Energy : from $(1) - (3)$, (5) , (7) , (10) , (11) , the set of the admissible configurations of the network is

$$Kin = V_+ \cap C \ , \ V_+ = \{ \overrightarrow{y} \in V \ || \ \partial_i \overrightarrow{y} \ | \geq 1 \ \text{on} \ \Omega \} \ . \tag{20}$$

Let us introduce $\alpha^+ = (\alpha + | \ \alpha \ |)/2$, the total energy $J = W + U$, the relaxed energy $J^{**} = W^{**} + U$ and the functional j , given by

$$W^{**}(\overrightarrow{x}) = \int_\Omega \left\{ \frac{K_1}{2} \left[\left(| \ \partial_1 \overrightarrow{x} \ | -1 \right)^+ \right]^2 + \frac{K_2}{2} \left[\left(| \ \partial_2 \overrightarrow{x} \ | -1 \right)^+ \right]^2 \right\} da,$$

$$j(\overrightarrow{x}) = \int_\Omega A \ | \ (\overrightarrow{x} - \overrightarrow{x}_R)_T \ | \ da \ , \ U(\overrightarrow{x}) = \ - F\left(\left[\overrightarrow{g} \ , \overrightarrow{h} \right], \overrightarrow{y} \right) \ .$$

For this particular functional , $J^{**} = QJ = \overline{J}$, where QJ is the quasicon-vex regularization of J and $\overline{J}$ is its lower semicontinuous regularization (see Dacorogna [4]). We set $I = J + j$, $I^{**} = J^{**} + j$ and we consider the problems

Problem 4.1 - Find $\overrightarrow{x} \in Kin$ such that $I(\overrightarrow{x}) = \inf_{Kin} \{I\}$ []

Problem 4.2 - Find $\overrightarrow{x} \in C$ such that $I^{**}(\overrightarrow{x}) = \inf_C \{I^{**}\}$ []

We have the following results :

Theorem 4.3 - 1) A configuration $\overrightarrow{x}$ corresponds to a solution of the problem 3.1.2 **if and only if** it is a solution of the problem 4.1
2) $\overrightarrow{x}$ is a solution of the problem 4.1 **if and only if** $\overrightarrow{x} \in Kin$ and $\overrightarrow{x}$ is a solution of the problem 4.2 .

3) The field of tensions $\overrightarrow{T}$ and the contact forces $\overrightarrow{r}$ are uniquely determined and are the same for the problems 3.1.2 , 4.1 and 4.2 .
4) $\overrightarrow{x}$ is a solution of the problem 4.1 **if and only if** $\overrightarrow{x} \in Kin$ and $\overrightarrow{x}$
generate the field of tension $\overrightarrow{T}$ and the efforts of contact $\overrightarrow{r}$.
5) The problem 4.2 has at least one solution . []

This result is not trivial , since Kin is a non convex set : it does not apply to the problem 3.1.1 , for which counter-examples of non-uniqueness of the field of tensions and contact forces can be exhibited (see Souza de Cursi [3]) .

5. A NUMERICAL METHOD

The theorem 4.3 gives us a method for the resolution of the problem 3.1.2 : in a first step , we solve the problem 4.2 , which is a convex closed coercive problem . This step gives us the field of tensions $\overrightarrow{T}$ and the efforts of contact $\overrightarrow{r}$. In a second step , we look for an admissible configuration $\overrightarrow{x} \in Kin$ which generates this field of tension and the same efforts of contact : this configuration is a configuration of equibrium . Thus , we shall establish a numerical method for the problem 4.2 in three steps :

5.1 – Step 1 : regularization of j

In this step , the non differentiable j is replaced by a differentiable j_δ ($\delta > 0$) , given by

$$j_\delta(\overrightarrow{x}) = \int_\Omega A\,\theta_\delta((\overrightarrow{x} - \overrightarrow{x}_R)_T)da \,,\ \theta_\delta(\overrightarrow{\xi}) = \sqrt{\delta^2 + |\overrightarrow{\xi}|^2} \ . \qquad (21)$$

We set $I_\delta^{**} = J^{**} + j_\delta$ and we consider the following problem

Problem 5.1.1 - Find $\overrightarrow{x}_\delta \in C$ such that $I_\delta^{**}(\overrightarrow{x}_\delta) = \inf_C \{I_\delta^{**}\}$ □

We have the following result :

Theorem 5.1.2 -   Let $\overrightarrow{x}$ be a cluster point of the sequence $\{\overrightarrow{x}_\delta\}_{\delta>0} \subset [H^1(\Omega)]^3$. Then $\overrightarrow{x}$ is a solution of the problem 4.2 . □

This result means that we have also the convergence of the fields of tensions and of the contact forces .

5.2 – Step 2 : penalty method

In this step , the condition $\psi(\overrightarrow{x}) \geq 0$ is treated by a penalty method : let us introduce $\alpha^- = \alpha^+ - \alpha$, $\Psi_n = n.\Psi$, where

$$\Psi(\overrightarrow{x}) = \frac{1}{2} \int_\Omega \left[(\psi(\overrightarrow{x}(a)))^- \right]^2 da \ . \qquad (22)$$

We set $I_{n,\delta}^{**} = J^{**} + j_\delta + \Psi_n$ and we consider the problem

Problem 5.2.1 - Find $\overrightarrow{x}_\delta \in V$ such that $I_{n,\delta}^{**}(\overrightarrow{x}_\delta) = \inf_V \{I_{n,\delta}^{**}\}$ □

We have the following result :

Theorem 5.2.2 -   Let $\overrightarrow{x}_\delta$ be a cluster point of the sequence $\{\overrightarrow{x}_{n,\delta}\}_{n>0} \subset [H^1(\Omega)]^3$. Then $\overrightarrow{x}_\delta$ is a solution of 5.1.1 . □

As in Theorem 5.1.2 , this result means that we have also the convergence of the fields of tensions and of the contact forces .

5.3 – Step 3 : reduction to a variational equation

Since 5.2.1 is a convex differentiable problem , it is **equivalent** to the following variational problem (we do not write the indexes n and δ)

$$\vec{x} \in V = \vec{x}_0 + V_0 \ , \\ a(\vec{x}, \vec{y},) = F\big([\vec{c}(\vec{x}), \vec{h}], \vec{y}\big), \forall \vec{y} \in V_0, \Bigg\}\quad (23)$$

where $a(\vec{x}, \vec{y}) = a_1(\vec{x}, \vec{y}) + a_2(\vec{x}, \vec{y})$,

$$a_i(\vec{x}, \vec{y}) = \int_\Omega K_i(|\,\partial_i\,\vec{x}\,| - 1)^+ \frac{\partial_i\,\vec{x}}{|\,\partial_i\,\vec{x}\,|} \cdot \partial_i\,\vec{y}\, da \quad (i = 1, 2);$$

$$\vec{c}(\vec{x}) = \vec{g} - n\psi^-(\vec{x})\text{grad}\psi(\vec{x}) + \frac{A(\vec{x} - \vec{x}_R)_T}{\sqrt{\delta^2 + |\,(\vec{x} - \vec{x}_R)_T\,|^2}}\ .$$

The variational problem (23) can be solved by a Finite Element Method (FEM . See for instance Zienkiewicz [5]).

5.4 – A numerical example

The following situation simulates the covering of a ball by a network : $\Omega = (0,1)^2$, $\Gamma_0 = \{a \in \partial\Omega \mid a^1 = 0\}$, the admissible region is $B = \{\vec{\xi} \in R^3 \mid (\xi_1 - 1/2)^2 + (\xi_2 - 1/2)^2 + (\xi_3)^2 \geq 4/25 \ , \ \xi_3 \geq 0\}$. We are interested in the quasistatic evolution (see section 3.2) of the net from the initial configuration $\vec{x}_0(a) = a^2\,\vec{e}_2 + , (a^1 + (a^1)^2/2)\,\vec{e}_3$, when the forces applied are $\vec{g} = -\vec{e}_3$, $\vec{h} = \vec{0}$, if $a^1 \neq 1$ and , for $a^1 = 1$, $\vec{h}(t) = t\,\vec{e}_1 + (1 - t)\,\vec{e}_3$, if $t \leq 1/2$; $\vec{h}(t) = (1 - t)(\vec{e}_1 + \vec{e}_3)$, if $t \geq 1/2$. We consider $\mu = 0.2$, $n = 100$, $\delta = 1E - 2$, $T = 1$ and the time step is $\Delta t = 0.05$. The variational equation (23) is approximated by a standard FEM involving an uniform grid made of $1 + M$ vertical and $1 + N$ horizontal straight lines V_i and $H_j (1 \leq i \leq 1 + M, 1 \leq j \leq 1 + N)$. V_1 corresponds to Γ_0 , the intersection of V_i and H_j is the point P_{ij} , the diagonal lines $(P_{i+1,j}, P_{i,j+1})$ generate the triangles and the unknowns are approached by polynomials of degree 1 on each triangle . Let $\vec{X}_{ij}$ be the approximated value of $\vec{x}(P_{ij})$. The value of $\vec{c}(\vec{x})$ at the point P_{ij} is approximated by $\vec{c}(\vec{X}_{ij})$. The unknowns are $\mathcal{X} = (\vec{X}_{ij})_{2 \leq i \leq 1 + M, 1 \leq j \leq 1 + N}$. They satisfy a nonlinear system of equations

$$\mathcal{E}(\mathcal{X}) = \mathcal{O} \ ; \ \mathcal{E}(\mathcal{X}) = (\vec{E}_{ij}(\mathcal{X}))_{2 \leq i \leq 1 + M, 1 \leq j \leq 1 + N} \ . \quad (24)$$

By reasons of limitation of room, we do not give the expressions of E_{ij} . (24) is solved by an iterative procedure : an initial guess $\mathcal{X}^{(0)}$ is given and we calculate $\mathcal{X}^{(1)}$, $\mathcal{X}^{(2)}$,..., by

$$\begin{cases} \vec{X}_{ij}^{(k+1)} = \vec{X}_{ij}^{(k)} - \omega\,\vec{E}_{ij}(\widetilde{\mathcal{X}}_{ij}^{(k)}) \\[2mm] \widetilde{\mathcal{X}}_{ij}^{(k)} = (\vec{X}_{pq}) \ ; \ \vec{X}_{pq} = \begin{cases} \vec{X}_{pq}^{(k+1)} \ , \ \text{if } (p < i) \text{ or } (p = i, q < j) \\[2mm] \vec{X}_{pq}^{(k)} \ , \ \text{otherwise.} \end{cases} \end{cases}$$

We set $h_1 = 1/M, h_2 = 1/N$. The quality of the approximated solution is controlled by the mean value residue

$$R_2 = \left(h_1 h_2 \sum_{i=2}^{1+M} \sum_{j=1}^{1+N} \left| \vec{E}_{ij}(\mathcal{X}^{(k)}) \right|^2 \right)^{1/2} .$$

The results for $M = N = 10$, $\omega = 0.01$ and $k = 250$ are given in the Table 1 . In Figure 1 , we show the final configuration of the network .

t	0.2	0.4	0.6	0.8	1.0
R_2	$3E - 2$	$4E - 2$	$1E - 2$	$8E - 3$	$8E - 3$

Table 1 - Results for $k = 250$.

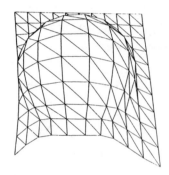 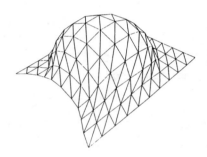

a) eye at $(1/2,0,1)$ b) eye at $(1,1,1)$
Figure 1 - The final configuration of the network .

REFERENCES

1. Souza de Cursi , J. E. 'Stress Unilateral Analysis of Mooring Cables' *Int. J. for Num. Meth. in Eng.* , Vol. 34 , no. 1 , pp 279 - 302 , 1992 .

2. Souza de Cursi , J. E. 'Statique des fils sans raideur à comportement unilatéral' *J. Méc. Th. Appl.* , Vol. 6 , no. 6 , pp 789 - 825 , 1987 .

3. Souza de Cursi , J. E. 'Un problème issu de l'étude numérique d'un fil sans raideur soumis au frottement sec ' *Annales de la Faculté des Sciences de Toulouse* , Vol. XI , no. 2 , pp 137 - 186 , 1990 .

4. Dacorogna , B. *Direct methods in the Calculus of Variations* Springer Verlag , Berlin , 1989

5. Zienkiewicz , O. C. *The Finite Element Method in Engineering Sciences* Mc Graw Hill , New York , 1977

Stability and bifurcation of plane cracks of arbitrary shape

P. Berest, Q.S. Nguyen, R.M. Pradeilles-Duval

Laboratoire de Mécanique des Solides, Ecole Polytechnique, 91128 Palaiseau, France

ABSTRACT

The extension of a plane crack of arbitrary shape in an elastic solid is discussed for G-based laws of propagation. It is shown that the rate of extension is governed by a variational inequality in which the second derivative of the potential energy and of the dissipated energy play a fundamental role. Crack surface is the principal unknown, the differentiation of energy must be performed with respect to a variable domain with moving boundary. Bifurcation and stability of the crack front curve can be discussed as in plasticity. The obtained results are illustrated by some simple analytical examples.

INTRODUCTION

The propagation of plane cracks of arbitrary shape is an interesting problem in fatigue or in fracture analysis. For example, the study of a plane crack of delamination propagating in laminated composites, or of interface cracks in thin films or in surface coatings of different kind, has been the subject of many discussions in the recent literature [1,3,9,10,14,15]. On the other hand, some models of damage mechanics also lead to study the extension of a damage zone in a solid [2,4,6,7,12,14]. The objective of this paper is to present some general results on the subject concerning the rate problem and stability or bifurcation analysis.

GENERAL EQUATIONS

An elastic solid with a propagating plane crack is a mechanical system undergoing irreversible transformation. The associated irreversible parameter is the crack surface, a plane domain Ω of boundary S as shown in Fig. 1.

Its evolution is associated with a total potential energy W :

$$W = \int_V w(\epsilon(u)) \, dV - \int_{S_T} F(\lambda).u \, ds \tag{1}$$

In this expression, $w(\epsilon)$ denotes the volumic density of elastic deformation and F is the applied forces, assumed to depend on a force or displacement control parameter λ.
If only quasi-static evolutions are considered, it is well known that the displacement field at equilibrium u can be implicitly defined as a function of the given state of crack Ω and of control λ :

$$u = u(\Omega,\lambda) \tag{2}$$

via the equilibrium equations :

$$\int_V w_{,\epsilon} \, \delta\epsilon \, dV - \int_S F \, \delta u \, ds = 0 . \tag{3}$$

The total potential energy can be then considered as a function of Ω and λ :

$$W = W(\Omega,\lambda) . \tag{4}$$

To introduce the generalized force associated with an extension of Ω, cf. [4,12], it is necessary to make the derivation of energy with respect to a domain $W_{,\Omega}$ by the techniques of derivation with respect to a geometric domain.

It is established that if $\delta\Omega$ denotes the rate of the normal extension of the present boundary S, then the following expression holds :

$$W_{,\Omega} \cdot \delta\Omega = - \int_S G \, \delta\Omega \, ds \tag{5}$$

where G denotes the energy release rate at a point of the moving surface S and represents the local value of generalized force G associated with the motion of Ω.

For example, for a plane crack in a three-dimensional solid, G is the limiting value of the local Rice-Eshelby integrals :

$$G = J^0 \quad \text{with} \quad J^0 = \text{Lim}_{\Gamma \to 0} \int_\Gamma (wn_1 - n.\sigma.u_{,n}) \, d\Gamma \tag{6}$$

For a damage zone, the expression of G is [12] :

$$G = [w - n.\sigma.u_{,n}] \tag{7}$$

and for a delamination crack in a composite plate or a thin film [3,14,15] :

$$G = [w - n.N.u_{,n} - n.M.\nabla\nabla w.n] \tag{8}$$

From (5) and from the energy balance, it follows that the dissipation (which is also the product of the entropy production by the temperature) is simply a product of forces and fluxes :

$$d = \mathbf{G} \cdot \dot{\Omega} = \int_S G(s) \cdot \dot{\Omega}(s) \; ds \qquad (9)$$

It may be useful to remark that in the same spirit, the second derivative of energy is :

$$\delta\Omega \cdot \mathbf{W}_{,\Omega\Omega} \cdot \delta\Omega = \int_S - \left[\delta G + \delta\Omega \frac{G}{R} \right] \cdot \delta\Omega \; ds \qquad (10)$$

where δG denotes the variation of G following the motion $\delta\Omega$ of Ω and R is the local curvature of S. A more symmetric expression of the second derivative can be obtained from the expression of δG in terms of $\delta\Omega$.

The G-based crack propagation law :

$$\begin{array}{ll} \text{If } G(s) < G_c \text{ then } \dot{\Omega}(s) = 0 & \text{(no propagation)} \\ \text{If } G(s) = G_c \text{ then } \dot{\Omega}(s) \geq 0 & \text{(possible propagation)} \end{array} \qquad (11)$$

is associated with the dissipation potential :

$$D(\dot{\Omega},\Omega) = \int_S G_c \; \dot{\Omega}(s) \; ds \quad \text{for } \dot{\Omega}(s) \geq 0 \qquad (12)$$

If G_c is a constant, the total mechanical energy Φ can be introduced as a function of the present state :

$$\Phi(\Omega,\lambda) = W(\Omega,\lambda) + G_c \int_\Omega da \qquad (13)$$

where the second term is the total potential energy and the third term represents the surface energy dissipated by crack extension.

RATE PROBLEM

The rate problem of propagation of the crack surface Ω consists in the obtention of the normal extension rate $\dot{\Omega}$ in terms of the control rate $\dot{\lambda}$ when the present state is assumed to be known. Local rate equations follow directly from (11). After time derivation, the identity $(G(s) - G_c) \; \dot{\Omega}(s) = 0$ leads to :

$$\dot{\Omega}(s) \geq 0 \text{ if } G(s) = G_c \text{ and if } \frac{dG}{dt}(s) = 0 \qquad (14)$$

$$\dot{\Omega}(s) = 0 \text{ if } G(s) < G_c \text{ or if } G(s) = G_c \text{ but } \frac{dG}{dt}(s) < 0 .$$

where $\frac{dG}{dt}$ denotes the normal derivative of G following the motion of the boundary.

These equations can also be written in an equivalent variational form. Indeed, after (14) :

$$\dot{\Omega}(s) \geq 0, \quad \frac{dG}{dt}(s) \leq 0 \text{ and } \frac{dG}{dt} \cdot \dot{\Omega} = 0 \text{ if } G(s) = G_c , \qquad (15)$$

it follows that :

$$\frac{dG}{dt} (s) \ (\ \delta\Omega - \dot{\Omega}(s) \ ) \ \geq 0 \quad \text{for all } \delta\Omega \geq 0 \tag{16}$$

or, in a global way :

$$\int_{S_c} \frac{dG}{dt} (s) \ (\ \delta\Omega(s) - \dot{\Omega}(s) \ ) \ ds \ \geq 0 \quad \text{for all admissible } \delta\Omega. \tag{17}$$

Admissible rates $\delta\Omega$ must satisfy $\delta\Omega(s) \geq 0$ on the portion S_c where the propagation limit is attained $G(s) = G_c$ and $\delta\Omega(s) = 0$ if $G(s) < G_c$.

Formally, from (5), (10) , (14) and (17), the rate $\dot{\Omega}$ is then a solution of the following variational inequality :

$$\dot{\Omega} (s) \ \geq 0 \ \text{on } S_c \ \text{and satisfies } \forall \ \delta\Omega(s) \ \geq O \ \text{on } S_c :$$

$$(\delta\Omega - \dot{\Omega}) \ . \ (\Phi,_{\Omega\Omega} \ . \ \dot{\Omega} \ + \ W,_{\Omega\lambda} \ . \ \dot{\lambda}) \ \geq 0 \tag{18}$$

where the second derivative $\Phi,_{\Omega\Omega}$ plays a fundamental role.

BIFURCATION AND STABILITY ANALYSES

As in incremental plasticity, the study of the rate problem enables us to follow step by step the evolution of the crack surface. For example, stability and bifurcation of the quasi-static response can be discussed as in plasticity by Hill's method [8,12] . The following propositions are then obtained :

The present equilibrium is stable in the dynamic sense if :

$$\delta\Omega \ . \ \Phi,_{\Omega\Omega} \ . \ \delta\Omega \ \text{is positive definite for } \delta\Omega(s) \geq 0 \text{ on } S_c . \tag{19}$$

The stability criterion (19) can also be written as :

$$\int_S - \delta G \ . \ \delta\Omega \ ds \ > 0 \quad \text{for any } \delta\Omega \neq O \text{ such that } \delta\Omega(s) \geq 0 \text{ on } S_c . \tag{20}$$

The present equilibrium is not a bifurcation point if the rate response is unique. Since uniqueness is ensured by a similar but more restrictive positive condition by relaxing the sign of $\delta\Omega(s)$ on S_c :

$$\delta\Omega \ . \ \Phi,_{\Omega\Omega} \ . \ \delta\Omega \ \text{is a positive definite for all } \delta\Omega , \tag{21}$$

condition (21) represents a sufficient condition of non-bifurcation.

ILLUSTRATION

As an illustration, consider the debonding of a thin film which represents the surface coating of a rigid half-space, due to the propagation of an interface crack Ω with internal pressure p, cf. Fig. 2 . The film is assumed to be a membrane in isotrope tension T. If u is the transverse displacement of the membrane at point x, the associated elastic energy is $w = \frac{1}{2} T |\nabla u|^2$.

If the pressure p is controlled, $p = \lambda$ and the total potential energy is :

$$W = \int_\Omega \frac{1}{2} T |\nabla u|^2 \, da - \int_\Omega \lambda u \, da . \qquad (22)$$

Local equations at equilibrium are :
$$T \Delta u + p = 0 \text{ in } \Omega , \quad u = 0 \text{ on } S . \qquad (23)$$

Since $W_{,\Omega} \cdot \delta\Omega = \int_\Omega (T \nabla u \cdot \nabla\delta u - \lambda \delta u) \, da + \int_S (w - \lambda u) \, \delta\Omega \, ds$

where δu is associated to $\delta\Omega$ by the perturbation boundary problem which follows from (23) :

$$T \Delta \delta u = 0 \text{ in } \Omega , \quad \delta u + \nabla u . n \, \delta\Omega = 0 \text{ on } S , \qquad (24)$$

finally one obtains :

$$W_{,\Omega} \cdot \delta\Omega = - \int_S w \, \delta\Omega \, ds . \qquad (25)$$

Thus $G(s) = w = \frac{1}{2} T |\nabla u(s)|^2$ and $\delta G = T \nabla u . \nabla\delta u + T\nabla u . \nabla\nabla u . n \, \delta\Omega$, the quadratic form to be considered is :

$$\delta\Omega \cdot \Phi_{,\Omega\Omega} \cdot \delta\Omega = \int_S -\delta G . \delta\Omega \, ds = \int_S - T \nabla u . (\nabla\delta u + \nabla\nabla u . n \, \delta\Omega) \, \delta\Omega \, ds . \qquad (26)$$

The last expression can also be written in a symmetric form as :

$$\int_\Omega T |\nabla\delta u|^2 \, da + \sqrt{2TG_c} \int_S u_{,nn} \, \delta\Omega^2 \, ds .$$

If the internal volume is controlled, i.e. if :

$$\int_\Omega u \, da = \lambda , \qquad (27)$$

the total potential energy is also given by the expression of the lagrangean :

$$W(\Omega,\lambda) = \int_\Omega w \, da - p \left[\int_\Omega u \, da - \lambda \right]$$

p is the lagrangean multiplier associated with the volume constraint (27) ; p and u are implicitly defined by (23) and (27).

Thus $W_{,\Omega} \cdot \delta\Omega = \int_{\Omega} (T \nabla u \nabla \delta u - p \, \delta u) \, da + \int_{S} (w - pu) \, \delta\Omega \, ds$

with $T \Delta \delta u + \delta p = O$ in Ω, $\delta u + \nabla u.n \, \delta\Omega = O$ on S, $\int_{\Omega} \delta u \, da = 0$. (28)

Finally, expressions (25), (26) still hold with a different definition of δu.

Consider for example the case of a circular interface crack of radius R, cf. Bérest [1]. Equations (23) give $u(r,\theta) = \frac{p}{4T} (R^2 - r^2)$. The propagation limit G_c is attained on the whole contour S when $p = p_c = \frac{2}{R} \sqrt{2TG_c}$ which is a limit value since equilibrium is not possible for $p > p_c$. Let us study the stability of the equilibrium when $p = p_c$:

A boundary extension rate $\delta\Omega(\theta)$ can be expanded in Fourier series :

$$\delta\Omega(\theta) = \delta a_0 + \sum_{1}^{\infty} (\delta a_j \cos j\theta + \delta b_j \sin j\theta) .$$ (29)

The associated rate δu defined by (24) is :

$$\delta u(r,\theta) = \frac{pR}{2T} \left\{ \delta a_0 + \sum_{1}^{\infty} (\delta a_j \cos j\theta + \delta b_j \sin j\theta) \left[\frac{r}{R}\right]^{j} \right\}$$

Relation (26) leads to :

$$\delta\Omega \cdot \Phi_{,\Omega\Omega} \cdot \delta\Omega = 2\pi G_c \left[-2 \delta a_0^2 + \sum_{1}^{\infty} (j-1) (\delta a_j^2 + \delta b_j^2) \right]$$

Thus, the considered equilibrium is unstable in mode 0 with pressure control.

In volume control, a similar result is obtained :

$$\delta\Omega \cdot \Phi_{,\Omega\Omega} \cdot \delta\Omega = 2\pi G_c \left[6 \delta a_0^2 + \sum_{1}^{\infty} (j-1)(\delta a_j^2 + \delta b_j^2) \right]$$

It is not difficult to check that (20) is satisfied while (21) is not. The considered equilibrium is stable but bifurcation is always possible in mode 1 since the boundary extension rate can be of the form $\delta\Omega(\theta) = \frac{1}{3} R \frac{\dot\lambda}{\lambda} + \dot a_1 \cos\theta + \dot b_1 \sin\theta$, where $\dot a_1$ and $\dot b_1$ are arbitrary small numbers such that $\delta\Omega(\theta)$ is non-negative.

The tunnel crack, cf. Fig. 2b where Ω is an infinite band of width 2R, is also an interesting example. Transverse displacement is now $u = \frac{p}{2T} (R^2 - x^2)$ after (23).

A symmetric mode of bifurcation of the crack front of the form :

$\delta\Omega(y) = \delta a + \delta b \cos ky$ when $x = R$, $\delta\Omega(y) = \delta a + \delta b \cos ky$ when $x = -R$ (30)

can be considered. In this case, it follows from (28) that :

$$\delta u = \frac{\delta p}{2T}(R^2 - x^2) + \frac{pR}{T}\delta a + \delta b \frac{pR}{T}\frac{chkx}{chkR}\cos ky \text{ with } \int_\Omega \delta u \, da = 0 \text{ thus } \delta p$$

$= -\delta a \frac{3p}{R}$ in volume control. By unit length, the quadratic form (26) is :

$$\delta\Omega \cdot \Phi,_{\Omega\Omega} \cdot \delta\Omega = 10 \, G_c \frac{1}{R}\delta a^2 + \delta b^2 \, G_c \frac{1}{2R}(kR \, thkR - 1) \text{ with } kL = 2\pi$$

Thus, a symmetric bifurcation of the front following a sinus curve of wave length L,

with $\frac{2\pi R}{L} \, th \, \frac{2\pi R}{L} = 1$, is always possible.

An skew-symmetric mode of bifurcation of the form :

$\delta\Omega(y) = \delta a + \delta b \cos ky$ when $x = R$, $\delta\Omega = -\delta a - \delta b \cos ky$ when $x = -R$ (31)

can also be considered. In this case :

$$\delta u = \frac{\delta p}{2T}(R^2 - x^2) + \frac{pR}{T}\delta a \frac{x}{R} + \frac{pR}{T}\delta b \frac{shkx}{shkR}\cos ky \text{ with } \int_\Omega \delta u \, da = 0 \text{ thus } \delta p$$

$= 0$ in volume control. By unit length, the quadratic form (26) is :

$$\delta\Omega \cdot \Phi,_{\Omega\Omega} \cdot \delta\Omega = G_c \frac{1}{2R}\delta b^2 (kR \coth kR - 1)$$

A skew-symmetric bifurcation is always possible following a translation mode (arbitrary δa) or a sinus mode of wave length L with $\frac{2\pi R}{L} \coth \frac{2\pi R}{L} = 1$.

REFERENCES

1. Bérest P. , Problèmes de Mécanique associés au stockage souterrain.
   Doctorat thesis, Paris, 1989.
2. Bui H.D. & Ehrlacher A., Propagation dynamique d'une zone endommagée.
   C.R. Acad. Sciences, t290, 1980.
3. Cochelin B , Flambage et délaminage dans les plaques composites stratifiées.
   Doctorat thesis, Metz, 1989.
4. Dems K. & Mroz Z., Stability conditions for brittle plastic structures
   with propagating damage surfaces.
   J. Struc. Mech., Vol 13, pp. 95, 1985.
5. Duvaut G. & Lions J.L., Les inéquations en mécanique et en physique.
   Dunod, Paris, 1972.
6. Ehrlacher A., Contribution à l'étude thermodynamique de la
   progression de fissure et à la mécanique de l'endommagement brutal.
   Doctorat thesis, Paris, 1985.
7. Fedelich B. & Bérest P., Torsion d'un cylindre élasto-fragile,
   Arch. Mech. Stos., Vol 40, pp. 5-6, 1988.
8. Hill R., A general theory of uniqueness and stability in elastic-plastic solids.
   J. Mech. Phys. Solids, pp. 236, 1958.
9. Hutchinson J.W., Thouless M.D., & Liniger E.G. Growth and

416   Free and Moving Boundary Problems

configurational stability of circular buckling driven film delamination.
Acta Metall. Mat., Vol. 40, pp. 295-308, 1992.

10. Jensen H.M., Thouless M.D. Effect of residual stresses in the blister test.
Report 439, The Technical University of Denmark, 1992.

11. Koiter W.T., On the stability of elastic equilibrium.
Ph.D. thesis, Delft, 1945.

12. Nguyen Q.S., Stability and bifurcation of standard dissipative systems.
CISM Course, Udine, 1991.

13. Nguyen Q.S., Stolz C., Energy methods in fracture mechanics.
IUTAM Symposium, Masson, Paris, 1987.

14. Pradeilles R. Délaminage des composites.
Doctorat thesis, Ecole Polytechnique, Paris, 1992.

15. Storakers B., Non linear aspects of delamination in structural members.
Theoretical and Applied Mechanics, ICTAM, Grenoble, 1988.

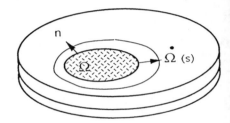

Fig.1 Propagation of a plane crack

Fig.2 Thin membrane under internal
pressure
       2a : Circular crack
       2b : Tunnel crack

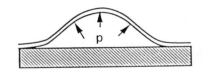

Fig. 2a

Fig. 2b

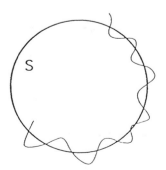

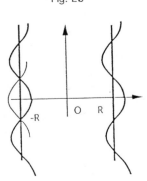

SECTION 12: MATHEMATICAL FORMULATIONS AND COMPUTATIONAL TECHNIQUES

Auxiliary principle technique for a class of nonlinear variational inequalities

M.A. Noor, E.A. Al-Said

Mathematics Department, College of Science, King Saud University, PO Box 2455, Riyadh 11451, Saudia Arabia

ABSTRACT

It is well known that moving, free, obstacle, unilateral, general equilibrium problems arising in elasticity, fluid flow through porous media, economics, transportation, pure and applied sciences can be studied in a unified general framework of variational inequalities. The ideas and techniques of variational inequalities are being applied in a variety of diverse fields and proved to be productive and innovative. One of the most difficult and important problems in this theory is the development of an efficient and implementable numerical method for solving these variational inequalities. In this paper, we use the auxiliary principle technique to prove the existence of a solution of a new class of variational inequalities and to suggest a new novel and general iterative algorithm. We also study the convergence criteria of this algorithm. Several special cases, which can be obtained from our main results, are also discussed.

INTRODUCTION

The last two centuries have seen increased attention paid by many research workers to the study of the variational principles. During this period, the variational principles have played an important and fundamental part as a unifying influence in pure and applied sciences and as a guide in the mathematical interpretation of many physical phenomena. In recent years, these principles have been enriched by the discovery of variational inequality theory, which is originally due to Stampacchia [1] and Fichera [2]. In 1971, Baiocchi [3] proved that the fluid flow through porous media (free boundary value problems) can be studied effectively in the framework of variational inequalities. Duvaut [4] extended the Baiocchi's technique to characterize the Stefens problems (moving boundary value problems) by a class of variational inequalities. Since then the variational inequality theory has been developed in several directions and with the aid of many new powerful and varied techniques, a large number of advances were made through cross pollination among many areas of mathematical, social, regional and engineering sciences, see, for example, [4,5,6,7,8] and the references therein for more details.

In 1988, Noor [10] introduced and studied a new class of variational inequalities. This new formulation extends various kinds of variational inequality problem formulation that have been introduced and enlarges the class of problems that can be studied by the variational inequality techniques in a unified and general framework. One of the main advantages of this theory is that the location of the free (moving) boundary becomes an intrinsic part of the solution and no special devices are needed to locate it. Inspired and motivated by the recent research work going on in this field, we introduce and consider a new class of variational inequalities. We remark that the projection technique and its variant forms cannot be applied to study the existence of a solution of this new class. In this paper, we use the auxiliary principle technique to study the existence of the solution of these variational inequalities. This technique deals with an auxiliary variational inequality problem and proving that the solution of the auxiliary problems is the solution of the original variational inequality problem. This technique is quite general and is used to suggest an iterative algorithm for computing the approximate solution of variational inequalities and related optimization problems.

In section 2, we introduce the variational inequality problem and review some basic results. The main results are proved in Section 3.

FORMULATION AND BASIC RESULTS

Let H be a real Hilbert space, whose inner product and norm are denoted by $< .,. >$ and $\| . \|$ respectively. Let K be a nonempty closed convex set in H. Given $T, g : H \to H$ continuous operators, we consider the problem of finding $u \epsilon H$ such that $g(u) \epsilon K$ and

$$< Tu, v - g(u) > + \phi(v) - \phi(g(u)) \geq 0, \quad \text{for all} \quad v \epsilon K, \tag{1}$$

where $\phi : H \to R$ is a convex, lower semi-continuous, proper and nondifferentiable functional. The inequality (1) is known as the mixed variational inequality.

SPECIAL CASE

I. If $g \equiv I$, the identity operator, then the problem (1) is equivalent to finding $u \epsilon K$ such that

$$< Tu, v - u > + \phi(v) - \phi(u) \geq 0, \quad \text{for all} \quad v \epsilon K, \tag{2}$$

a problem originally studied and considered by Duvaut and Lions [4]. The existence of its solution has been considered by Glowinski, Lions and Tremolieres [6], Kikuchi and Oden [7] and Noor [10] using the auxiliary variational principle technique.

II. If $\phi(u) \equiv 0$, then problem (1) reduces to the problem of finding $u \epsilon H$ such that $g(u) \epsilon K$ and

$$< Tu, v - g(u) > \geq o, \quad \text{for all} \quad v \epsilon K, \tag{3}$$

a problem introduced and studied by Oettli [11], Isac [12] and Noor [9] independently in different contexts and applications.

III. If $\phi(u) \equiv 0$, $K^* = \{u \epsilon H, \ < u, v > \geq 0, \text{ for all } v \epsilon K\}$ is a polar cone of the convex cone K in H and $K \subset g(K)$, then problem (1) is equivalent to finding $u \epsilon H$ such that

$$g(u) \epsilon K, \quad Tu \epsilon K^* \quad \text{and} \quad < Tu, g(u) > > 0, \tag{4}$$

which is known as the general nonlinear complementarity problem. The problem (4) is quite general and includes many previously known classes of linear and nonlinear complementarity problems as special cases. For the iterative algorithms, convergence analysis and extensions of the problem (4), see Noor [13].

IV. If $\phi(u) \equiv 0$, and $g \equiv I$, the identity operator, then problem (1) is equivalent to finding $u\epsilon K$ such that

$$< Tu,\ v - u > \geq 0, \quad \text{for all } v\epsilon K, \tag{5}$$

which is known as the classical variational inequality problem originally introduced and studied by Stampacchia [1] and Fichera [2] in 1964.

It is clear that problems (2) - (5) are special cases of the problem (1). In brief, the problem (1) is the more general and unifying one, which is one of the main motivations of this paper.

DEFINITION. A mapping $T : H \to H$ is said to be:

(a) **Strongly monotone**, if there exists a constant $\alpha > 0$ such that

$$< Tu - Tv,\ u - v > \geq \alpha \| u - v \|^2, \quad \text{for all } u, v\epsilon H$$

(b) **Lipschitz continuous**, if there exists a constant $\beta > 0$ such that

$$\| Tu - Tv \| \leq \beta \| u - v \|, \quad \text{for all } u, v\epsilon H.$$

In particular, it follows that $\alpha \leq \beta$. If $\beta = 1$, then T is said to be nonexpansive.

MAIN RESULTS

In this section, we prove the existence of a solution of the general variational inequality (1) by using the auxiliary principle technique and suggest an iterative algorithm.

THEOREM 1. Let the operators $T, g : H \to H$ be both strongly monotone and Lipschitz continuous, then there exists a solution $u\epsilon H$ such that $g(u)\epsilon K$ satisfying the variational inequality problem (1).

PROOF. We use the auxiliary principle technique of Noor [10,13,14] and Glowinski, Lions and Tremolieres [6] to prove the existence of a solution of the problem (1). For a given $u\epsilon H$ such that $g(u)\epsilon K$, we consider the problem of finding a unique $w \epsilon H$ such that $g(w) \epsilon K$ satisfying the auxiliary variational inequality

$$<w, v-g(w)>+\rho\phi(v)-\rho\phi(g(w))\geq<u,v-g(w)>-\rho<Tu,v-g(w)>, \qquad (6)$$

for all $v \epsilon K$, where $\rho > 0$ is a constant.

Let w_1, w_2 be two solutions of (6) related to $u_1, u_2 \epsilon H$ respectively. It is enough to show that the mapping $u \rightarrow w$ has a fixed point belonging to H satisfying (6). In other words, it is sufficient to show   that   for $\rho > 0$,

$$\| w_1 - w_2 \| \leq \theta \| u_1 - u_2 \|,$$

with $0 < \theta < 1$, where θ is independent of u_1 and u_2. Taking $v = g(w_2)$ (respectively $g(w_1)$) in (6) related to u_1 (respectively u_2), we have

$$<w_1,g(w_2)-g(w_1)>+\rho\phi(g(w_2))-\rho\phi(g(w_1))\geq<u_1,g(w_2)-g(w_1)>-\rho<Tu_1,g(w_2)-g(w_1)>$$

and

$$<w_2,g(w_1)-g(w_2)>+\rho\phi(g(w_1))-\rho\phi(g(w_2))\geq<u_2,g(w_1)-g(w_2)>-\rho<Tu_2,g(w_1)-g(w_2)>$$

Adding these inequalities, we have

$$< w_1 - w_2, g(w_1) - g(w_2) > \leq < u_1 - u_2 - \rho(Tu_1 - Tu_2), g(w_1) - g(w_2) >,$$

from which, we obtain

$$\eta \| w_1 - w_2 \|^2 \leq \| u_1 - u_2 - \rho(Tu_1 - Tu_2) \| \| g(w_1) - g(w_2) \|$$

$$\leq \xi \| u_1 - u_2 - \rho(Tu_1 - Tu_2) \| \| w_1 - w_2 \|, \qquad (7)$$

where $\eta > 0$ and $\xi > 0$ are the strongly monotinicity and Lipschitz continuity constants of the operator g.

Since T is a strongly monotone Lipschitz continuous operator, so

$$\| u_1 - u_2 - \rho(Tu_1 - Tu_2) \|^2 \leq \| u_1 - u_2 \|^2$$
$$-2\rho < Tu_1 - Tu_2, u_1 - u_2 >$$
$$+\rho^2 \| Tu_1 - Tu_2 \|^2$$

$$\leq (1 - 2\rho\alpha + \beta^2\rho^2) \| u_1 - u_2 \|^2 . \qquad (8)$$

Combining (7) and (8), we obtain

$$\| \omega_1 - \omega_2 \| \leq \frac{\sqrt{1 - 2\rho\alpha + \beta^2\rho^2}}{k} \| u_1 - u_2 \|, \quad \text{with } k = \frac{\xi}{\eta} \neq 0.$$
$$= \theta \| u_1 - u_2 \|,$$

where

$$\theta = \frac{\sqrt{1 - 2\rho\alpha + \rho^2\beta^2}}{k} < 1 \quad \text{for} \quad | \rho - \frac{\alpha}{\beta^2} | < \frac{\sqrt{\alpha^2 - \beta^2(1 - k^2)}}{\beta^2},$$

$\alpha > \beta\sqrt{1 - k^2}$ and $k < 1$.

Since $\theta < 1$, so the mapping $u \to \omega$ defined by (6) has a fixed point $u \equiv \omega \epsilon H$, which is the solution of the variational inequality (1).

REMARK 3.1.   We note that various projection, linear approximation, relaxation and decomposition algorithms that have been proposed and analyzed for solving variational inequalities may be considered as special cases of the auxiliary variational inequality problem (6). To be more specific, we show that the projection technique is a special case of the auxiliary problem (6). For this purpose, we take $\phi(v) \equiv 0$, $g \equiv I$, the identity operator in (6). In this case, for given $u \epsilon K$, the auxiliary problem (6) is equivalent to finding a unique $\omega \epsilon K$ such that

$$< \omega, v - \omega > \geq < u, v - \omega > -\rho < Tu, v - \omega >, \quad \text{for all } v \epsilon K,$$

from which it follows that

$$\omega = P_K[u - \rho Tu], \tag{9}$$

where P_K is the projection of H into K. It is well known that the map defined by (9) has a fixed point $\omega = u$ for $0 < \rho < \frac{2\alpha}{\beta^2}$, see Noor [15] for full details. Thus we conclude that $u = P_K[u - \rho Tu]$ is the solution of the variational inequality problem (5) and the converse is also true. This shows that the projection method is a special case of the auxiliary principle technique. We like to point out that the auxiliary principle technique is applicable to study the existence of the solution of some kind of variational inequalities, whereas the projection technique is not.

REMARK 3.2. It is clear that if $\omega = u$, the ω is the solution of the variational inequality (1). This observation enables to suggest an iterative algorithm for finding the approximate solution of the variational inequality (1) and its various special cases.

ALGORITHM 3.1.

(a) At $n = 0$, start with some initial value $\omega_0 \epsilon H$.

(b) At step n, solve the auxiliary problem (6) with $u = \omega_n$. Let ω_{n+1} denote the solution of the problem (6).

(c) If $\| \omega_{n+1} - \omega_n \| \leq \varepsilon$, for given $\varepsilon > 0$, stop. Otherwise repeat (b).

CONCLUSION

In this paper, we have considered and studied a new class of variational inequalities, which includes the known ones as special cases. We have also shown that the auxiliary principle technique can be used not only to study the problem of the existence of solution of variational inequalities, but also to suggest a novel and innovative iterative algorithm. By an appropriate choice of the auxiliary problem, one is able to select a suitable iterative method to solve the variational inequality and related optimization problems. Development and improvement of an implementable algorithm for various classes of variational inequalities deserve further research efforts.

REFERENCES

1. Stampacchia, G. 'Formes bilineaires coercities sur les ensembles convexes', C.R. Acad. Sci., Paris, 258 (1964), 4413-4416.

2. Fichera, G. 'Problemi elastostatici con vincoli unilaterali: il problema di signorini con ambigue condizione al contorno. Atti. Acad. Naz. Lincei. Mem. Cl. Sci. Fiz. Mat. Nat. Sez. Ia, 7(8), (1963-64), 91-140.

3. Baiocchi, C. and Capelo, A. 'Variational and Quasi-variational Inequalities', J. Wiley and Sons, London, 1981.

4. Duvaut, D. and Lions, J.L. 'Les Inéquations en Mechanique et en

5. Crank, J. 'Free and Moving Boundary Problems'. Clarendon Press, Oxford, 1984.

6. Glowinski, R., Lions, J.L. and Tremolieres, R. 'Numerical Analysis of Variational Inequalities ', North-Holland, Amsterdam, 1981.

7. Kikuchi, N. and Oden, J.T. 'Contact Problems in Elasticity'. SIAM, Philadelphia, 1988.

8. Noor, M.A., Noor, K.I. and Rassias, Th. M. 'Some aspects of variational inequalities', J. Comput. Appl. Math. (1993), in Press.

9. Noor, M.A. 'Quasi variational inequalities'. Appl. Math. Letters, 1(1988), 367-370.

10. Noor, M.A. 'General nonlinear variational inequalities', J. Math. Anal. Appl. 126(1987), 78-84.

11. Oettli, W. 'Some remarks on general nonlinear complementarity problems and quasi-variational inequalities', Pre-print, University of Mannheiny Germany, 1987.

12. Isac, G. A special variational inequality and the implicit complementarity problem, J. Fac. Sci. Univ. Tokyo, 37(1990), 109-127.

13. Noor, M.A. 'General algorithm and sensitivity analysis for variational inequalities', J. Appl. Math. Stoch. Anal. 5(1992), 29-42.

14. Noor, M.A. 'An iterative algorithm for nonlinear variational inequalities', Appl. Math. Letters. 5(4) (1992), 11-14.

15. Noor, M.A. 'General nonlinear variational inequalities', to appear.

Discretization proposal for finite elements with moving boundaries

L. Traversoni

Division de Ciencias Básicas e Ingeniería, Departamento de Ingeniería de Procesos e Hidráulica, Hidrología, Universidad Autónoma Metropolitana, (Iztapalapa), México D.F., México

1   Abstract

A completely new method, based on natural neighbors is proposed first to discretize the shape changing domain and afterwards to perform, using the same method, interpolation in the Finite Element method.

2   Natural neighbors and covering spheres

Natural neighbors may be defined as follows:

For every set $V = \{p_1, p_2, \ldots, p_m\}$ of m different points on E. And for each i on I_m is defined the set

$$T_i = \{x \in E : d(x, p_i) < d(x, p_j), \quad j \in I_m \setminus \{i\}\},$$

of *Voronoi polytopes* related to V.

Every pair of points whose Voronoi polytopes have common frontiers, are called *Natural Neighbors*; for each point there always exists a set of Natural Neighbors

The interpolation in some point P is performed using its natural neighbors as follows.

Let P be a point not belonging to V, and let $V = V1, V2, \ldots., Vm$ be the subset of V formed by the natural neighbors of P and let $Im = z1, z2, \ldots., zm$ be some assigned values of a function $U(z)$. Related to the values on the above points it may be defined the value at P as follows:

$$U(P) = \sum C(i) z_i$$

where:

$$C(i) = \frac{A(i)}{A(P)}$$

$A(i) =$ Intersection of the tile of V_i with the tile of P $A(P) =$ Tile of P

In two dimensions, the above refers to the areas of the tiles, in three the volumes, etc.

Definition

Let now V be a set of m different points on E, with $m > n$, not contained on a subspace of E of dimmension less than n. An open sphere $\mathcal{E}$ on E is called *Covering Sphere* related to V, if and only if :

i) $\mathcal{E}$ contains no point of V.

ii) The frontier of $\mathcal{E}$ contains at least $n + 1$ points of V.

The set of Covering Spheres related to V will be named $\mathcal{S}$. This construction is always possible and non empty and its cardinality, shape and other characteristics depend upon the number and distribution of V. There are some important properties of this construction, as was shown by Traversoni [1 and 2] :

i) Covering Spheres have their centers at the vertices of the Voronoi tessellation and for that reason they are a dual construction of Voronoi Tessellation.

ii) Every Delaunay triangle (or simplex in higher dimensions) is circumscribed by a Covering Sphere.

iii) Every Voronoi tile is completely covered by the spheres which have at their frontier the point of V which generates the tile. This also includes the open tiles because there are considered spheres generated by the points in the sides of the convex hull of V and the point at the infinity (the sphere is then the semispace not containing V).This also means that every point of $\mathcal{E}$ which is not in V belongs to at least one Covering Sphere.

iv) If $\mathcal{E}$ is a Covering Sphere of V the set of $n + 1$ points on its frontier is called the set of*generators* of $\mathcal{E}$.

The interpolant may be redefined using the covering spheres with the aid of the first property. This is very important because in the building algorithm the centers of the spheres as well as their radius must be stored. In that way, it is not necessary to calculate any new point in order to perform the interpolation; they are all stored as centers of spheres. In each case only the correct ones must be found.

To calculate for example the weight of A, all the vertices of the figure formed by intersecting tiles (darker in the figure 1) are centers of circles having A as generator. The general tile (that of P) is formed by the centers of the last four circles, all which have P as generator.

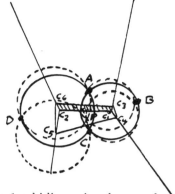

figure 1 a bidimensional example

However, there is another important link between the spheres and Sibson's interpolant: they generate a partition such that the interpolant is defined in each tile as:

Let $V = \{v_1, v_2, \ldots, v_m\}$ be a collection of given points on the euclidean space E of dimension n.

The notation $\mathcal{S} = \{E_1, E_2, \ldots, E_s\}$ will be given to the set of Covering Spheres of V. Each E_j is an open sphere containing at least $n + 1$ points of V on its frontier and none in its interior.

In the set $\mathcal{S}$ are included the open semispaces containing on its frontier some face of dimension $n - 1$ of the convex hull of V. Such semispaces are considered as spheres of infinite radius with its center on the point at the infinity of E.

Covering Spheres overlap, but starting with them a partition $\mathcal{P}$ of the space E can be built as follows. For each subset J of I_s the following is defined

$$A_J = \{x \in E : x \in E_j \text{ if } j \in J, \text{ y } x \notin E_k \text{ if } k \in I_s \backslash J\}$$

and

$$\mathcal{P} = \{A_J : J \subseteq I_s \text{ y } A_J \neq \emptyset\}.$$

Note that $A_\emptyset = V$ because the elements of V are the only points not contained in any of the Covering Spheres.

3   The Finite Element application

3.1   Basic statements

The purpose is to substitute the linear or other interpolant used in, for example a Galerkin formulation (the trial function) by the above interpolant. In this case the "elements" are the zones shown in Figure 2. For a point P internal to one element, for example a triangle (ABC) on the figure 3 the

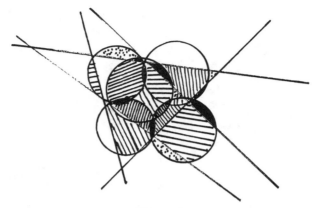

Figure 2
The subdivision of the plane done with
the intersection of covering spheres

linear interpolation depends upon the weights calculated with barycentric coordinates:

$$
\frac{\begin{bmatrix} x_p & y_p & 1 \\ x_a & y_a & 1 \\ x_b & y_b & 1 \end{bmatrix}}{\begin{bmatrix} x_a & y_a & 1 \\ x_b & y_b & 1 \\ x_c & y_c & 1 \end{bmatrix}}, \quad
\frac{\begin{bmatrix} x_p & y_p & 1 \\ x_a & y_a & 1 \\ x_c & y_c & 1 \end{bmatrix}}{\begin{bmatrix} x_a & y_a & 1 \\ x_b & y_b & 1 \\ x_c & y_c & 1 \end{bmatrix}} \quad and \quad
\frac{\begin{bmatrix} x_p & y_p & 1 \\ x_b & y_b & 1 \\ x_c & y_c & 1 \end{bmatrix}}{\begin{bmatrix} x_a & y_a & 1 \\ x_b & y_b & 1 \\ x_c & y_c & 1 \end{bmatrix}},
$$

The above leads to:

$$\phi_a = [(x_b y_c - x_c y_b) + (y_b - y_c)x + (x_c - x_b)y]/2A$$

$$\phi_b = [(x_c y_b - x_a y_c) + (y_c - y_a)x + (x_a - x_c)y]/2A$$

$$\phi_c = [(x_a y_b - x_b y_a) + (y_a - y_b)x + (x_b - x_a)y]/2A$$

where:

$$2A = (x_b y_c - x_c y_b) - x_a(y_c - y_b) + y_a(x_c - x_b)$$

and

$$\phi_a + \phi_b + \phi_c = 1$$

When natural coordinates are used for the same 3 points the result is the same but when four points ABCD are used the expression depends upon the centers of the related covering circles, the example of figure 3 is illustrated:

$$\phi_a = (x_4 y_3 - x_3 y_4 + x_3 y_1 - x_1 y_3 + x_1 y_2 - x_2 y_1 + x_2 y_4 - x_4 y_2)/2A_t$$

$$\phi_b = (x(y_5 - y_4) - y(x_5 - x_4) + x_5 y_4 - x_4 y_5 - x(y_5 - y_2) + y(x_5 - x_2)$$

$$-x_5 y_2 + x_2 y_5 - x(y_2 - y_4) + y(x_2 - x_4) - x_2 y_4 + x_4 y_2)/2A_t$$

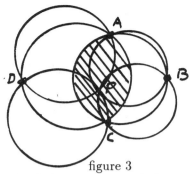

figure 3

Four points ABCD generate two circles, a generic point P
in the shadowed area generate with ABCD other four circles

$$\phi_c = (x_6 y_5 - x_5 y_6 + x_5 y_1 - x_1 y_5 + x_1 y_2 - x_2 y_1 + x_2 y_6$$
$$-x_6 y_2 - x(y_1 - y_2) + y(x_1 - x_2) - x_1 y_2 + x_2 y_1)/2A_t$$
$$\phi_d = (x(y_3 - y_6) - y(x_3 - x_6) + x_3 y_6 - x_6 y_3 - x(y_3 - y_1) + y(x_3 - x_1)$$
$$-x_3 y_1 + x_1 y_3 - x(y_1 - y_6) + y(x_1 - x_6) - x_1 y_6 + x_6 y_1)/2A_t$$

Here $2A_t$ is the area of 3456, then the result is a rational cuartic. However the representation based in Bernstein polynomials is a better choice. In that case, the general expression of a weighting function becomes:

$$S_f(p) = \sum_{|i|=1} B_{\mathbf{i}}^r(\mathbf{p}) f(v_{\mathbf{i}}),$$

where $B_{\mathbf{i}}^r(\mathbf{p})$ is a Bernstein polynomial of degree r in r variables, one for each natural neighbor of p, and the p_i are p's Sibson coordinates. In the present case $r = 4$ The expression of $B_{\mathbf{i}}^r(\mathbf{p})$ is:

$$B_{\mathbf{i}}^r(\mathbf{p}) = \binom{r}{\mathbf{i}} p_1^{i_1} p_2^{i_2} \cdots p_r^{i_r},$$

which can also be stated as:

$$\frac{r!}{i_1! i_2! \cdots i_r!} p_1^{i_1} p_2^{i_2} \cdots p_r^{i_r}.$$

In the linear case $p_1 + p_2 + \cdots + p_r = 1$, are the Sibson's coordinates whose rational expression was shown above and the binomial term is one.

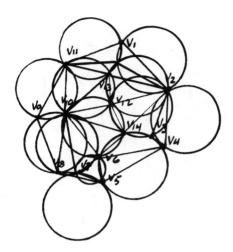

Figure 4
An example with 14 points

The Bernstein expression is general because $r(p) \geq 1$ may be taken and then the formula is more interesting leading to higher approximation orders.

Now, the weighting functions may be incorporated in the general Galerkin (or other) formulation which is mantained without change because Sibson's coordinates are also local coordinates, leading to similar simplifications in the integrations.

3.2   Implementation

To exemplify the application of the method, Figure 4 will be an important aid. In it, a set of 14 points with its corresponding covering circles has been drawn, also, one of the 48 valid Delaunay triangulations is drawn (there are so many because there are more than 3 points in many of the circumferences). If the triangulation is taken as discretization, in the equation of, for example V_{12} the elements used are $V_{12}V_2V_{13}$, $V_{12}V_{13}V_{10}$, $V_{12}V_{10}V_{14}$, and $V_{12}V_{14}V_2$.

To use the new method, first the circles with V_{12} as generator are identified in this case they are the ones defined by the sets $V_{12}V_2V_{13}$, $V_{12}V_{14}V_3V_2$, $V_{12}V_{10}V_6V_{14}$ and $V_{12}V_{13}V_{11}V_{10}$. This means that $V_{13}, V_{11}, V_{10}, V_6, V_{14}, V_3 and V_2$ are the natural neighbors of V_{12} and with them the equation of V_{12} will be built.

The second step is to remove V_{12} and build the circles that can be made with its natural neighbors, V_{12} will be necesarily inside of them or in their frontiers in this case such circles are the generated as follows: $V_2V_{14}V_{13}$ and $V_{13}V_{10}V_{14}$ which have V_{12} on their interior and $V_{13}V_{11}V_{10}$ $V_{10}V_6V_{14}$, $V_{14}V_3V_2$ with V_{12} on its frontier which are not used in V_{12}'s equation.

Now the equation can be stated as described above using $V_2, V_{13}, V_{10} and V_{14}$ as neighbors.

If the desired approximation goes further than the rational cuartics provided by the easiest case, the condition to be applied is the continuity of the directional derivatives in the neighbors (with their directions pointing in each one to the other neighbors).

4   The advantages in moving boundaries

4.1   General advantages

One of the most important problems related to moving boundaires is the location of such boundaires, covering spheres provide an easy tool for such location. There are two basic ways to treat the problem, one to modify, for example expanding and contracting the net or the other, to find the boundary between two different conditions in a fixed net. In both approximations this kind of discretization is useful because it works with local considerations so the modifications will be strictly restricted to the changing zones.

However, the most important advantage of this new method is its higher order of approximation which leads to better conditioned siffness matrices. As is well known fast changing boundaires mean many times, several orders of magnitude of changes in the parameters characterizing the nodes, C_1 and even C_2 continuity provided by the method are a good tool to deal with such problems.

4.2   An example

The method has been applied to coastal regions simulation, particularly to coast changes on beaches due to the remotion and deposition of sand by the incoming waves.

The problem is that several zones emerge and others are submerged during the simulation the model then, has to deal with the creation and removal of nodes. In each creation and removal the node has to be located in the discretization and also its characteristics (when creation is the case) must be obtained by interpolation.

The present method provides the oportunity to deal with all the problems with the same tool.

5   References

1) Traversoni *Algunos aspectos de la triangulacion de Delaunay en el plano* Monografias de la Academia de Ciencias de Zaragoza 1990

2) Traversoni and Palacios *Hierarchical Covering Spheres of a given set of points* Curves and Surfaces Academic Press 1991

Invited Paper

Mechanisms of shock generation in variable bubble point systems

I. Herrera[a], R. Camacho[b], A. Galindo[c]

[a]*Instituto de Geofísica, National University of Mexico (UNAM), Apdo Postal 22-582, Mexico D.F., Mexico*

[b]*PEMEX and UNAM, Mexico City, Mexico*

[c]*Instituto Mexicano del Petroleo and UNAM, Mexico City, Mexico*

ABSTRACT

In a sequence of papers the authors have investigated shock modeling in miscible displacement, specially in connection with variable bubble-point problems in Petroleum Engineering. The conclusions in connection with the mechanisms of shock generation are summarized here. The main conclusion is that there is a clear difference between the mechanisms of shock generation in miscible and immiscible displacements. In particular, Bucley-Leverett Theory which has been the main tool to understand shocks in immiscible displacement, is not applicable to shocks in miscible displacement models. In addition, some of the implications of these results, for the numerical modeling of shocks in miscible displacement are discussed.

1 INTRODUCTION

In a sequence of papers [1, 2, 3], the authors have investigated the different kinds of shocks that can be generated when modeling petroleum reservoirs and the procedures available for numerically modeling them. This paper is devoted to summarize our conclusions, so far, in connection with shock generation.

When discussing this topic, it is necessary to distinguish between "miscible" and "immiscible" displacement. By immiscible displacement, it is usually understood [4], one in which the different phases involved do not mix at all and there is not mass exchange between them. This is the case, for example, when water is injected through some wells, in secondary recovery.

On the other hand, if complete mixing or "miscibility" is attained, so that only one phase is formed, the term "miscible" displacement is most frequently applied. This is the case, for example, when CO_2 is injected to form a single fluid phase with the resident hydrocarbon.

Another situation that can occur [1], to which we will refer as "partial mixing", is the case when two or more phases can exchange mass but in which complete mixing does not take place, so that each one of the different phases keeps its own identity. This happens, for example, in reservoirs containing liquid oil and soluble gas, when the bubble point varies and a gas phase is present, at least in part of the region modeled.

The starting point for the understanding of shocks in immiscible displacement, was the classical Buckley-Leverett theory [5-7], which was further enlighten by the work of Cardwell and Sheldon [8,9], who explained clearly the way in which shocks are generated in such processes. The mechanism in this case, is similar to that occuring in the theory of inviscid compressible fluids, in which shocks are generated when characteristics intersect. For a more complete explanation of these points, the reader is referred to [1].

Shocks which occur when the phases are treated as partially miscible, as is the case when a gas front advances into a region occupied by undersaturated liquid oil, are not generated by the crossing of characteristics and have not received as much attention. In this paper it is shown, that such shocks are generated by the sudden transformation of an undersaturated oil particle into a saturated one, when such particle is reached by a saturating phase, as a gas phase. For immiscible displacement, it is generally accepted that shocks can occur only when capillary forces are neglected. On the other hand, for partially miscible displacement, the results summarized in this paper indicate that shocks may occur even when capillary forces are taken into account, in the beta or black-oil model. This last statement implies an evolution in the understanting of the processes of shock generation, with respect to previous works (see for example [1]).

One of the most successful methods that have been proposed for modeling shocks in immiscible displacement, is "front tracking". This was introduced by Richtmyer [10], and was developed extensively by Glimm, McBryan and coworkers (see, for example [11]). Many descriptions of the method at different states of development have been published (see, for example [12] or [13]). The reader is referred to [1], for a more detailed discussion.

One of our conclusions, which is specially relevant for the numerical modeling of shocks, is that the front-tracking method, which is based on the use of characteristics, is not applicable to partially miscible displacement, as is explained in Section 5. Due to this fact, it is necessary to look for competitive alternatives. For this purpose, the authors have proposed a procedure: the Eulerian-Lagrangian modeling of shocks [3]. This method is being tested at present, and some publications have already been devoted to it [1,2]. However, additional research which is needed, is underway. The interested reader is referred to the above publications, since in this paper we have prefered restricting our attention to the mechanisms of shock generation, exclusively.

To give our developments a firm basis, the results presented in this article are derived from first principles. Thus, Section 2 is devoted to present the basic equations, which constitute the starting point of our developments. Section 3, in which shock generation in immiscible displacement is discussed, the classical Buckley-Leverett theory is revisited. Shock generation in partially miscible displacement is discussed in Section 4. Some of the implications that the results presented have in the modeling of shocks, are examined in Section 5.

2 THE BASIC EQUATIONS

To give to our developments a firm physical and mathematical basis, we start from first principles. In the case of multi-phase systems, each phase α moves with its own particle velocity $\underline{v}^\alpha$. Here, $\alpha = 1, \ldots, N$, where N is the total number of components. In any phase there may be several components, but all components contained in the same phase move with the same velocity. The balance equations satisfied by any intensive property ψ^α associated with component α, are (see the Appendix):

$$\psi^\alpha_t + \nabla \cdot (\psi^\alpha \underline{v}^\alpha) - \nabla \cdot \underline{\tau}^\alpha = g^\alpha \qquad (1a)$$

and

$$[\psi^\alpha(\underline{v}^\alpha - \underline{v}_\Sigma) - \underline{\tau}^\alpha] \cdot \underline{n} = g^\alpha_\Sigma \qquad (1b)$$

Here, the vector $\underline{\tau}^\alpha$, is the **flux** of ψ^α across surfaces in space, while the quantities g^α and g^α_Σ represent **external supply** of ψ^α [14,15], per unit volume and unit time, in the case of g^α, while g^α_Σ represents **external supply** of ψ^α through the discontinuity, per unit area and unit time. In addition, $\underline{v}_\Sigma$ stands for the velocity with which the discontinuity moves. In all the applications that follow, the intensive properties are densities (mass per unit of total volume) of each one of the components of the systems to be considered. In them, the fluxes $\underline{\tau}^\alpha$, are produced by diffusive processes such as molecular diffusion and dispersion.

Consider a "black oil" or "beta" model [16], which is based on the following assumptions:

a).- There are three phases: water, liquid oil and gas (whose particle velocities will be denoted by $\underline{v}^w$, $\underline{v}^o$ and $\underline{v}^g$, respectively);

b).- Water and oil are immiscible, while gas is soluble only in liquid oil; i.e. the water and gas phases consist of only one component, while the liquid oil is made of two components (dissolved gas and non-volatile oil). This implies that the total number of components are four and that the latter two components move with the same velocity; and

c).- No physical diffusion is present. This includes both molecular diffusion and that induced by the randomness of the porous medium (dispersion).

It is important to observe that these assumptions do not exclude capillary pressure.

In what follows, the notations $\bar{\rho}_o$ and $\bar{\rho}_{dg}$, for the effective densities of non-volatile oil and dissolved gas, respectively, together with the relation

$$\bar{\rho}_{dg} = \bar{R}_s \bar{\rho}_o \equiv \frac{\rho_{gSTC}}{\rho_{oSTC}} R_s \bar{\rho}_o \tag{2}$$

will be used. Here, the factor R_s is the "solution gas:oil ratio" [16].

A straight-forward application of Equ. (1a), yields:

$$(\phi\, S_w \rho_w)_t + \nabla\cdot(\phi\, \rho_w S_w \underline{v}^w) = 0 \tag{3}$$

$$(\phi\, S_o \bar{\rho}_o)_t + \nabla\cdot(\phi\, \bar{\rho}_o S_o \underline{v}^o) = 0 \tag{4}$$

$$(\phi\, S_o \bar{R}_s \bar{\rho}_o)_t + \nabla\cdot(\phi\, \bar{R}_s \bar{\rho}_o S_o \underline{v}^o) = g^o_{Ig} \tag{5}$$

$$(\phi\, S_g \rho_g)_t + \nabla\cdot(\phi\, \rho_g S_g \underline{v}^g) = g^g_{Io} \tag{6}$$

as the governing differential equations of the black oil model [16]. Here, g^o_{Ig} is the mass of gas that is dissolved in the liquid oil per unit volume per unit time, while g^g_{Io} is the mass of dissolved oil that goes into the gas phase, per unit volume per unit time, and the extraction terms have been set equal to zero. Clearly

$$g^o_{Ig} + g^g_{Io} = 0 \tag{7}$$

for mass conservation.

When shocks occur, each one of the four components must satisfy the jump conditions which are implied by mass balance. By virtue of Equ. (1b), they are:

$$[\phi\, \rho_w S_w(\underline{v}^w - \underline{v}_\Sigma)]\cdot\underline{n} = 0 \tag{8a}$$

$$[\phi\, \bar{\rho}_o S_o(\underline{v}^o - \underline{v}_\Sigma)]\cdot\underline{n} = 0 \tag{8b}$$

$$[\phi\, \bar{\rho}_o S_o \bar{R}_s(\underline{v}^o - \underline{v}_\Sigma)]\cdot\underline{n} = g^o_{\Sigma g} \tag{9a}$$

$$[\phi \, \rho_g S_g (\underline{v}^g - \underline{v}_\Sigma)] \cdot \underline{n} = g^g_{\Sigma_o} \qquad (9b)$$

In addition, Darcy's Law requires:

$$[p_1] = 0 \; ; \; 1 = w, \, o, \, g \qquad (10)$$

Above, the quantities $g^o_{\Sigma g}$ and $g^g_{\Sigma o}$ stand for the exchange of mass between the gaseous phase and the liquid oil which takes place on Σ. As before, mass conservation requires:

$$g^o_{\Sigma g} + g^g_{\Sigma o} = 0 \qquad (11)$$

When these quantities are different from zero, and this is the case at the gas front when it advances into a region of undersaturated oil, a mass exchange concentrated on the surface Σ, between the gaseous and the liquid oil phases must occur. This is in contrast with the quantities g^o_{Ig} and g^g_{Io} of Equs. (5) and (6), which represent a mass exchange distributed on a volume and not concentrated on a surface.

3 IMMISCIBLE DISPLACEMENT

In previous work [1], an analysis of the different processes of shock generation that can occur in multiphase flow, has been carried out. In that research, two different processes of shock generation have been identified. Namely:

i).- Intersection of characteristics, just like in flow of compressible fluids; and ii).- The sudden transformation of an undersaturated particle into a saturated one.

The first one of these mechanisms takes place in immiscible displacement. Such process is described by the classical Buckley-Leverett Theory. On the other hand, the second one occurs in partially miscible displacement, as for example, when gas invades a region of undersaturated oil.

A.- Immiscible Displacement

In this case, shocks are generated by the first of these mechanisms, exclusively [1]. For the sake of completeness and comparison, Buckley-Leverett Theory is revised briefly in this Section, where, our discussion will be restricted to the case

when only two phases are present and each one of them is made
of one component: non-volatil oil and the displacing fluid. No
mass exchange between these phases is assumed and capillary
pressure is neglected.

The Darcy velocities are defined by:

$$\underline{u}_\alpha = \phi \, S_\alpha \, \underline{v}^\alpha \; ; \qquad \alpha = o \text{ and } D \text{ (displacing fluid)} \qquad (12)$$

Using them, Equs. (3) and (4) can be written as:

$$(\phi \, S_D \rho_D)_t + \nabla \cdot (\rho_D \underline{u}_D) = 0 \qquad (13a)$$

$$(\phi \, S_o \rho_o)_t + \nabla \cdot (\rho_o \underline{u}_o) = 0 \qquad (13b)$$

The "total Darcy velocity" is defined by

$$\underline{u}_T = \underline{u}_D + \underline{u}_o = \phi \{ S_D \, \underline{v}^D + S_o \, \underline{v}^o \} \qquad (14)$$

When capillary pressure and gravity forces are neglected, Darcy
velocities are given by

$$\underline{u}_l = - \frac{\underline{\underline{k}} k_{rl}}{\mu_l} \nabla p, \quad l = o, D \qquad (15)$$

and the total Darcy velocity, as well as the velocity of
the displacing fluid, are colinear. Thus,

$$\underline{u}_D = f_D \underline{u}_T, \qquad (16)$$

where f_D is a proportionality factor. In view of this
equation, one can replace $\underline{u}_D$ by $f_D \underline{u}_T$, in Equ. (13a), to obtain

$$(\phi \, S_D \rho_D)_t + \nabla \cdot (\rho_D f_D \underline{u}_T) = 0 \qquad (17)$$

When the fluids are incompressible, the density of the
displacing fluid can be cancelled out, in this equation. If in
addition, the solid matrix is also incompressible, such
equation reduces to

$$(S_D)_t + \phi^{-1} \nabla \cdot (f_D \underline{u}_T) = 0 \qquad (18)$$

Equations (14) to (16), together imply

$$f_D(S_D) = \frac{1}{1 + \dfrac{k_{ro} \mu_D}{k_{rD} \mu_o}} \qquad (19)$$

When the liquid phases and the solid matrix are incompressible,
Equs. (13) together imply that $\nabla \cdot \underline{u}_T = 0$. Hence, Equ. (18), can be
written as

$$(S_D)_t + \phi^{-1} f'_D \underline{u}_T \cdot \nabla S_D = 0 \qquad (20)$$

because f_D is function of S_D, only. Here, f'_D stands for the derivative of f_D with respect to S_D. This equation is a first order differential equation for S_D and when complemented with suitable boundary conditions, it can be solved uniquely for S_D. Such equation states that the rate of advance of a point that has a certain fixed saturation, equals the total Darcy velocity $\underline{u}_T$, multiplied by the factor $\phi^{-1}f_D'$. Here, no gravity segregation has been taken into account, but it is not difficult to incorporate it (see, for example [12]).

Buckley and Leverett [5,6], were the first to derive the one-dimensional version of Equ. (20). For such case, one has

$$(S_D)_t + \phi^{-1}f_D'\underline{u}_T \partial S_D/\partial x = 0 \qquad (21)$$

Writing q_T for the total rate of flow through a section, the total Darcy velocity can be expressed as $\underline{u}_T = q_T/A$, where A is the cross-sectional area, and Equ. (21) becomes:

$$(S_D)_t + (q_T/A\phi)f_D' \partial S_D/\partial x = 0 \qquad (22)$$

This is the classical Buckley-Leverett equation. If f_D' is non-constant, the space-time curves in which S_D remains constant will intersect, in general, leading to multi-valued solutions which are non-physical. The problem is similar to that occurring in the study of compressible fluids, either supersonic flow or the piston problem, and is solved by introducing discontinuous solutions or shocks. The same is done in multidimensional problems.

Using Equ. (12) and the incompressibility of the liquid phases and the solid matrix, the jump conditions (8), can be written as:

$$[\underline{u}_D] = \phi[S_D]\underline{v}_\Sigma \qquad (23a)$$

$$[\underline{u}_o] = \phi[S_o]\underline{v}_\Sigma \qquad (23b)$$

Adding up these two equations, it is seen that

$$[\underline{u}_T] = 0 \qquad (24)$$

i.e., the total Darcy velocity $\underline{v}_T$, is continuous. Making use of this result and of Equs. (16) and (14), it is seen that

$$[\underline{u}_D] = [f_D]\underline{u}_T = \phi[f_D]\{S_D \underline{v}^D + S_o \underline{v}^o\} \qquad (25)$$

which when combined with (23a), yields

$$\underline{v}_\Sigma = \frac{[f_D]}{[S_D]} \{S_D \underline{v}^D + S_0 \underline{v}^0\} = \phi^{-1} \frac{[f_D]}{[S_D]} \underline{u}_T \qquad (26)$$

This relation was first derived by Sheldon and Cardwell [25],
for one-dimensional problems. As has been presented here, it
applies to problems in several dimensions, as well.

B. - <u>Shock</u> <u>Formation</u> <u>in</u> <u>Immiscible</u> <u>Displacement</u>

According to the discussion presented in Section 3, for
immiscible displacement, in the absence of capillary forces,
the points in which the saturations remain constant move with
velocity $\phi^{-1}f'_D\underline{u}_T$. Let $x_c(S_D,t)$, be the position at time t, of a
point at which the saturation is S_D. Then, such a point satisfies
the differential equation

$$\frac{\partial x_c}{\partial t}(S_D,t) = \phi^{-1}f'_D(S_D)\underline{u}_T \qquad (27)$$

The solutions of Equ. (27), define straight lines in the
space-time plane, since the slope is constant in each one of
them.

Assume, $x_I(S_D)$ is the initial position, at time equal to
zero, of a point in which the saturation of the displacing
fluid is S_D. Then:

$$x_c(S_D,t) = x_I(S_D) + t\phi^{-1}f'_D(S_D)\underline{u}_T \qquad (28)$$

and the solution of the partial differential equation (21),
will be single valued, unless the equation

$$\frac{\partial x_c}{\partial x}(S_D,t) = x'_I(S_D) + t\phi^{-1}f''_D(S_D)\underline{u}_T = 0 \qquad (29)$$

is satisfied for some S_D. Clearing for t, one gets:

$$t = -\frac{\phi x'_I(S_D)}{f''_D(S_D)\underline{u}_T} = -\frac{\phi}{S'_{DI}f''_D(S_D)\underline{u}_T} \qquad (30)$$

where $S_{DI}(x)$ is the initial distribution of S_D and a prime is
used to denote the derivative of such function. A shock has to
be introduced at the minimal time (t_{sh}) which satisfies (30).
Under the assumption that the velocity $\underline{u}_T$ is positive, a t
satisfying Equ. (30) would be positive, only if $S'_{DI}f''_D(S_D)<0$.
If this latter condition is fulfilled, t_{sh} is obtained when
$|S'_{DI}f''_D(S_D)|$ is maximum, in Equ. (30).

On the other hand, let $x_\Sigma(t)$ be the position of the shock
at time t. According to Equ. (26), one has

$$\frac{dx_\Sigma}{dt} = \phi^{-1}\frac{[f_D]}{[S_D]}\underline{u}_T \qquad (31)$$

In general, the saturation S_D at the shock varies with time. A necessary condition for remaining constant, is that the shock moves with the velocity of a point which keeps fixed the value of S_D; i.e.:

$$v_\Sigma = \frac{\partial x_c}{\partial t}(S_D, t) = \phi^{-1}f'_D(S_D)\underline{u}_T \qquad (32)$$

In view of Equ. (26), this condition is

$$f'_D(S_D) = \frac{[f_D]}{[S_D]} \qquad (33)$$

Equ. (33) can be fulfilled during a finite period of time, only if the shock advances into a region of constant S_D. A special case of this situation is when $S_D \equiv 0$ ahead of the shock ($S_{D+}=0$). For this case:

$$f'_D(S_D) = \frac{f_D}{S_D} \qquad (34)$$

since $f_D(0)=0$. A point satisfying Equ. (34), can be obtained drawing a tangent to the curve $f_D(S_D)$ from the origin. This is the graphical construction first suggested by Buckley and Leverett [22]. Such construction is the basis of the simplified method for computing oil recovery, due to Welge [7].

In the more general situation in which S_D is a constant different from zero, ahead of the shock ($S_{D+} \neq 0$), the relation (33) in its more general form, must be fulfilled. It can be written more explicitly, as:

$$f'_D(S_D) = \frac{f_D(S_{D+}) - f_D(S_{D-})}{S_{D+} - S_{D-}} \qquad (35)$$

A point S_{D+} satisfying such condition can be obtained drawing a tangent to the curve $f_D(S_D)$ from the point $(S_{D-}, f_D(S_{D-}))$.

4 PARTIALLY MISCIBLE DISPLACEMENT

In Section 3, we have seen that in immiscible displacement shocks correspond to discontinuities of the saturation fluid S_D and that shocks are generated when space-time lines carrying constant values of S_D, intersect. In the present Section, it will be shown that on the contrary, in miscible displacement, shocks are associated with discontinuities of the solution gas:oil ratio R_s and that lines carrying constant values of R_s can not intersect. Thus, the intersection of characteristics as a shock generating mechanism must be ruled out, in this case.

In addition, it will be shown that when a particle of undersaturated oil is reached by a gas front, the transition from an undersaturated state to a saturated one, is discontinuous and generates a shock.

A. - Bubble-Point Conservation Principle

In this Section, two phases will be considered: liquid oil and gas. As was explained previously, in a Beta or Black Oil model, diffusion is excluded. Due to this fact, the following general result holds.

The Bubble-Point Conservation Principle.
In the absence of a gas phase, oil particles conserve their bubble- point.

Proof. When the gas phase is not present, the governing differential equations are:

$$(\phi \, S_o \bar{\rho}_o)_t + \nabla \cdot (\phi \, \bar{\rho}_o S_o \underline{v}^o) = 0 \qquad (36)$$

$$(\phi \, S_o \bar{R}_s \bar{\rho}_o)_t + \nabla \cdot (\phi \, \bar{R}_s \bar{\rho}_o S_o \underline{v}^o) = g^o_{Ig} \qquad (37)$$

In the presence of (36), Equ.(37) can be replaced by

$$\phi \, S_o \bar{\rho}_o \{(\bar{R}_s)_t + \underline{v}^o \cdot \nabla \bar{R}_s\} = g^o_{Ig} \qquad (38)$$

Observe that when the gas phase is not present $g^o_{Ig}=0$ and Equ.(38) may be reduced to

$$(R_s)_t + \underline{v}^o \cdot \nabla R_s = 0 \qquad (39)$$

This equation states that in the absence of a gas phase, R_s remains constant on particles moving with the velocity of the oil phase, $\underline{v}^o$. Thus, R_s remains constant on oil particles and the bubble-point is conserved.

B. - Shock Generation

This imposes some limitations on the paths that the value of R_s on an oil particle can describe on the R_s-p plane (see, Fig. 1). The one shown in Fig. 1a, is feasible and corresponds to the well known phenomenon which occurs when a single-phased mixture of oil and gas, starting at state "n", is depressurized beyond the bubble point, so that free gas becomes available and the liquid oil remains saturated when depressurization is continued. Then the mixture is pressurized again until all the gas present is dissolved and the liquid oil becomes undersaturated, finally reaching state "n+1", in Fig. 1a. Of course, such path is reversible: we can start at state "n+1" and by successive depressurization and pressurization, reach state "n". Observe that the point at which the mixture will leave the saturation curve when it is repressurized, depends on the amount of free gas available. In actual reservoir models, such amount of gas is supplied by the gas phase, which in turn is determined by the relative motion of the gas phase, with respect to the oil.

On the other hand, on an oil particle, the values of R_s cannot follow a trajectory such as the one joining points "n" and "n+1", in Fig. 1b, since it implies that the R_s changes without reaching the bubble point. That is, that R_s changes when the gas phase is absent, so that the bubble-point conservation principle is violated.

It seems that in actual models, when dealing with variable bubble-point problems, it is more efficient to replace Equ. (37) by the "bubble-point conservation principle", instead of integrating both Equs. (37) and (38) simultaneously, as is usually done. When this approach is followed, in the absence of a gas phase all trajectories of particles are horizontal, in the $p-R_s$ plane. Trajectories like the one shown in Fig. 1b, which are usually included (see for example, Figs. 12.6b and c, of [16]), must be excluded when an oil particle is followed.

On the other hand, a trajectory such as the one illustrated in Fig. 1c, is admissible for an oil particle. It corresponds to an oil particle which is initially undersaturated (point "n") so that the gas phase is absent necessarily, and at some point the oil particle is reached by a gas phase (point SH) so that it suddenly becomes saturated and under further pressurization R_s moves on the saturation curve. Such trajectory has a point of discontinuity at SH and in actual reservoir models, it gives rise to a discontinuous front or shock. This is the mechanism of shock generation which is the main subject of the present paper.

When a gas front advances into a region of undersaturated oil the surface where the properties are discontinuous will be denoted by Σ and will be referred to, as the shock. On Σ, the jump conditions (8b) and (9), must be satisfied. They are:

$$[\phi \, \bar{\rho}_o S_o (\underline{v}^o - \underline{v}_\Sigma)] \cdot \underline{n} = 0 \qquad (40a)$$

$$[\phi \, \bar{\rho}_o S_o \bar{R}_s (\underline{v}^o - \underline{v}_\Sigma)] \cdot \underline{n} = g^o_{\Sigma g} \qquad (40b)$$

$$[\phi \, \rho_g S_g (\underline{v}^g - \underline{v}_\Sigma)] \cdot \underline{n} = g^g_{\Sigma o} \qquad (40c)$$

Notice, in one side of Σ no free gas is available, while the other one is occupied by the advancing gas. To be specific, the unit normal vector "$\underline{n}$" to Σ will be taken pointing towards the side of the advancing gas. Then $S_{g-} = 0$, and only the gas properties on the positive side are defined. Thus, in what follows the subindex "plus" will be dropped when referring to the gas properties.

In the developments that follow, a formula for the "jump of a product" that has been used extensively in previous work by Herrera [16-19], will be applied. It is:

$$[rs] = \dot{r}[s] + \dot{s}[r] \qquad (41)$$

where the dot stands for the "average" across the surface of discontinuity. More precisely, for any function "r", one has

$$\dot{r} = (r_+ + r_-)/2 \qquad (42)$$

In the presence of (8b), Equ. (9a) can be written as:

$$\phi \, \bar{\rho}_o S_o (\underline{v}^o - \underline{v}_\Sigma) [\overline{\dot{R}_s}] \cdot \underline{n} = g^o_{\Sigma g} \qquad (43)$$

However, the product $\phi \bar{\rho}_o S_o (\underline{v}^o - \underline{v}_\Sigma)$ is continuous, by virtue of Equ. (6b). Thus

$$\phi \, \bar{\rho}_o S_o \overline{(\underline{v}^o - \underline{v}_\Sigma)} = \phi_+ \bar{\rho}_{o+} S_{o+} (\underline{v}^o_+ - \underline{v}_\Sigma) \qquad (44)$$

and (43) becomes

$$\phi_+\bar{\rho}_{o+}S_{o+}(\underline{v}^o_+-\underline{v}_\Sigma)[\bar{R}_s]\cdot\underline{n} = g^o_{\Sigma g} \qquad (45)$$

Furthermore, adding Equs.(45) and (9b), it is obtained:

Let us define the "retardation factor ε" by:

$$(\underline{v}_\Sigma - \underline{v}^o_+)\cdot\underline{n} = \varepsilon(\underline{v}^g - \underline{v}^o_+)\cdot\underline{n} \qquad (47)$$

Observe that $\underline{v}_\Sigma - \underline{v}^o_+$, is the relative velocity of the advancing gas front with respect to the oil, while $\underline{v}^g - \underline{v}^o_+$ is the relative velocity of the particles in the gas phase also with respect to the oil. The retardation factor ε, which as will be seen is always positive and less than one, expresses how smaller the relative velocity of the gas front is in comparison to that of the gas.

Noticing that

$$(\underline{v}^g-\underline{v}_\Sigma) = (\underline{v}^g - \underline{v}^o_+) - (\underline{v}_\Sigma - \underline{v}^o_+) \qquad (48)$$

and clearing for ε in Equ.(12), it is seen that

$$\varepsilon = \cfrac{1}{1 + [R_s]\cfrac{\rho_{o+}S_{o+}}{\rho_g S_g}} \qquad (49)$$

The whole system of jump conditions can now be replaced by Equs.(8), together with (47), where ε is given by Equ. (49). Observe that, as stated, $0<\varepsilon\leq1$, since $R_{s+}\geq R_{s-}$. This shows that the relative velocity of the gas front with respect to the oil, is not equal to the relative velocity of the gas, but it is reduced by a "retardation factor" ε.

5.- NUMERICAL IMPLICATIONS

One of the most effective procedures for dealing with shocks in Petroleum Engineering, is the Front-Tracking Method [10-13]. Such method is based on the use of characteristics, since a Riemann problem is solved at each time step (see [1], for example). However, the shock which occurs in partially miscible displacement and which have been described in Section 4 of this paper, is not generated by the crossing of characteristics. Thus, the Front-Tracking Method is not applicable. In such situations alternative procedures must be applied. A procedure, that has been proposed by the authors is Eulerian-Lagrangian, modeling of shocks (see [1,2]). This method is being the subject of research at present whose results will be reported elsewhere.

REFERENCES

1.- Herrera, I., A. Galindo and R. Camacho., Shock Modelling in Petroleum Engineering, Chapter 7 of the book Computational Methods for Moving Boundary Problems in Heat and Fluid Flow, L.C. Wrobel Ed, Computational Mechanics Publications, 1993.

2.- Herrera, I., A. Galindo and R. Camacho, "*Shock Modelling in Variable Bubble Point Problems of Petroleum Engineering*", Computational Modelling of Free and Moving Boundary Problems, **Vol. 1: Fluid Flow**, Eds. L.C. Wrobel and C.A. Brebbia, Computational Mechanics Publication, pp. 399-415, 1991.

3.- A. Galindo., Herrera, I., R.G. Camacho and L. Chargoy., "Eulerian-Lagrangian Approach to the Modeling of Shocks in Petroleum Reservoirs", 7th IMACS International Conference on Computer Methods for Partial Differential Equations, Brunswickm N,J., June 1992

4.- Ewing, R.E., "*Problems Arising in the Modeling of Processes for Hydrocarbon Recovery*", **The Mathematics of Reservoir Simulation**, Ed. R.E. Ewing, Frontiers in Applied Mathematics Vol. 1, SIAM, Philadelphia, 3-34, 1983.

5.- Leverett, M.C.,"Capillary Behaviour in Porous Solids", Trans. AIME, 1941, 142, 152.

6.- Buckley, S.E. and Leverett, M.C.: "Mechanics of Fluid displacement in sands". Trans., AIME (1942) 146, 107.

7.- Welge, H.J.,"A Simplified Method for Computing Oil Recovery by Gas or Water Drive", Petroleum Trans. AIME, 1952, 195, pp 91-98.

8.- Cardwell, W.T.,"The Meaning of the Triple Value in Noncapillary Buckley-Leverett Theory", T.P. 808, Trans. AIME, 1959, 216, pp 271-276.

9.- Sheldon, J. W., Cardwell, W. T., "One-Dimensional, Incompressible, Noncapillary, Two-Phase Fluid in a Porous Medium", Petroleum Trans. AIME, 1959, 216, pp 290-296.

10.- Richtmyer, R.D., *Difference Methods for Initial Value*

Problems, Interscience Publ., New York, 1957.

11.- Glimm, J., E. Isaacson, D. Marchesin and O. McBryan, *Front Tracking for Hyperbolic Systems,* Adv.Appl.Math. **2**, 91-119, 1981.

12.- Colella, P., P. Concus and J. Sethian, *Some Numerical Methods for Discontinuous Flows in Porous Media,* in **The Mathematics of Reservoir Simulation,** R.E. Ewing, Ed., Frontiers in Applied Mathematics Vol. 1, SIAM, Philadelphia, 161-186, 1983.

13.- Bratvedt F., K. Bratvedt, C.F. Buchholz, T. Gimse, H. Holden and N.H. Riseboro, *Front Tracking for Groundwater Simulations,* Computational Methods in Water Resources IX, Vol. I: Numerical Methods in Water Resources, T.F. Russell et al. Eds., CM Publications, Elsevier Applied Science, 97-104, 1992.

14.- Allen, B.M., Herrera I. and Pinder G.F., "Numerical Modeling in Science and Engineering", John Wiley & Sons, New York, 1988.

15.- Herrera, I. and Allen, M.B., "Modelación Computacional de Sistemas en Ciencias e Ingeniería", Comunicación Técnica No 9, Serie Docencia e Investigación, Instituto de Geofísica, UNAM 1986.

16.- Aziz, K., and Settari, A., Petroleum Reservoir Simulation, Ed. Applied Science Publishers Ltd, London, 1979

APPENDIX

The reader can find a convenient presentation of the "Balance Equations of Continuum Mechanics", in [14]. They have been written in Equs. (1). However, our notation differs slightly from the notation of [14] and also Equ. (1b) is in a form slightly more general than that presented in [14]. Thus, this Appendix is devoted to explain those differences.

In the notation here followed, which was introduced in [15], the mass M^α of any component α, in a region Ω is written as

$$M^\alpha = \int_\Omega \psi^\alpha(\underline{x}, t)d\underline{x} \qquad (A.1)$$

In particular, the masses of water, non-volatile oil, disolved gas and gas in the gas phase, are:

$$M^w = \int_\Omega \phi S_w \rho_w d\underline{x}; \quad \overline{M}^o = \int_\Omega \phi S_o \overline{\rho}_o d\underline{x}; \quad \overline{M}^{dg} = \int_\Omega \phi S_o \overline{\rho}_{dg} d\underline{x}; \quad M^g = \int_\Omega \phi S_g \rho_g d\underline{x} \quad (A.2)$$

This permits identifying

$$\psi^w = \phi S_w \rho_w; \quad \overline{\psi}^o = \phi S_o \overline{\rho}_o; \quad \overline{\psi}^{dg} = \phi S_o \overline{\rho}_{dg}; \quad \psi^g = \phi S_g \rho_g \quad (A.3)$$

Then (3) to (6) follow by sustitution of (A.3) into (1a), and (8) and (9) by sustitution of (A.3) into (1b).

In addition, Equ. (1b) is more general than Equ. (1.3-6) of [14], because we have included the term g_Σ^α which accounts for the possibility of having mass supply through a discontinuity surface. As was explained at the end of Section 2, this is essential in order to be able to model a gas front which advances into a region occupied by undersaturated oil.

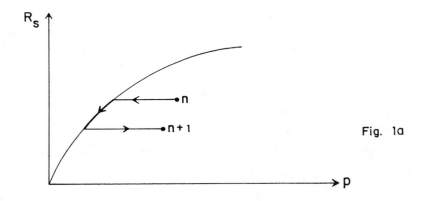

Fig. 1a

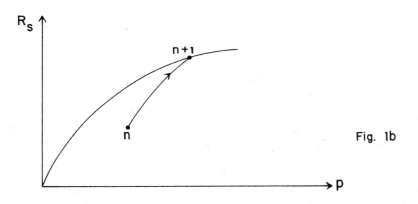

Fig. 1b

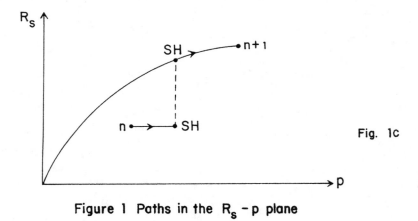

Fig. 1c

Figure 1 Paths in the $R_s - p$ plane

A model of the electrochemical machining process

H. Hardisty, A.R. Mileham, H. Shirvani
School of Mechanical Engineering, Univeristy of Bath, Bath BA2 7AY, UK

ABSTRACT

A computer package has been developed, based on the finite element method (FEM), which simulates the electrochemical machining (ECM) process. A finite element (FE) package has been used to determine the two-dimensional potential distribution in the electrolyte that fills the space between the advancing tool and the eroding workpiece. This yields the flux or current density distribution which, together with Faraday's Law of electrolysis allows the erosion of the workpiece to be predicted for a small time step. A series of algorithms have been developed to effect the automatic remeshing of the FE grid which is necessary, at the end of each time step, to simulate the movement of the tool/electrolyte and electrolyte/tool boundaries. Thus the computer package provides a continuous, realistic, two-dimensional model of the ECM process without interaction from an external operator. Simulation results showing a flat tool machining a stepped workpiece are presented.

INTRODUCTION

ECM is a non conventional metal removal process in which a current is made to pass through an electrolyte solution flowing between a cathode tool and an anode workpiece . The gap between the tool and work is typically below 1 mm and this together with a dc voltage of between 10-20 V produces very high current densities. Under these conditions the work surface is dissolved at a rate described by Faraday`s laws of electrolysis. ECM is ideally suited to the machining of complex shaped components made from high strength heat resistant alloys as found in the aerospace and nuclear industries, Jain [1].

The ECM process is complex and non-linear in nature and a significant level of experience is required to operate the process successfully, Mileham [2]. This is particularly so for tool design, in which several trial and error iterations, often taking several months are typically required to specify a tool shape that will machine a required profile to the prescribed accuracy. There is a need for a process model to be developed that will enable tool profiles to be specified `Right-First-Time`without the need for expert modification.

Mathematical models of the ECM process have been reported that have been used to predict certain two-dimensional work profiles under particular processing conditions, Kozak [3], Kozak [4], Ozis [5]. The Finite Element Method (FEM) has also been used, but only steady state solutions of very simple tool shapes have been modelled to date. Some theoretical analysis of numerical methods has been carried out on dynamic moving boundary problems, Christiansen [6]. No attempt appears to have been made to simulate continuous erosion or to solve the difficult moving boundary problem.

This paper describes an FE based model of the ECM process and assesses its ability to simulate the erosion of a stepped workpiece by a flat tool.

ECM THEORY

a) One-Dimensional Analysis

When a current I (Amp) is passed through an electrolyte between plane parallel electrodes, the quantity of material Q (mm^3) which is removed from the workpiece is given by Faraday's Law:-

$$Q = \frac{A\,I\,t}{\eta\,\rho 96500} \qquad (1)$$

Where,

Q = Volume of material removed, mm^3 η = Valency of work material
A = Atomic Weight of work material   I = Current, amp
96500 = Faraday's constant, coulomb/g   t = Time, s
ρ = Density of the work material, g/mm^3

At any instant,when the tool and workpiece are separated by a distance y (mm) and the constant voltage V is maintained between them, the current is given by Ohm's Law:-

$$I = \frac{kA_xV}{y} \qquad (2)$$

Where, k = Electrical Conductivity of the electrolyte, mho/mm.
A_x = Cross-Sectional area normal to current flow, mm^2.

Alternatively Ohm's Law may be expressed in terms of the flux J (A/mm^2), sometimes termed the current density :-

$$J = \frac{kV}{y} \qquad (3)$$

Equations (1) and (3) can be combined to yield the rate E at which the surface of the work is eroded:-

$$E = \frac{C}{y} \qquad (4)$$

Where $C = \dfrac{AkV}{\eta\rho 96500}$ = constant

In practice the tool is fed towards the workpiece at a steady linear velocity F. For this case the rate of change of the gap distance y (measured relative to the surface of the tool) is given by the differential equation:-

$$\frac{dy}{dt} = E - F \qquad\qquad = \frac{C}{y} - F \qquad (5)$$

Equation (5) may be integrated to yield the time taken for the gap to change from an initial value y_0 at time zero, to a final value of y at time t.

$$t = \frac{1}{F} (y_0 - y) + \frac{C}{F^2} \ \ln\left\{ \frac{(y_0 - C/F)}{(y - C/F)} \right\} \qquad (6)$$

It is perhaps worth emphasising that although in a fixed coordinate system erosion always causes the work surface to move in a direction away from the tool, this is not so for the system used here where the coordinates move with the tool. In this latter system y may either increase or decrease depending on the initial value of y_0, see Figure 1.

Inspection of equation (5) shows that when the erosion rate E becomes equal to the feed rate F, the rate of change of y is zero, and the relative gap size has an "equilibrium" value.

$$y_E = \frac{C}{F} \qquad (7)$$

b) Two-Dimensional Analysis
When the shape of either the tool or workpiece, or both, is not planar, the distribution of electrical potential in the electrolyte has a complex two-dimensional shape. For this case the vector flux (equation 3) will have x and y components which depend upon the value of the local partial derivatives of the potential. At any instant, for a homogeneous electrolyte, the potential distribution must satisfy Laplace's equation.

It should be noted that equation (3) is analogous to Fourier's Law for the conduction of heat. The FEM can be used to solve not only problems of mechanical stress, but also to model heat flow in thermal analysis, Hardisty [7]. Thus the contours of electrical potential which produce a flow of electric current through materials of differing electrical conductivity are directly analogous to contours of temperature, and heat fluxes through materials of differing thermal conductivity.

Test Cases - Previous Validation of Computer Package

A comprehensive series of tests has been carried out on the computer package for the case of one-dimensional erosion with two plane parallel surfaces, Hardisty et al [8]. Erosion was simulated with both a stationary and a moving tool; the effects of changing the principal parameters (F, y_0, Δ, etc) were investigated. A comparison of computer predictions with equation (6), and also with the theoretical relation for a stationary tool, showed good agreement. The tests demonstrated that the simulation package embodied the essential characteristics of the dynamic erosion process. The one-dimensional cases constitute the fundamental framework for the two-dimensional test described below.

THE ECM PROCESS MODEL

The ECM process model has been developed using a proprietary FE package, ANSYS [9]. This was chosen because of its file handling facilities that allow user macros to communicate with the FE model while it is running. A two-dimensonal mesh, consisting of uniform square elements, has been used to construct the model. Each element is assigned a material type that defines it as being part of the tool, electrolyte or workpiece. A voltage is applied between the tool and work and the model solves the complex potential distribution in the electrolyte, which in turn is used to provide a current density map of the work/electrode interface and the current density acting on each work surface element.

The simulation is based on discrete time-steps, during which, erosion is simulated by changing the eroded elements material type from work to electrolyte. Similarly, at the end of a time-step, tool feed is simulated by changing the electrolyte interface elements to tool elements. Thus at the end of a time-step a new mesh condition is created that is then automatically used as the input for the next time step to achieve a process of continuous erosion.

It should be noted that:- $F = \dfrac{dy}{dt} = \dfrac{\Delta}{\Delta t}$

It also follows that when equilibrium is reached the erosion rate will become equal to one element per time step. Because of the finite size of the elements in the FE mesh, when the gap y approaches its equilibrium value, the programme performs a repeating pattern in which the tool advances, and the work recedes, by one element.

The algorithms and methodologies developed for the model provide an incremental simulation of the ECM process that contains moving boundaries, automatic remeshing, continuous program cycling and a uniform square mesh that can accommodate any tool shape within its confines.

DESCRIPTION OF THE ECM GEOMETRY TO BE SIMULATED

The simulation to be analysed consisted of a flat, planar tool fed at uniform velocity towards a right-angle corner as represented by step 1 of Figure 3. The following conditions were used:-

Size of FE element (Δ)	0.05 mm	Critical flux	0.392 A/mm^2
Time-step (Δt)	3.45 s	Equilibrium gap (y_E)	7.6Δ
Feed rate (F)	0.0145 mm/s	Initial gap Small (y_{OS})	Δ
		Large (y_{OL})	16Δ

At time zero, the two-dimensional shape of the electrolyte can be regarded as a combination of two, one-dimensional parallel gaps. Initially, the small gap was much less than, and the large gap was greater than, the equilibrium distance y_E. This particular two-dimensional shape was selected because it is a natural extension of the one-dimensional validation tests already completed, Hardisty et al [8].

Provided that the left and right boundaries of the rectangular mesh are sufficiently distant from the central corner, then at these edges the flux in the electrolyte will be essentially one-dimensional. Thus, at the edges the development of the gap size with time should be predictable from equation (6). As erosion proceeds, both gaps should approach their equilibrium distance, the small gap enlarging, the large gap decreasing. In the limiting asymptotic case, of very long times, the corner will have disappeared and the work will become a straight line parallel to the tool, and at a distance y_E from it.

DISCUSSION OF COMPUTER PREDICTIONS

The simulation program was run for a total of 29 time-steps. During the first step, because of the high rate of erosion in the small gap, the program performed 5 cycles but subsequently there were two cycles per time-step. During each cycle the FE package solves for the two-dimensional flux distribution in the electrolyte, and the program erodes the work accordingly. The changing shape of the surface, as the tool descends and the work-piece erodes, is shown diagrammatically in Figure 3. A typical flux distribution in the electrolyte is shown in Figure 2. It can be seen that the flux is increased in the vicinity of the external (convex) corner, and correspondingly decreased within the internal (concave) corner. At the edges away from the influence of the corners, the shape of the flux is essentially one-dimensional.

In the first few time-steps, because of the rapid erosion, the small gap quickly attains its equilibrium value of approximately 7/8 elements. Thereafter the previously mentioned repeating pattern of erosion is set up. The high fluxes produce erosion of the convex corner. In the large gap fluxes are low and the gap closes largely because of the tool movement. A consequence of the extremely low fluxes in the concave corner is that the shape of this corner persists through the early stages of erosion (to step 9 in Figure 3). At the edges of the boundary, the change in gap size with time, as predicted by the computer has been compared with that of one-dimensional theory, equation (6). Agreement is good. Also after 29 time-steps the work profile becomes straight and parallel to the tool and the repeating pattern occurs at the correct equilibrium distance, in agreement with equation (6). It can be observed from Figure 3 that successive profiles all show a characteristic stepped shape. This is a consequence of the discrete nature of the FE mesh, the algorithm used to simulate erosion, and the time-stepping process. These steps in the profile themselves cause local flux distortions over the surface. These distortions are minimised by decreasing the mesh size.

Although in general terms the erosion of the corner proceeds in a manner which might be reasonably expected, no theory is presently available which can be used to check predictions of the changing shape of the corners as erosion proceeds. However validation work is being actively pursued and it is hoped to check computer predictions against experimental results in the near future.

CONCLUSIONS

1) A novel computer simulation of the two-dimensional, moving boundary ECM erosion process using FE methods has been designed and developed.
2) The continuous erosion process has been simulated as a series of time-steps, at each of which, the complex flux distribution in the electrolyte is calculated. Algorithms, external to the FE package, have been developed to determine those elements, if any, which must be eroded during a time-step.
3) The erosion of a stepped workpiece by a flat tool has been simulated to the point where equilibrium was reached and a flat workpiece attained. Erosion in the one-dimensional areas was seen to conform to theory and in the two-dimensional region of the step, erosion profiles were produced that were similar to those expected in practice.
4) Further research is being carried out to extend and improve the program and to investigate the use of key point techniques to model contoured surfaces.

REFERENCES

1. Jain V.K., Rajurkar K.P., 1991, "An integrated approach for tool design in ECM", Precision Eng, Vol 13, No 2, pp 111-124.
2. Mileham A.R., Harvey S.J. "Current Efficiency variations in ECM", 5th Poly Symp on Manufacturing Eng,Brighton, May 1986, pp 155-164.
3. Kozak J. et Al, 1991, "Computer simulation of pulse ECM", J of Mats Process Tech, Vol 28, pp 149-157.
4. Kozak J. et Al, 1991 "Computer modelling of ECM with rotating electrode", J of Process Tech, Vol 28, pp 159-167.
5. Ozis T., 1991 "An efficient approach to the solution of the two-dimensional ECM problem", J of Comp & App Maths, Vol 36, pp 239-246.
6. Christiansen S., 1990 "A stability analysis of a Eulerian solution method for moving boundary problems in ECM", J of Comp & App Maths, Vol 33, pp 269-296.
7. Hardisty H., Abboud J., Aug 1988 Dubrovnik, "Thermal analysis of microelectronic systems using FE modelling", XXth Int Symp on Heat Transfer in Electronic & Microelectronic Equipment, ICHMT.
8. Hardisty H., Mileham A.R.,Shirvani H.,"A Finite Element Simulation of the ECM Process", Annals of CIRP, Vol 42/1, Aug 1993.
9. ANSYS-PC/Thermal, Strucom Ltd,188-196 Canterbury Rd,Croydon, England

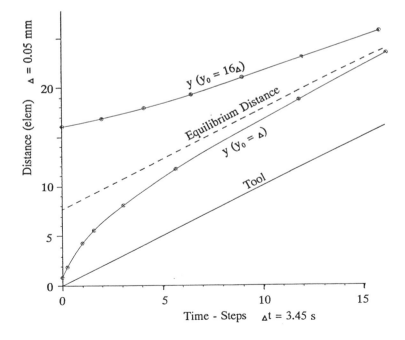

Figure 1. Characteristics of Erosion with a Tool Moving
at a Uniform Rate

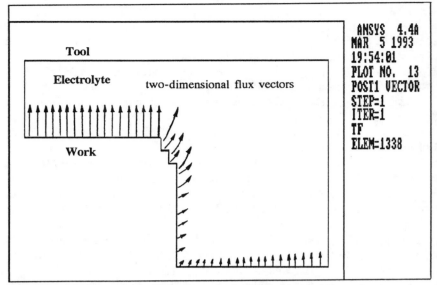

Figure 2. Flux vector plot at the end of the first time-step; arrows
indicate the relative size and direction of the flux.

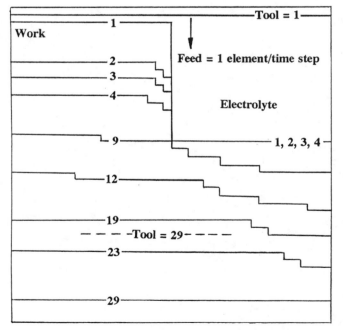

Figure 3. Simulated Erosion Profiles- From initial
step (1) to final flat surface (29)

Existence of solution and numerical simulation for an elastic journal bearing

J. Durany, G. García, C. Vázquez

Department of Applied Mathematics, University of Vigo, 36280 Vigo, Spain

ABSTRACT

A particular elastohydrodynamic lubrication problem is modelled in this work. The presence of elasticity, lubrication and cavitation gives place to a non linear coupled system of variational equations. An existence result is concluded by means of a constructive algorithm that decouples the elastic hinged plate biharmonic equation and the lubrication-cavitation Elrod-Adams free boundary problem.

INTRODUCTION

Since the presentation of the governing equations for the lubrication problem in the hydrodynamic case (see Reynolds [13]) a lot of effort has been done in the domain of elastohydrodynamic lubrication in three areas: mathematical modelling, theoretical analysis and numerical solution algorithms. In this work the authors try to contribute in the previous three aspects for a particular elastohydrodynamic problem concerning to journal bearing devices.

Modellization requires to take into account the following main features of the physical problem: the fluid hydrodynamic displacement, the formation of bubbles inside the fluid (cavitation) and the deformation of the boundary surfaces. The first physical aspect is mathematically modelled by Reynolds´ equation formally justified from Stokes´ equations by Bayada-Chambat [2]. The second aspect arises when the values of the pressure of the lubricant are below the one of saturation pressure. In this case the presence of air bubbles inside the lubricant makes Reynolds´ equation no longer valid in this part of the domain (cavitation region). Between the different cavitation models Elrod-Adams´ one has lately revealed the more realistic (see Bayada-Chambat [3]). The third phenomenon is the elastic deformation of the surfaces in contact by the effect of the fluid pressure. The particular characteristics of the contact and the surfaces justify the use of different elasticity equations. In elastohydrodynamic lubrication contacts the three aspects are coupled each other. Therefore the resulting equations that govern each problem are also coupled.

In this paper the lubrication problem that appears in a journal bearing device with an elastic thin bearing is considered (see *Figure 1.a.*). The thinness of the bearing allows to approximate the elastic behaviour of it by means of plates equation. A similar problem has been mathematically studied in Cimatti

[8] by using a variational inequality model for the cavitation. Herein, we consider the Elrod-Adams model for cavitation and the resulting coupled problem is posed. The existence of solution result is obtained by means of an algorithm that essentially decouples the hydrodynamic and the elastic part of the problem.

The numerical algorithm here proposed follows the theoretical proof of existence and it requires the solution of a nonlinear elliptic second order free boundary problem and a linear fourth order plate equation. For the first one we follow the idea already developed in Bermudez-Durany [5] and Durany-Vázquez [9] in the hydrodynamic case (i.e. rigid surfaces). For the biharmonic equation with Dirichlet and periodic boundary conditions a mixed formulation that involves the solution of second order elliptic problems is implemented (see Glowinski-Pironneau [11]).

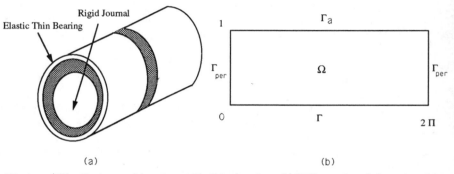

Fig.1.: a)Elastic journal bearing with thin bearing. b)Bidimensional domain of the problem.

FORMULATION OF THE EQUATIONS.

The journal bearing device basically consists in a cilindrical shaft that rotates inside a cylindrical bearing. The gap between them is lubricated by means of an isoviscous and incompressible fluid supplied through a circumferential groove (see *Figure 1.a*). The consideration of a thin bearing and the use of Elrod-Adams model for cavitation leads to the following set of equations

Find (p, θ, w) such that :

$$\frac{\partial}{\partial x}((h+w)^3\frac{\partial p}{\partial x}) + \frac{\partial}{\partial y}((h+w)^3\frac{\partial p}{\partial y}) = 6v_0 s\frac{\partial}{\partial x}(h+w) \quad p > 0 \ \text{ and } \ \theta = 1 \ \text{ in } \ \Omega^+$$
(1)

$$\frac{\partial}{\partial x}(\theta(h+w)) = 0, \quad p = 0 \ \text{ and } \ 0 \leq \theta \leq 1 \ \text{ in } \ \Omega_0$$
(2)

$$(h+w)^3\frac{\partial p}{\partial n} = 6sv_0(1-\theta)(h+w)\cos(n,i), \quad p = 0 \ \text{ on } \ \Sigma$$
(3)

$$p = 0 \ \text{ on } \ \Gamma$$
(4)

$$p = p_a \quad on \; \Gamma_a \tag{5}$$

$$p \; is \; 2\pi - x \; periodic \tag{6}$$

$$\eta \Delta^2 w = p \quad in \quad \Omega \tag{7}$$

$$w = \Delta w = 0 \quad on \quad \Gamma \cup \Gamma_a \tag{8}$$

$$w \quad and \quad \Delta w \; 2\pi - x \; periodic \tag{9}$$

where the unknowns p, θ and w denote the fluid pressure, the saturation function and the deformation of the elastic bearing respectively.

The data are the initial rigid gap h, the constant angular velocity s, the viscosity ν_0 and the supply pressure p_a and the flexure rigidity η of the bearing. The rigid gap is classically approximated in terms of the difference between the radii C and the eccentricity β $(0 < \beta < 1)$ in the form

$$h(x) \quad = \quad C(1 + \beta \cos(x)) \tag{10}$$

The sets that appear in the strong formulation of the problem are, see *Figure 1.b.*,

$$
\begin{aligned}
\Omega &= (0, 2\pi) \times (0, 1) \\
\Omega_0 &= \{(x, y) \quad p(x, y) = 0\} \\
\Gamma &= \{(x, y) \in \partial\Omega \; / \; y = 0\} \\
\Gamma_a &= \{(x, y) \in \partial\Omega \; / \; y = 1\} \\
\Gamma_{per} &= \{(x, y) \in \partial\Omega \; / \; x = 0 \; or \; x = 2\pi\}
\end{aligned}
$$

where Ω corresponds to the mean plane of the gap (so x represents the radial coordinate and y is the axial coordinate). Equations (1)-(6) correspond to the mathematical model of a thin film fluid displacement considering the possibility of cavitation. Equations (7)-(9) govern the hinged plate behaviour of the thin bearing. The introduction of the new variable p^* defined by

$$p^*(x, y) \quad = \quad p(x, y) - p_a y \tag{11}$$

provides a suitable weak formulation of Equations (1)-(9) given by

Find $(p^*, \theta, w) \in M_0 \times L^\infty(\Omega) \times L_0$ such that :

$$\int_\Omega (h + w)^3 \nabla p^* \cdot \nabla\varphi \, dx dy \quad = \quad \int_\Omega (h + w)\theta \frac{\partial\varphi}{\partial x} \, dx dy$$
$$- \; p_a \int_\Omega (h + w)^3 \frac{\partial\varphi}{\partial y} \, dx dy \quad \forall \varphi \in M_0 \tag{12}$$

$$\eta \int_\Omega \Delta w \, \Delta\psi \, dx dy \quad = \quad \int_\Omega (p^* + p_a y) \, \psi \, dx dy \quad \forall\psi \in L_0 \tag{13}$$

$$p^* \geq -p_a y \tag{14}$$

$$H(p^* + p_a y) \leq \theta \leq 1 \tag{15}$$

where H denotes the Heaviside function and

$$M_0 = \{\varphi \in H^1(\Omega) \,/\, \varphi = 0 \text{ on } \Gamma \cup \Gamma_a \text{ and } \varphi \; 2\pi - x \text{ periodic}\} \tag{16}$$
$$L_0 = \{\psi \in H^2(\Omega) \,/\, \psi = \Delta\psi = 0 \text{ on } \Gamma \cup \Gamma_a \text{ and } \psi \; 2\pi - x \text{ periodic}\} \tag{17}$$

where $H^1(\Omega)$ and $H^2(\Omega)$ denote the classical Sobolev spaces.

EXISTENCE OF SOLUTION.

The mathematical analysis consists in the proof of existence of solution for Equations (12)-(15). It is based on the construction of an algorithm that generates a sequence $\{(p_n, \theta_n, w_n)\}$ in the space $M_0 \times L^\infty(\Omega) \times L_0$ converging to the solution.

Next paragraph is devoted to the description of the algorithm :

STEP 1 : Let be $p_0^* = w_0 = 0$ and $\theta_0 = 1$

Problem 1.1 - Find $(p_1^*, \theta_1) \in M_0 \times L^\infty(\Omega)$ such that

$$\int_\Omega (h + w_0)^3 \nabla p_1^* \, \nabla\varphi \, dx dy = \int_\Omega (h + w_0)\theta_1 \frac{\partial\varphi}{\partial x} \, dx dy$$
$$- p_a \int_\Omega (h + w_0)^3 \frac{\partial\varphi}{\partial y} \, dx dy \;\; \forall \varphi \in M_0 \tag{18}$$

$$p_1^* \geq -p_a y \tag{19}$$

$$H(p_1^* + p_a y) \leq \theta_1 \leq 1 \tag{20}$$

Problem 1.2 - Find $w_1 \in L_0$ such that

$$\eta \int_\Omega \Delta w_1 \, \Delta\psi \, dx dy = \int_\Omega (p_1^* + p_a y) \, \psi \, dx dy \;\; \forall \psi \in L_0 \tag{21}$$

This first step takes into account that $w_0 = 0$ and that $h(x)$ is a $2\pi - x$ periodic function. So

$$\int_\Omega (h + w_0)^3 \frac{\partial\varphi}{\partial y} \, dx dy = 0 \tag{22}$$

$$0 < C(1 - \beta) \; \leq \; h \leq C(1 + \beta) \qquad (23)$$

The previous arguments reduce Problem 1.1 to the one already treated in Alvarez [1]. Existence, uniqueness of solution and the regularity property $p_1^* \in C(\overline{\Omega})$ have been proved. The classical results of existence and uniqueness of solution for Problem 1.2 can be found in Rektoris [12], for example. In Cimatti [8] the regularity property $w_1 \in H^3(\Omega)$ is obtained. The fact that p_1 is non negative and the application of the weak maximun principle twice conclude that w_1 is also nonnegative (provided the boundary conditions imposed for w_1).

The consideration of p_1^* as test function in Problem 1.1, the application of the Holder inequality and the lower bound of h lead to the $H^1(\Omega)$ estimate for p_1^*

$$[\int_\Omega h^2 \mid \nabla p_1^* \mid^2 \, dxdy]^{\frac{1}{2}} \; \leq \; K(\Omega, \beta, C) \qquad (24)$$

where $K(\Omega, \beta, C)$ is a constant. The above results and the equation (21) conclude that (see Bayada-Durany-Vázquez [4] for details)

$$\parallel p_1 \parallel_{H^1(\Omega)} \; \leq \; K_1(\Omega, \beta, C) \qquad (25)$$
$$\parallel w_1 \parallel_{H^2(\Omega)} \; \leq \; K_2(\Omega, \beta, C) \qquad (26)$$

STEP n :

Problem n.1 - Find $(p_n^*, \theta_n) \in M_0 \times L^\infty(\Omega)$ such that

$$\int_\Omega (h + w_{n-1})^3 \nabla p_n^* \, \nabla \varphi \, dxdy \; = \; \int_\Omega (h + w_{n-1}) \theta_n \frac{\partial \varphi}{\partial x} \, dxdy$$
$$- \; p_a \int_\Omega (h + w_{n-1})^3 \frac{\partial \varphi}{\partial y} \, dxdy \;\; \forall \varphi \in M_0 \;\; (27)$$

$$p_n^* \; \geq \; -p_a y \qquad (28)$$

$$H(p_n^* + p_a y) \leq \; \theta_n \; \leq 1 \qquad (29)$$

Problem n.2 - Find $w_n \in L_0$ such that

$$\eta \int_\Omega \Delta w_n \, \Delta \psi \, dxdy \; = \; \int_\Omega (p_n^* + p_a y) \, \psi \, dxdy \;\; \forall \psi \in L_0 \qquad (30)$$

At the end of the $(n - 1)$-th step the corresponding n-independent estimates of type (25) and (26) for the functions $(p_{n-1}^*, \theta_{n-1}, w_{n-1})$ were obtained. For the sake of simplicity we rewrite Problem n.1 in the new notation.

Problem n.1 - Find $(p_n^*, \theta_n) \in M_0 \times L^\infty(\Omega)$ such that

$$\int_\Omega l^3 \nabla p_n^* \nabla \varphi \, dx dy = \int_\Omega l \theta_n \frac{\partial \varphi}{\partial x} \, dx dy$$
$$- p_a \int_\Omega l^3 \frac{\partial \varphi}{\partial y} \, dx dy \quad \forall \varphi \in M_0 \tag{31}$$

$$p_n^* \geq -p_a y \tag{32}$$

$$H(p_n^* + p_a y) \leq \theta_n \leq 1 \tag{33}$$

where

$$l(x, y) = h(x) + w_{n-1}(x, y) \tag{34}$$

and therefore

$$0 < k_0 \leq \| l \|_{C(\overline{\Omega})} \leq k_1 \tag{35}$$

with k_0 y k_1 constants independents of n. The existence of solution for Equations (31)-(33) is obtained by means of the regularization of the function θ and the consideration of the following regularized problem :

Find $p_\epsilon^* \in M_0$ such that

$$\int_\Omega l^3 \nabla p_\epsilon^* \nabla \varphi \, dx dy = \int_\Omega l \, H_\epsilon(p_\epsilon^* + p_a y) \frac{\partial \varphi}{\partial x} \, dx dy$$
$$- p_a \int_\Omega l^3 \frac{\partial \varphi}{\partial y} \, dx dy \quad \forall \varphi \in M_0 \tag{36}$$

$$p_\epsilon^* \geq -p_a y \tag{37}$$

where the function H_ϵ is an approach of the Heaviside graph defined by

$$H_\epsilon(t) = \begin{cases} 1 & t > \epsilon \\ \dfrac{t}{\epsilon} & 0 \leq t \leq \epsilon \\ 0 & t \leq 0 \end{cases} \tag{38}$$

Theorem 1 *For $q_\epsilon^* \in L^2(\Omega)$ given there exists a unique function $p_\epsilon^* \in M_0$ that is a solution of the linear problem*

$$\int_\Omega l^3 \nabla p_\epsilon^* \nabla \varphi \, dx dy = \int_\Omega l \, H_\epsilon(q_\epsilon^* + p_a y) \frac{\partial \varphi}{\partial x} \, dx dy$$
$$- p_a \int_\Omega l^3 \frac{\partial \varphi}{\partial y} \, dx dy \quad \forall \varphi \in M_0 \tag{39}$$

Proof : It is a consequence of Lax-Milgram theorem.

Theorem 2 *The regularized problem* $(36) - (37)$ *has a unique solution.*

Proof : The existence is achieved by means of Schauder fixed point theorem applied to the operator defined by the solution of the linear Equation (39) as in the work of Alvarez [1]. The uniqueness is based in the use of special functions (see Brezis-Kinderleher-Stampacchia [7] and Vázquez [14]) and the upper and lower bounds of l.

Theorem 3 *The Problem n.1 has at least a solution.*

Proof : From Equation (37) the function $p_\epsilon^* + p_a y$ is non negative and the set

$$M_0^+ \ = \ \{\varphi \in M_0 / \varphi + p_a y \geq 0\} \tag{40}$$

is weakly closed in M_0. Moreover $p_\epsilon^* \in M_0^+$.

Easy computations allow us to obtain $H^1(\Omega)$ estimates for p_ϵ^* independents of the parameter ϵ. Thus, from compacity arguments we deduce that there exists $p_n^* \in M_0^+$ such that

$$\{p_\epsilon^*\} \quad \rightarrow \quad p_n^* \ in \ H^1(\Omega) \ weak \tag{41}$$

where $\{p_\epsilon^*\}$ is really a subsequence of $\{p_\epsilon^*\}$. By the same argument there exists $\theta_n \in L^2(\Omega)$ such that

$$0 \leq \theta_n \leq 1 \quad and \quad H_\epsilon(p_\epsilon^* + p_a y) \rightarrow \theta_n \ weak \tag{42}$$

and the convergences are in the $L^2(\Omega)$ weak and $L^\infty(\Omega)$ weak-* topologies. The convergences achieved allow to pass to the limit in the parameter ϵ in the regularized problem and conclude that (p_n^*, θ_n) is a solution of Problem 1.

Proposition 1 *The function p_n^* is continuous in $\overline{\Omega}$.*

Proof : The continuity in Ω is a classical result of regularity properties for solutions of second order elliptic problems. The continuity in the boundary follows from an argument analogous to the one used in Alvarez [1] (see Vázquez [14], for details).

With respect to Problem n.2 the existence and uniqueness of solution w_n is a classical result for the biharmonic operator (see Rektoris [12], for example). Moreover taking into account that p_n^* is non negative the weak maximum principle implies that w_n is also non negative. The regularity property $w_n \in H^3(\Omega)$ (and therefore $w_n \in C^1(\overline{\Omega})$) is obtained in Cimatti [8]).

Finally the analogous estimates of step 1 for p_n and w_n are obtained:

$$\| p_n \|_{H^1(\Omega)} \ \leq \ K_3(\Omega, \beta, C) \tag{43}$$

$$\| w_n \|_{H^2(\Omega)} \ \leq \ K_4(\Omega, \beta, C) \tag{44}$$

where $K_3(\Omega, \beta, C)$ and $K_4(\Omega, \beta, C)$ denote constants independent of n.

The following theorem concludes the existence of solution for the problem here posed as the limit of the sequence that has been built up by means of the algorithm.

Theorem 4 *The problem $(12) - (15)$ has at least a solution.*

Proof: The previous estimates and the compacity arguments imply the convergences

$$\exists p^* \in M_0 \;/\; p_n^* \;\rightarrow\; p^* \; in \; H^1(\Omega) \; weak$$
$$\exists w \in L_0 \;/\; w_n \;\rightarrow\; w \; in \; H^2(\Omega) \; weak$$
$$\exists \theta_n \in L^\infty(\Omega) \;/\; \theta_n \;\rightarrow\; \theta \; in \; L^2(\Omega) \; and \; in \; L^\infty(\Omega) \; weak$$

and consequently

$$\Delta w_n \;\rightarrow\; \Delta w \; in \; L^2(\Omega) \; weak$$
$$p_n^* \;\rightarrow\; p^* \; in \; L^2(\Omega) \; weak$$
$$\nabla p_n^* \;\rightarrow\; \nabla p^* \; in \; L^2(\Omega) \; weak$$
$$\theta_n \;\rightarrow\; \theta \; in \; L^2(\Omega) \; weak$$

Finally by passing to the limit in n in the Equations (27) and (30) it is deduced that the triple (p^*, θ, w) is a weak solution of the elastohydrodynamic problem of Equations (12)-(15) here treated.

NUMERICAL SOLUTION

For the numerical solution we propose to follow the theoretical algorithm which has been presented in the last paragraph in order to obtain the existence of solution. First we decouple the hydrodynamic and the elastic part (problem $n.1$ and $n.2$ respectively). For the lubrication subproblem $n.1$ we adopt the ideas already developed in Bermúdez-Durany [5] by introducing an "artificial evolutive" problem and the total derivative. The numerical approach of the linear fourth order Problem $n.2$ is based in a classical equivalent mixed formulation (see Glowinsky-Pironneau [11]) which essentially involves the solution of two second order linear elliptic problems:

$$-\Delta \chi = p \quad in \quad \Omega \tag{45}$$

$$\chi = 0 \; on \; \Gamma_0 \cup \Gamma_a \quad and \quad 2\pi - x \; periodic \tag{46}$$

$$-\eta \, \Delta w = \chi \quad in \quad \Omega \tag{47}$$

$$w = 0 \; on \; \Gamma_0 \cup \Gamma_a \quad and \quad 2\pi - x \; periodic \tag{48}$$

So the global numerical algorithm here proposed remains as follows

- Initialize $p_0 = p_a y$, $w_0 = 0$ and $\theta_0 = 1$.

- Step n.1.: Compute (p_n, θ_n) as solution of

$$\int_\Omega (h + w_{n-1})^3 \nabla p_n \nabla \varphi \, dx dy \; + \; \int_\Omega (h + w_{n-1}) \theta_n \frac{D\varphi}{Dt} \, dx dy \; = \; 0 \; \forall \varphi \in M_0 \tag{49}$$

$$H(p_n) \leq \; \theta_n \; \leq 1 \tag{50}$$

- Step n.2.: Compute w_n in two steps :

$$\int_\Omega \nabla \chi_n \nabla \psi \, dx dy \; = \; \int_\Omega p_n \psi \, dx dy \; \forall \psi \in L_0 \tag{51}$$

$$\eta \int_\Omega \nabla w_n \nabla \psi \, dx dy \; = \; \int_\Omega \chi_n \psi \, dx dy \; \forall \psi \in L_0 \tag{52}$$

where for the sake of simplicity a *-notation has been dropped in Equation (49) in all the "artificially time dependent" functions defined by

$$\varphi_*(x, y, t) \; = \; \varphi(x, y) \tag{53}$$

After introducing the "artificial" velocity field $v(x, y) = (-1, 0)$, the total derivative

$$\frac{D\varphi_*}{Dt} \; = \; -\frac{\partial \varphi}{\partial x} \tag{54}$$

appearing in Equation (49) is approached by means of the method of characteristics (see Durany-Vázquez [9]) and the resulting nonlinear problem is solved by duality algorithms (see Bermúdez-Moreno [6]). A finite element technique of type P_1-Lagrange triangular elements is used as space discretization in all linear problems. A more detailed explanation about the numerical solution and several test examples are presented in Durany-García-Vázquez [10].

References

[1] Alvarez, S.: " Problemas de Frontera Libre en Teoría de Lubrificación". Ph.D. Thesis. University Complutense of Madrid. (Spain), 1986.

[2] Bayada, G. Chambat, M.: "The Transition between the Stokes Equation and the Reynolds Equation: A Mathematical Proof". Appl. Math. Optim., 14, pp. 73–93, 1986.

[3] Bayada, G. Chambat, M.: "Sur Quelques Modelizations de la Zone de Cavitation en Lubrification Hydrodynamique".*J. of Theor. and Appl. Mech.*, Vol. 5, N. 5, pp. 703–729, 1986.

[4] Bayada, G. Durany, J. Vázquez, C.: "Existence of Solution for a Lubrication Problem in Elastic Journal Bearing Devices with Thin Bearing". (to appear).

[5] Bermudez, A. Durany, J.: "Numerical Solution of Cavitation Problems in Lubrication." *Comp. Meth. in Appl. Mech. and Eng.*, 68, pp. 55–65, 1988.

[6] Bermudez, A. Moreno, C.: "Duality Methods for Solving Variational Inequalities." *Comput. Math. Appl.*, 7, pp. 43–58, 1981.

[7] Brezis, H. Kinderlehrer, Stampacchia, G.: "Sur une Nouvelle Formulation du Probléme de l'Écoulement á travers une Digue".*C.R.Acad.Sci. Paris.* Sér. A-B, 187, pp. 711–714, 1978.

[8] Cimatti, G.: "Existence and Uniqueness for Nonlinear Reynolds Equations". *Int. J. Eng. Sci.* Vol 24, N. 5, pp. 827–834, 1986.

[9] Durany, J. Vázquez, C.: "Numerical Approach of Lubrication Problems in Journal Bearing Devices with Axial Supply." in *Numerical Methods in engineering '92, (Eds: Ch. Hirsch et al.)*, Elsevier Science Publishers, pp. 839–844, 1992.

[10] Durany, J. García, G. Vázquez, C.: "Finite Element Approximation of Lubrication Problems with Cavitation in Elastic Journal-Bearings." *Proceedings of VIII International Conference on Finite Elements in Fluids*, Barcelona (Spain), 1993 (to appear).

[11] Glowinski, R. Pironneau, O.: "Sur la Résolution Numérique du Probleéme de Dirichlet pour l'Opérateur Biharmonique par une Méthode Quasi-directe". *C.R.Acad.Sci. Paris.* Sér. 282 A, pp. 223–226, 1976.

[12] Rektoris, K.: *"Variational Methods in Mathematics Science and Engineering"*. Reidel, 1977.

[13] Reynolds, O.: "On the Theory of Lubrication and its Applications to M.Beauchamp Tower´s Experiments". *Phil. Trans. Roy. Soc.* , London A117, pp. 157-234, 1886.

[14] Vázquez, C.: *"Análisis Matemático y Resolución Numérica de Problemas de Lubricación con Cavitación"*. Ph.D. Thesis, Publications of University of Santiago de Compostela (Spain), 1992.

Mass transfer in turbulent flow

A. Jahanmiri[a], E.T. Woodburn[b]

[a] *Chemical Engineering Department, Shiraz University, Shiraz, Iran*
[b] *Department of Chemical Engineering, UMIST University, UK*

ABSTRACT

In order to assess the effect of turbulence on the rate of mass transfer in the liquid phase, work has been carried out on gas absorption by liquid flowing over spheres.

The hydrodynamics of the liquid flow over spheres was modelled incorporating eddy viscosity. The coefficients of the eddy viscosity expression were evaluated by measuring the liquid hold-up over a string of twenty spheres of 3.7 cm diameter. The range of the liquid Reynolds numbers was between 30-600. The form of eddy viscosity was found to be of the form:

$$V_t = 7.8 \times 10^{-5} \cdot Re^{2.21} \cdot (y_o - y)^2$$

Mass transfer in the liquid film flowing over a sphere was modelled based on eddy diffusivity [1] incorporating the hydrodynamic model results for physical or chemical absorption accompanied by a instantaneous reaction and a pure or mixed gas phase. The system of partial differential equations of mass transfer with moving boundaries was solved numerically in order to obtain the concentration profiles of the reactants, position of the plane of reaction, and the rate of absorption. The predicted results agreed well with the experimental results. The mass transfer analysis revealed that the rate of gas absorption increases with increasing the liquid flow rate and the liquid reactant concentration in the chemical absorption processes.

INTRODUCTION

The effect of radial turbulent mixing in absorption films has not been comprehensively treated yet if early turbulent mixing could be induced in film of liquid over packing then liquid film resistance could be significantly reduced if not eliminated.

Turbulence could be induced either by wave motion on the surface or through eddies generated as a consequence of high velocity gradients in thin films. Different shapes of packing have been used for the experimental study. Stephen and Morris [2] used circular disks, with the vertical plane of each disk being at right angles to the one above. Although this may well develop turbulence it has some difficulties [3]. Spherical packing has been used as a simpler and an alternative packing piece by many investigations [4-9] in gas absorption processes. In this system liquid flows over each sphere and, on passing through the meniscus between the packing elements cause an interruption similar to that between packing pieces in packed tower. The existing mathematical analysis for this system has been developed based on laminar flow and the liquid surface has been assumed to be ripple free. Comparisons between the theoretical and the experimental results show that, when the liquid flow rates are low, agreement was achieved based on the assumption of laminar ripple-free flow (Figure 1).

Lynn et al. [5] used a simple method of solving the hydrodynamics of liquid flow over a sphere in the laminar flow region. The thickness and velocity profile of liquid film were found as:

$$y_0 = \left(\frac{3 \nu Q}{2 \pi R g Sin^2 \theta} \right) 1/3 \tag{1}$$

$$u = u_i (1 - y^2/y_0^2) \tag{2}$$

$$u_i = \left(\frac{9g}{32 \nu \pi^2} \right)^{1/3} Q^{2/3} R^{-2/3} Sin^{-1/3} \theta \tag{3}$$

Mass transfer in laminar flow over sphere has been analyzed both experimentally and theoretically [4,5,7,8]. Davidson et al. [7] derived a mass transfer equation in the liquid film by considering an element bounded by two stream lines and the two radial lines. If there is no convection across the stream lines and if diffusion in the flow direction is neglected then the following partial differential equation is deduced:

$$u\left(\frac{\partial C}{\partial \theta}\right) = \frac{DR}{y_0^2}\left(\frac{\partial^2 C}{\partial P^2}\right) \tag{4}$$

For small depth of penetration solution of the above equation gives [7]:

$$(C-C_0)/(C_i-C_0) = erfc(P/2\sqrt{D\varphi}) \tag{5}$$

The experimental and the theoretical rate of CO_2 absorption with pure water show an agrement only for the low liquid flow rate [4] (Figure 2).

The divergence in both hydrodynamics and mass transfer results may be due to the fact that as the free surface of the liquid film flows down by gravity effect, it is disturbed by wave motion and ripples. It was found theoretically that laminar motion is unstable for any value of Reynolds number, while experiments lead to the conclusion that there exits a critical value of Reynolds number for the transition from laminar state to the wave-motion (N_{Re}=7) [10]. However the analysis of the liquid film flow accompanied with wave-motion is valid up to Reynolds number of about 120-130 , [11,12]. At these Reynolds number the dominating mechanism of momentum and mass transfer is probably due to unsteady molecular diffusion into a largely laminar fluid which is intermittently mixed by eddies associated with the surface wave structure. At higher liquid flow rates the laminar and wave treatment does not satisfy the experimental results, and also does not predict the existence of wave-motion on the free surface of the liquid.

In turbulent flow the liquid moves in a very irregular manner causing an exchange of momentum from one portion of the liquid to another in a manner similar to the molecular momentum transfer but on a much larger scale. In the vicinity of the wall the motion of the eddies is damped because they can not move radially, and the transfer process depends on molecular motion. Near the wall the controlling molecular transfer is very slow, but the distances are small while in the main turbulent stream the transfer by eddies is rapid.

The eddies are characterized by their velocities and by the distance over which these velocities change significantly. By analogy with Newton's law for laminar flow one of the earliest proposal for turbulent shear stress is [13]:

$$\tau_t = -\mu_t \frac{\partial u}{\partial y}$$ (6)

If it is assumed that both the molecular and eddy transport take place by parallel processes, then two coefficients may be added together. Therefore the total shear stress, (τ_T) is:

$$\tau_T = -(\mu + \mu_t) \frac{\partial u}{\partial y}$$ (7)

The main difficulties in analyzing the turbulent flow is associated with the turbulent viscosity.

HYDRODYNAMICS

Levich [14] has analyzed the general nature of turbulent motion qualitatively at developed turbulent state. The scale of motion in turbulent flow is one of the characteristic of the eddies over which the velocities of eddies are changed. His results show that, the scale of motion decreases from turbulent zone to the solid surface, and the rate of reduction increases. In general the variation of eddy viscosity in the turbulent film has been show to be described by a single expression as:

$$v_t = ay_1^n$$ (8)

where the power n is varied from 1 to 4, and a is a function of physical and flow characteristics, and y_1 is the distance measured from the solid wall. By analogy with the results of analysis of mass transfer study in turbulent flow over the flat surface in terms of eddy diffusion [1], the coefficient a is assumed as:

$$a = A.Re^B$$ (9)

Then the eddy viscosity in term of y, the distance from free surface is considered as:

$$v_t = A.Re^B(y_o - y)^n$$ (10)

where:

$$Re = \frac{4\phi}{2\pi R v \sin\theta}$$ (11)

A differential element of liquid flow as shown in Figure (3) is considered to obtain flow equation. The

assumptions made for analysis are:
1-The thickness of the liquid film is very small
compared to the radius of sphere (R >> y_0)
2-Steady state condition
3-Newtonian flow
4-Neglect changes in the rate of momentum in the flow
direction
5-Neglect acceleration effect in the flow direction.

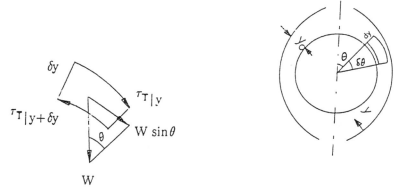

Figure 3. Liquid film over sphere and force acting on element.

Force balance on the differential element and taking differential gives:

$$gsin\theta=-\frac{\partial}{\partial y}(v_T\frac{\partial u}{\partial y})$$ (12)

The boundary conditions are:

$$u=0 \quad at \quad y=y_o$$ (13)

$$-\mu_T\frac{\partial u}{\partial y}=\tau_i \quad at \quad y=0$$ (14)

where, τ_i is the shear stress on the liquid surface caused by the gas flow.

Depending on the value of n in Equation (10) different forms of velocity distribution are obtained. The values 2 and 3 were used in this study, if n is equal to 2 the velocity distribution is obtained as:

$$u=\frac{gsin\theta}{a}[\frac{y_o-\tau_i/\rho gsin\theta}{\sqrt{v/a}}tan^{-1}(\frac{y_o-y}{\sqrt{v/a}})+1/2ln(\frac{v/a}{v/a+(y_o-y)^2})]$$ (15)

To assess the velocity of the hydrodynamics

analysis in terms of the undetermined coefficients of the eddy viscosity, it is to predict the hold up of the liquid over a sphere, and then to check the prediction against experiment.

$$u_{av} = \frac{g\sin\theta}{ay_o} \left[\frac{2y_o - \tau_i/\rho g\sin\theta}{2} \ln\left(\frac{\nu/a}{\nu/a + y_o^2}\right) + \frac{y_o(y_o - \tau_i/\rho g\sin\theta)}{\sqrt{\nu}/a} \right. $$
$$\left. \times \tan^{-1}\frac{y_o}{\sqrt{\nu}/a} + y_o \right] \qquad (17)$$

On the other hand the average velocity in the film is equal to:

$$u_{av} = Q/2\pi R y_o \sin\theta \qquad (18)$$

where Q is the liquid flow rate.

The thickness of the liquid film is determined by solving the above equations for y_0 implicity.

The contact angle for the top of the first sphere is found by determining the thickness of the liquid film over the rod.

MASS TRANSFER

Mass transfer in turbulent flow over the flat surface in terms of eddy diffusion has been studied in the past [12-20]. Levich [14] studied the diffusional flux in turbulent flow by considering the nature of the turbulent motion near the free surface of the liquid. He quoted that at Pr>>1, we can assume the major diffusional resistance is offered by diffusion sublayer. Then the mass-flux could written as $D_t \partial c/\partial y$ where, D_t is the turbulent diffusion coefficient. He found the turbulent coefficient decreases as the liquid surface is approached as:

$$D_t \alpha y^2 \qquad (19)$$

where y is the distance measured from the free surface.

Later on King [15] analyzed the liquid phase mass transfer processes to and from a free liquid interface involving a damped eddy diffusivity in the vicinity of the surface. He used a general form, ay^n for eddy diffusivity, and analyzed the mass transfer coefficient as a function of age of element of surface for different values of power n from zero to infinity.

Lamourelle and Sandal [1] followed the methods

adapted by Levich [14] and King [15] and tented mass transfer near a free surface in terms of eddy diffusivity by measuring the mass transfer coefficient of the liquid phase for gas absorption into a turbulent liquid flowing down a long wetted-wall column. They used helium, hydrogen, oxygen and carbon dioxide absorption into distilled water over a Reynolds number range between 1300-8300. The results were interpreted in terms of an eddy diffusivity with the general form of, ay^n. It was shown that the eddy diffusivity increases as the square of the distance from the interface and confirmed the conclusion of previous investigators such as Levich [14] and Davies [20]. By comparing with the experimental results it was found that the eddy diffusivity in the vicinity of the free surface is:

$$D_t = 7.9 \times 10^{-5} . Re^{1.675} . y^2 \qquad (20)$$

Later on, the above form for eddy diffusivity was confirmed in gas absorption accompanied by first order and instantaneous chemical reaction [16-19].

Equation (18) is valid for the regions adjacent to the free surface. However as a valid form it was used in this study over the whole film thickness, obviously in a real film the turbulence will decrease near the support wall but this not modelled because, of the large schmidt number as usually encountered in gas absorption, the major resistance to mass transfer occurs close to the free surface. So it is important to know the eddy diffusivity is only accurate in this region. The magnitude of the error, involved in this assumption was estimated by using a more realistic eddy diffusivity distribution in the bulk of liquid and it was found that, the mass transfer coefficient differed by less than 0.05% [18].

By considering a differential ring of liquid film write down a solute mass balance and taking differential gives:

$$u \frac{\partial C}{\partial \theta} = R \frac{\partial}{\partial y} \left(D_T \frac{\partial C}{\partial y} \right) \qquad (21)$$

Where D_T is the total diffusivity which is considered as:

$$D_T = D + \acute{a} y^2 \qquad (22)$$

where:

$$\acute{a} = 7.9 \times 10^{-5} . Re^{1.678} \qquad (23)$$

The similar assumptions as considered before, are made here.

In physical absorption if the gas phase is pure then the concentration is constant over the whole of the liquid film is:

$$C_A = C_{AI} \quad at \quad \theta = \theta_1 , \quad 0 \leq y \leq y_o \tag{24}$$

$$\frac{\partial C_A}{\partial y} = 0 \quad at \quad y = y_o , \theta_1 \leq \theta \leq \mathcal{Q}_2 \tag{25}$$

$$C_A = A_{Ai} \quad at \quad y = 0 , \quad \theta_1 < \theta < \theta_2 \tag{26}$$

In chemical Absorption if an instantaneous reaction takes place in the liquid film between the dissolved gas (A) and the reagent (B), a hypothetical surface where the concentration of both component are zero exist (plane of reaction). Concentration distribution in the liquid phase are described by a system of two partial differential equations as:

$$u \frac{\partial C_A}{\partial A} = R \frac{\partial}{\partial y} ((D_A + \acute{a}y^2) \frac{\partial C_A}{\partial y}) \quad 0 \leq y \leq \lambda \tag{27}$$

$$u \frac{\partial C_B}{\partial \theta} = R \frac{\partial}{\partial y} ((D_B + \acute{a}y^2) \frac{\partial C_B}{\partial y}) \quad \lambda \leq y \leq y_o \tag{28}$$

If the soluble gas is absorbed from a gas mixture then the boundary condition becomes:

$$C_B = C_{BI} \quad at \quad \theta = \theta_1 \tag{29}$$

$$\frac{\partial C_B}{\partial y} = 0 \quad at \quad y = y_0 \tag{30}$$

$$\alpha \acute{D}_A \frac{\partial C_A}{\partial y} \big|_{y=\lambda} = -\acute{D}_B \frac{\partial C_B}{\partial y} \big|_{y=\lambda} \tag{31}$$

$$C_A = 0 \quad at \quad \theta = \theta_1 \tag{32}$$

$$-D_A \frac{\partial C_A}{\partial y} \big|_{y=0} = kg (P_{A0} - P_{Ai}) \tag{33}$$

$$P_{Ai} = HC_{Ai} \tag{34}$$

where:

$$\acute{D}=D+\alpha\lambda^2 \tag{35}$$

At the plane of reaction, whose location is a function of y and θ, the concentration of reactants is zero and the motion of the plane of reaction is descried as [21]:

$$\frac{d\lambda}{d\theta}=-\left(\frac{\partial C_A/\partial\theta}{\partial C_A/\partial y}\right)\Big|_{y=\lambda} \tag{36}$$

The motion of the plane of reaction and the concentration profiles qualitatively sketched in Figure (4).

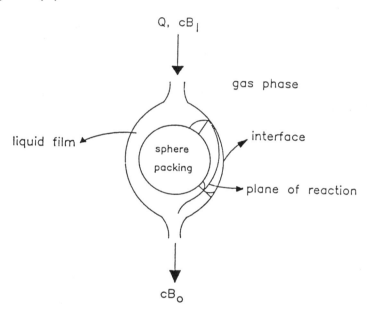

Figure 4. Motion of plane of reaction in liquid film.

Numerical method was used for solving the system of partial differential equations. Since the boundaries of the system (ie. the thickness of the film and the position of the plane of reaction) are varying a dimensionless variable was used as:

$$P = y/y_0 \tag{37}$$

By using finite difference, the partial differential equation (20) is changed to:

Where the coefficient A, B, C and the right hand side are known. These set of equations may be written

$$A_{i,j}\ C_{i-1,j} + B_{ij}\ C_{i,j} + E_{i,j}\ C_{i+1,j} = F_{i,j}\ C_{i,j-1} \qquad \textbf{(38)}$$

in matrix form as:

$$W\ V = X \qquad \textbf{(39)}$$

The first matrix is a three diagonal and the others are column matrix. The answer is:

$$V = W^{-1}\ X \qquad \textbf{(40)}$$

EXPERIMENTAL PROCEDURE

The apparatus used consists of a cylindrical column of 70 cm height contain a string of twenty polypropylene spheres each of 37 mm diameter, which mounted on a rod Figure (5). The liquid flow rate was in the range of (0-17 m/s). The carrier gas was supplied form cylinder B and the soluble gas from cylinder A. In order to measure the variation of gas concentration, side stream sample points were considered.

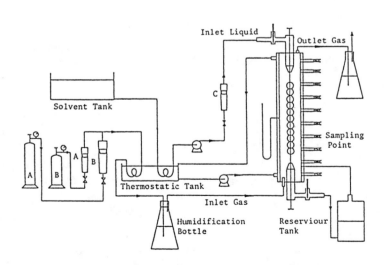

Figure 5. Schematic diagram of experimental apparatus.

In hydrodynamic studies, the liquid hold-up was measured for different flow rates. Hold-up consist of two parts, dynamic and static hold-up. The effect of various surfactant was tested by using three different surface agents.

Mass transfer experiments were carried out by measuring the rate of gas absorption and the gas concentration profile in the column for both physical and chemical systems. Different gas-liquid systems were used. Ammonia-water,carbon dioxide-water for physical absorption and carbon dioxide-sodium hydroxide solution, hydrogen sulphide-NTA.Fe^{3+} for chemical absorption were used.

RESULTS AND DISCUSSION

The hold-up prediction obtained from the hydrodynamic model for two value 2 and 3 for power n in Equation (10). The experimental and predicted results are shown in Figure (6). The experimental results show that the measured hold-up increases rapidly at lower liquid flow rate and dose not show a substantial deviation with different surface active agents. The solid line shows the hydrodynamic model result for the value of n = 2 which is the best curves through the experimental results after varying the constants A and B. The dotted curves show the predicted hold-up for laminar flow. The laminar and turbulent flow predictions have similar shapes and they start to diverge from each other at a Reynolds number of about 50 and the divergence increases with liquid flow rate. A possible reason for the experimental hold-up results, below the Reynolds number of 140, lying below the predicted curves,could be that at low liquid flow rated, the wetting of sphere is not complete.

By comparing the predicted results for two values 2 and 3 for power n and the experimental results, there appears to be little difference between the two predictions. However n = 2 seems to give slightly better agreement so it was the basis for mass transfer prediction. Then the Equation (10) change to:

$$v_t = 7.8 \times 10^{-5}.Re^{2.21}(y_0 - y)^2 \qquad \textbf{(41)}$$

A typical velocity profile in the liquid film at the equator if we assume no shear on the liquid surface is shown in Figure (7). The effect of shear surface caused by increasing the upward gas flow is illustrated in Figure (8).

Analysis of mass transfer in the turbulent regains was in terms of eddy diffusivity base on Equation (19). A typical concentration of reactants in the liquid film at different angles is shown in Figure (9). To examine the validity of the assumption made the form of eddy diffusivity, arrange of experiments were carried out.

The experimental and predicted results for CO_2 absorption by water in terms of the liquid side mass transfer coefficient (K_l) are shown in Figure (10). The predicted results, by turbulent assumption match well with those of the experimental results for Reynolds number higher than 250. In the lower range the predicted results are higher than the experimental and as mentioned before this may be due to incomplete wetted surface of the sphere. The laminar flow results, shown by dotted line is located under the experimental and predicted turbulent results. Their divergence increases by increasing the liquid flow rate, to which is attributed the effect of turbulence in the liquid film.

In the second part, the concentration profile, using two systems, in the column were examined. These included the physical absorption of ammonia from air by pure water, and hydrogen sulphide from air by Fe^{3+} chelated by NTA solution. The experimental results are shown with the predicted results in Figures (11) and (12). The results show that the model predictions are in agreement with those of the experimental ones which lead to the conclusion the reliability of the mass transfer analysis.

NOMENCLATURE

A	Eddy viscosity coefficient
a	Eddy viscosity coefficient
a´	Eddy diffusivity coefficient
B	Reynolds Power in eddy viscosity
C	Concentration in liquid film (mol/lit)
C_0	Concentration at the point of entry (mol/lit)
D	Molecular diffusivity (m^2/s)
g	Gravity acceleration (m/s^2)
n	Power in eddy viscosity or eddy diffusivity expression
P	Dimensionless liquid film thickness
Q	Liquid flow rate (m^3/s)
R	Radius of sphere (m)
u	Velocity (m/s)
y	Distance measured from liquid surface (m)
y_0	Liquid film thickness on sphere (cm)
y_1	Distance from wall (m)
θ	Angle measured from top of sphere (rad)
λ	Position of plane of reaction measured from interface (m)

ρ Liquid density
τ Shear stress (Pa)
ν Kinematic viscosity (m^2/s)
Δ_0 Thickness of liquid film (m)

SUBSCRIPTS
A   Solute gas
B   Liquid reactant
i   Condition at liquid
t   Turbulent
T   Total
i   Grid number in radial direction
j   Grid number in flow directio

REFERENCES

1   Lamourelle,A.P. and O.C. Sandall,Chem.Eng.Sci., 27,1035,1972
2   Stephen,E.J. and G.A.Morris,Chem. Eng. Progr., 47, 232, 1951
3   Taylor,R.F.& Roberts,Chem. Eng. Sci.,5,168,1951
4   Davidson,J.R. et al.,Trans. Instn. Chem. Eng., 37,122,1959
5   Lynn,S.,J.R. Straatemerier and H. Kramers,Chem. Eng. Sci.,4,63,1955
6   Yoshida,F. and T.Koyanagi Ind. Eng. Chem.,50, 365,1958
7   Davidson,J.F. and E.J. Cullen,Trans. Instn. Chem.,35,150,1968
8   Wild,J.D.,and O.E. Potter,I. Chem. E. Symposium Seris,28,30,1968
9   Tamir,A., J.C. Merchak and P.D. Virkar, Chem. Eng.,35,1393 1988
10   Ruckenstein,E. and C.Berbente,Chem. Eng. Sci., 20,795,1965
11   Banerjee,S.,E.Rhodes and D.S.Scott,Chem.Eng. Sci.,22,43,1967
12   Bunch,D.W. and M.R.Strunk, AIChE.J. 11,1108,1965
13   Bird,R.B.,W.E.Stewart and E.N.Lightfoot, "Transport Phenomena", Wiley, New York, 1960
14   Levich,V.G.,"Physicochemical Hydrodynamics", Pretice-Hall, 1962
15   King,C. J., I&EC. Fundamentals, 5, 1, 1966
16   Kayihan,R. and O.C.Sandall, AIChE J.,20,402,1974
17   Sandall,O.C.,Int. J. Heat Mass Transfer,17,459, 1974
18   Menez,G.D. and O.C.Sandall,Ind. Eng. Chem. Fundam.,13,72,1974
19   Mendez,F. and O.C.Sandall, AIChE J.,21,534,1975
20   Davies,J.T., Proc. R. Soc., A290, 515, 1966
21   Astarita,G.,"Mass Transfer with Chemical Reaction", Elsevier Publishing Company, p.55,1967

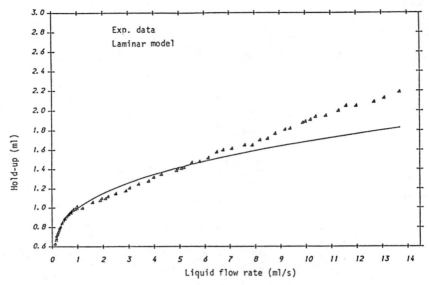

Figure 1: Experiment and Predicted data of the hold-up for one sphere by Davidson et at [4]

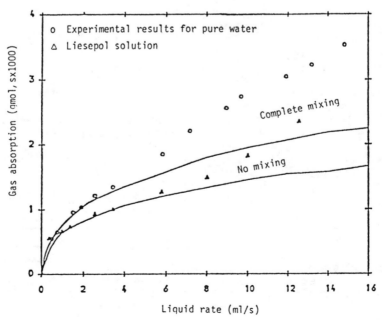

Figure 2: Carbon dioxide absorption by two sphere [4]

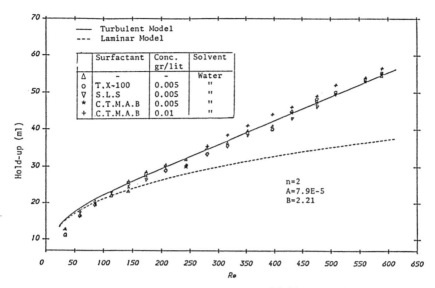

Figure 6: Experimental and Predicted data of hold-up as a function of Reynolds number for different surfactant

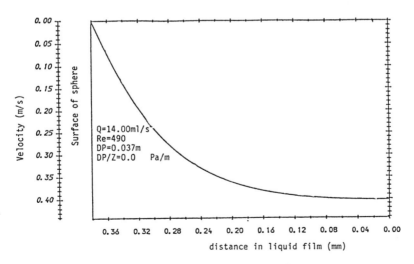

Figure 7: Velocity profile in liquid film at equator

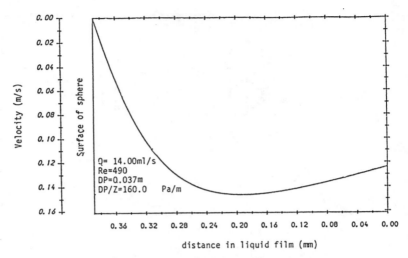

Figure 8: Velocity profile in liquid film at equator

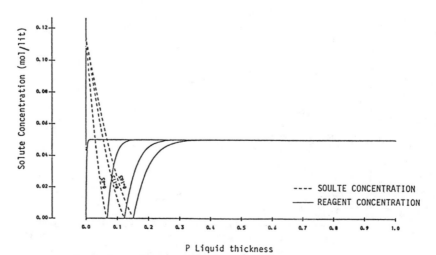

P Liquid thickness

Figure 9: Concentration profiles at different angles

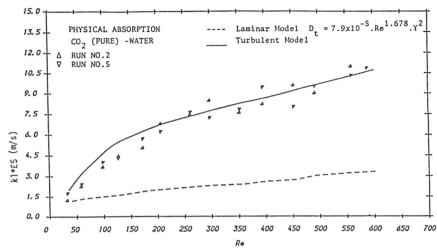

Figure 10: Experimental and Predicted Liquid Side Mass Transfer Coefficients

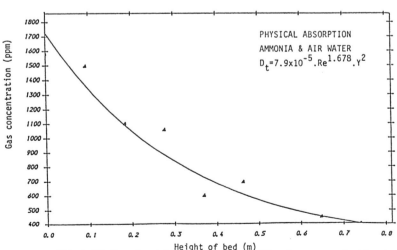

Figure 11: Experimental and Predicted profile of gas concentration in
absorption column

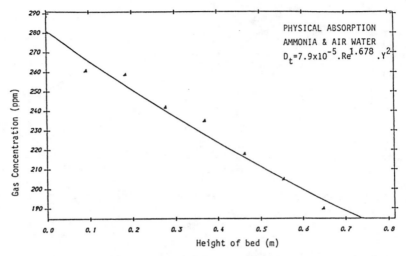

Figure 12: Experimental and Predicted profile of gas concentration in absorption column

Authors' Index

Computational Mechanics Publications

Computational Methods for Free and Moving Boundary Problems in Heat and Fluid Flow

Edited by **L.C. WROBEL** *and* **C.A. BREBBIA,**
Wessex Institute of Technology, Southampton, UK
The mathematical modelling of free and moving boundary problems is characterized by the presence of one or more surfaces which are initially unknown or move throughout the analysis. The determination of the location of these surfaces is an important part of the solution procedure, generally involving the use of iterative or time-marching algorithms. This volume concentrates on computational methods of the solution of practical engineering problems with emphasis on boundary and finite elements.

Series: Computational Engineering

ISBN: 1853122211; 1562521454 (US, Canada and Mexico) Jan 1993 412pp £110.00/$220.00

Advanced Computational Methods in Heat Transfer

Edited by: **L.C. WROBEL** and **C.A. BREBBIA,**
both of Wessex Institute of Technology, UK and
A.J. NOWAK, *Silesian Technical University, Poland*
These two volumes contain the edited versions of papers presented at the Second International Conference on Advanced Computational Methods in Heat Transfer held in Milan in 1992.
The set of two volumes are available at a price of £300.00/$600.00 ISBN: 185312172X; 1562521012

Conduction, Radiation, and Phase Change

Volume 1
ISBN: 1853121991; 156252125X (US, Canada, Mexico) July 1992 806pp £158.00/$316.00

Natural/Forced Convection and Combustion Simulation

Volume 2
ISBN: 1853122009; 1562521268 (US, Canada, Mexico) July 1992 720pp £142.00/$284.00

Computational Modelling of Free and Moving Boundary Problems

Edited by: **L.C. WROBEL** *and* **C.A. BREBBIA,**
Wessex Institute of Technology, Southampton, UK
These two volumes contain edited versions of the papers presented at the First International Conference on Computational Modelling of Free and Moving Boundary Problems, held in Southampton, UK, in July 1991.
The conference promoted the interaction between engineers, applied mathematicians and numerical analysts involved in the creation, development and application of computational methods to free and moving boundary problems. In particular, the conference provided a useful connection between scientists working in different areas of application but using similar numerical techniques.

SET ISBN: 1853121428 £116.00/$198.90

Fluid Flow
Volume 1
ISBN: 1853121576; 1562520849 (US, Canada, Mexico) July 1991 464pp £66.00/$116.00

Heat Transfer
Volume 2
ISBN: 1853121584; 1562520857 (US, Canada, Mexico) July 1991 332pp £66.00/$116.00

Boundary Element Technology VII

Edited by: **C.A. BREBBIA,** *Wessex Institute of Technology, UK, and* **M.S. INGBER,** *University of New Mexico, USA*
This book contains the edited versions of the papers presented at the Seventh International Conference on Boundary Element Technology, held at the University of New Mexico in Albuquerque in June 1992. This book deals with a series of advances in Boundary Elements, particularly in the field of electrical and electromagnetic problems and fluid Flow. The book is of primary importance to those researchers, engineers in industry and code developers who need to be aware of the latest developments in BEM.

ISBN: 1853121681; 1562520970 (US, Canada, Mexico) June 1992 964pp £200.00/$400.00

Computational Mechanics Publications
Ashurst Lodge
Ashurst
Southampton, SO4 2AA, UK
Tel: 44(0)703 293223 Fax: 44(0)703 292853

Computational Mechanics Inc
25 Bridge Street
Billerica
MA 01821, USA
Tel: 508 667 5841 Fax: 508 667 7582